COMPUTER READINGS SERIES

An Introduction to Computer Systems

EDWARD O. JOSLIN

College Readings Inc.
Post Office Box 2323
Arlington, Virginia 22202

Second Printing, January, 1970

COMPUTER READINGS SERIES
An Introduction to Computer Systems

Library of Congress Catalog Card Number 71-98170

To Carole and Laurie

PREFACE

Teaching an introductory course in data processing is a difficult task in the education of today's youth. Advances are being made daily both in the technology and the applications of data processing equipment. The limited number of textbooks available for an introductory course are not current because of the time lag inherent in the publication of most texts. Instructors are tasked with two full time jobs, learning the newest advances in the state-of-art and teaching, and the courses they teach must be flexible enough to suit the needs of various types of students.

It is because of my experience in teaching courses in data processing that this book exists today. I was spending much time reviewing the literature and selecting articles to provide currentness in courses. Permission to reprint articles was required if an article was to be duplicated. This often proved a long, and sometimes costly, process. Sending students to the school library was another alternative tried, but forty students trying to obtain an average of two articles a week from many different publications also proved unsatisfactory (Especially when most students put off their reading assignments until the night before a test or report was due). I decided a book of current readings, covering a broad spectrum, was a necessary addition to the student's required texts. Unfortunately, the book envisioned did not exist, so I decided to create such a book.

I went through the tedious task of selecting the articles ("How broad a selection? Am I hitting hard enough in this area, too hard in that area?"). I received the required permissions to reprint the selected articles, and found a method for reducing the publisher's required production cycle to less than four months.

In this book, one will not find any magazine article previous to 1967, and the majority of articles are from 1968 and 1969. I am in no way inferring that articles prior to this time period are not excellent sources of information, but I do feel that the information from pre-1967 articles is included in the newer data processing texts. This book is primarily intended to supplement such texts.

I have divided the book into three sections: background, applications, and technology. The background section is a survey of the data processing industry as a whole. In this section the student will receive views from many different vantage points as to what a computer is, how it works, what is its past, present and future, how it fits in an organizational structure, and who is involved with the computer, from manufacturers of equipment to computer programmers.

The applications section gives specific examples of the varied uses of computers, its impact on different types of businesses and the results obtained in each. Certain articles become very specific in the technological requirements of implementing the computer system, and others give a broad brush treatment. Thus, the student wishing only exposure and the student requiring detailed knowledge upon which to build will both find suitable material to fill their needs.

The technology area surveys the hardware and software components of a computer system as it exists today and as it may exist tomorrow. The first articles cover different types of input and output equipment and procedures. The remaining articles address the hardware and software requirements of computers.

I have not designed the book to fill all the requirements of introducing data processing courses to students (For instance, I still will send my students to the library for reading assignments, but at a greatly reduced rate). I have tried to make the book as flexible as possible. The ultimate benefit the student receives from the book will depend on the imagination of the instructor, and his knowledge of the individual student's aptitude and ability. That is as it should be.

I wish to thank the authors of the articles selected for putting their thoughts in print, the publishers of the articles for granting permission to use their material, and my family for providing me with the time and encouragement to bring this project to a successful conclusion.

Edward O. Joslin
Washington, D. C.
August, 1969

TABLE OF CONTENTS

I. BACKGROUND

II. APPLICATIONS

III. TECHNOLOGY

I

BACKGROUND

AN OVERVIEW OF THE INFORMATION PROCESSING AND COMPUTER COMMUNITY

Willis W. Alexander
President
The American Bankers Association
New York, New York

During the past decade, banking has probably felt the impact of EDP more than any other industry. In this short span of time, banking has progressed from the lowest to one of the highest positions on the scale of computer use and now has the largest single industry investment in EDP equipment.

The effects of EDP on banking have been both direct and indirect. Banking's increased ability to respond to the growing and changing needs of its customers illustrates the direct impact. The indirect impact is exemplified by the dramatic changes both in organizational structure and managerial requirements.

As we look to the future, we can foresee further effects. Among the most significant will be the bank's ability to link all of the customer's accounts in one overall relationship, thus pinpointing customer services and marketing efforts. This capability will truly add a new dimension to "full service banking." We anticipate that the use of sophisticated EDP applications will not be limited to large banks. Data communications and small computer developments will expand the already imaginative use of EDP by small banks.

In broader perspective, EDP will contribute to a significantly changed monetary and payments system. In recognition of this, The American Bankers Association recently set up a Monetary and Payments System Committee which, with four task forces, will examine the operational, legislative, marketing and economic planning requirements for such evolution. Only with such planning can banks fully utilize EDP capabilities and serve all the financially-related needs of their customers.

The expanding applications of EDP imposes the requirement that data processing managers become as skilled in the problem side of the ledger as they now are in the process side. EDP creates as well as solves problems and it is only as these problems can be foreseen and avoided by alert and sharpened management skills that EDP can achieve its fullest potential.

Bernard A. Galler
President
Association for Computing Machinery
New York, New York

Looking to the future, I believe we shall see developments in three major areas; the networking of computers, the development of large data bases and the proper use of the man in the system.

Although people have tended to think of computer networks primarily in terms of identical computers in different geographic areas sharing the work load, I believe the future development in this area will emphasize distinctive capabilities at each of several centers, such as unique hardware facilities, or specialized data bases; and the network will provide facilities utilizing these capabilities from remote points. The major problems here will be the establishment of communication and interface conventions between independent autonomous systems.

Large data bases will become much more common, as the cost of storage continues to decrease. On the other hand, we shall demand more and more that these data bases be flexible, easily modified and instantaneously accessed. Much more research will have to go into the techniques for organizing these data bases and for searching them efficiently. People who develop such data bases will have to face up to the large systems problems which are involved.

These problems inevitably dictate the kind of questions which can be asked on large data management systems, and the kinds (and costs) of changes that can be made in them. These problems are not insurmountable, but we must be realistic about the costs involved. It would help if computer scientists at universities would consider these problems more seriously. Many researchers do not give a high priority to information retrieval, and those who are interested usually do not tackle the hard problems of really large data bases.

We will have to find better ways to use the man in computer systems. In problems of pattern recognition, decision-making based on uncertain information, error correction and so on, the man can play an important role. There are many areas in which the computer can do a very good approximate job, and if it were only possible to include the man at that point to indicate the appropriate direction in which improvements could be found, the system could be very successful.

As a simple example, while the computer recognition of speech is not yet fully developed, one could even today use the approximate recognition that is available, feeding it back to the speaker (or his secretary) for improvement. Coupled with a learning procedure, so that the algorithm could adapt to the idiosyncrasies of the speaker, the system could learn rapidly to do a very good job in that situation. The extension of this philosophy to management situations, as well as many other areas, should be obvious.

I am optimistic about the future in these areas. I would guess that five years from now we shall regard these problems as well in hand, and we shall be looking for new directions. I am certainly looking forward to it.

Ralph E. Kent
President
American Institute of Certified Public Accountants
New York, New York

Inasmuch as certified public accountants are among the primary advisors to business organizations as well as government and nonprofit entities, they are very much aware of the great contributions which EDP makes to effective management.

CPAs often have occasion to counsel clients regarding EDP equipment and software, selection of data processing centers, adequacy of controls in systems and optimum use of electronically processed data. In their function as independent auditors, CPAs also are called upon to examine and render opinions on financial statements derived from electrically produced data.

It follows that training in EDP has become an integral part of certified public accountants' professional capability. In recognition of this fact, the American Institute of Certified Public Accountants has, among other things, published for the information of members *Auditing & EDP*, a volume of over 300 pages by Gordon B. Davis, professor at the University of Minnesota, and six *Computer Research Studies* prepared for the AICPA by System Development Corp. It also conducts periodically courses for its members.

A number of CPA firms have installed fairly extensive EDP equipment for handling their own work, and some firms provide data processing for clients. As a consequence of this development, the American Institute has added provisions to its Code of Professional Ethics regarding the EDP function.

Because of their wide and varied experience in the business world, and particularly because of their special training in gathering, analyzing and evaluating quantitative data, CPAs are in an excellent position to help corporations and other organizations obtain decision-making data not available previously, or obtainable only at prohibitive cost—data which could be the input for a management science approach to operations.

Thus there is a close affinity between accountancy and EDP technological developments, and it can be expected that CPAs will continue to play a major role in assisting managements to derive maximum benefit from the powerful tool of EDP.

Issac L. Auerbach
President
Auerbach Corporation
New York, New York

The future of the data processing industry will rest, in great part, with its ability to meet and adopt to the ever changing needs of the people and institutions which it serves. This can best be done, perhaps, by channeling greater effort into the development of new applications which utilize the already existing equipment and know-how, rather than by an insistent concentration on new equipment design.

One of the most significant developments utilizing this concept is the newly emerged capability we call "dedicated services." These are specially designed systems created to support specific industries, markets or applications, on a regional or national basis, with a complete range of information services. The growth figures in the past two years alone indicate the need and acceptance of this specialized service. The market for dedicated services approached $75 million in 1968, up from $30 million in 1967, and is expected to exceed $650 million in 1972. Such services should, in fact, be the fastest growing segment of the data processing services market.

The recent formation of Honeywell-Auerbach Computer Services Inc. attests to my belief in the importance of dedicated service companies in the future. By providing advanced data management systems for business and industry, such a firm can uniquely serve the three basic levels of business management—planning, policy and strategy—with the most complete tools and information. This concept comes close to being "all things" to selected industries, because it provides in one package the advanced equipment, the system programs, the human and financial resources, and the organization suited to the task and the environment. It is, essentially, one-stop shopping, and that quality alone makes it the most desirable service that can be offered to the business world—a world whose operations and information requirements will grow even more complex in the future. Dedicated service companies are structured to meet and deal with such complexity.

C. Mathews Dick, Jr.
President
Business Equipment Manufacturers Association
New York, New York

To speak of information processing is to speak of a very broad, but nonetheless singular, concept. For whether we are concerned with hardware, software, service bureaus, data banks or any other facet of data processing, we are really dealing with a means to a common end. And this end, the liberation of man's time in the handling of the overwhelming masses of information being generated daily, requires a far wider scope of effort than that which could be put forth by just the data processing industry itself.

The computer, by all means, is the hub of the information processing universe. In fact, it is the nucleus about which all good information processing systems must be built. But it is well to remember that the computer is not the entire universe. For without the many satellite services afforded by noncomputer devices and systems, the all-embracing concept of information processing would collapse. For it is the combination of the computer with many different ancillary equipments, each located in its best functional environment and integrated into a single configuration, that really constitutes a total information processing facility.

For this reason, it is no longer sufficient to concern ourselves with just our own particular piece in the puzzle. To build a computer output terminal for the sake of a single application, to design a business form without considering all the equipment with which it may be used, or to record data in an optical character font that is incompatible with many reading devices in common use throughout the world, is to follow the narrow path indeed.

As I see it, the destiny of information processing lies in the willingness and earnestness with which individual companies and professionals will work together to provide a totally integrated information service to the whole of the world community.

Dick Brandon
President
Brandon Applied Systems, Inc.
New York, New York

It is impossible to forecast the future of data processing in toto in the short space available; nor can it be done using history as a principal guide. As a result, any forecaster has to focus on smaller elements to try and determine what will happen. Three major areas suggest themselves: the application of computers, the developments in hardware, and the future of data processing people.

There are two significant developments facing the data processing industry in this area. First, we are finally reaching the point where we can talk about and design common data base systems, central information systems supplying answers on request. Although we have not yet reached the era of the management information system, with a lot of management education and luck, within the next five years we will be able to provide reasonable responses to management requests from a central data base.

Second, and far more important, is the area of social application. Society's real payout from computer use will not come in business; instead it will be in the application of computers in education, medicine, transportation, urban planning and welfare. These are virtually untouched if one recognizes, for example, that educational methodology today is little different from the way it was a hundred years ago. Thus the computer could make a major contribution which should begin in the next five years, and whose impact will be felt by millions of people.

Although it is easy, historically, to forecast dramatic changes in hardware, it is likely that "gradualism" will affect the computer as well. It is probable that the "fourth generation" will not be a dramatically different system, but one which is gradually remade with new and faster components. Better and more diverse peripherals, with emphasis on remote hard-copy and CRT devices, will team up with photo-optic memories, non-impact electronic beam printers and voice output systems, to provide a more flexible, responsive system, capable of congeniality with the human user. The boundaries of use are no longer hardware boundaries. It is obvious that software and people costs will limit our use of these resplendent devices, so that better answers in the software area have to be found simultaneously.

Data processing management, already beset by numerous people problems, will find these problems getting worse rather than better. A projection of shortages offers a dismal result in an industry whose requirements increase by 40% per year, whose supply increases by about 20% per year, and which starts with a shortage of close to 100,000 qualified people already. In addition, the requirements are changing. The people needed to implement complex, management level systems, using complicated hardware and software, are systems analysts and systems programmers at least five times better trained and qualified than today's average practitioner. Our qualitative shortage in the future may be worse, therefore, than our quantitative lacks appear today. Education and training are the only possible solutions available.

But, of course, every cloud has a silver lining. Salaries will naturally increase, and so will the status, prestige and management position of data processing managers. If they can keep up with the changing field and meet the challenges of the 70's head-on, they will be able to claim a deserved position in the top management of their organizations.

J. Daniel Couger
Assistant Dean
School of Business, University of Colorado
Colorado Springs, Colorado

Four years ago Dr. Herbert Simon made the following prediction in his book, *The Shape of Automation,* ". . . there is every prospect that we will soon have the technological means . . . to automate all management decisions, non-programmed as well as programmed."

Considerable progress has been made toward computerizing programmable managerial decisions. Considerably more research is necessary to assist the manager in the non-programmable area of decision making. A proper beginning is the design of effective manager-computer interactive systems to facilitate decision making. Through reports from the lay media (newspapers, TV and motion pictures), one might conclude that manager-computer interactive systems have been implemented in many organizations. Data processing professionals are aware of the realities—few such systems are in operation. Neither hardware nor software have held up such development—the constraint has been the manager.

But this barrier is on the verge of a breakthrough. First, the manager will be much better educated to participate in the design of such a system. After lagging behind industry for a number of years, educational programs for management have reversed directions and are including a large amount of computer-oriented materials.

Second, instead of operating virtually independently, industrial organizations and universities have begun cooperative research activities. Examples are programs at the Universities of Minnesota and Pennsylvania. The industry--university research teams head by Minnesota's Dr. Gordon Davis have accomplished significant research on computer-assisted financial planning. A similar approach by Dr. James Emery of Pennsylvania has produced some valuable research results on cost and value of information. At the University of Colorado we have the research center, CYSYS, an acronym for Cybernetics Systems Synergism. Through our behavioral studies of response patterns in manager-computer interactions, we are gaining a good understanding of the decision making environment. The result should be truly synergistic—producing a total effect greater than the two effects (man and machine) produced independently.

If industry and academic institutions continue to expand their cooperative research activities, some of the exciting developments in the near future will occur in the area of manager-computer interactive systems.

Dr. Harvey S. Gellman
President
DCF Systems Ltd.
Toronto, Ontario

The expanding use of time sharing systems are likely to have a marked effect on the data processing manager and his job. Of course, such systems are already entrenched in the data processing community and there seems little doubt that most organizations will use time-sharing facilities.

A large organization with several regional computer installations will probably move to a central, large-scale, time sharing system, to do most of the data processing work for the entire organization. Each regional office will then use a small-scale computer for small local data processing tasks. The regional computer will transmit data to the central system, which will handle the bulk of the processing work for each region. Thus, the regional office will not need a large data processing staff and the administrative responsibilities of the regional data processing manager will be sharply reduced.

The typical small organization will probably not have its own computer installation. Instead, it will use a terminal connected to a commercial time sharing service bureau.

There is also a trend toward the establishment of "complete" data processing service bureaus. These can provide a wide range of services, so the customer will not need to hire his own data processing staff. I believe that the computer service business will evolve into a problem-solving service, selling the customer answers instead of only machine time.

These structural changes in the data processing industry will, I believe, have profound effects on data processing managers. In the past, the data processing manager has often been accused of being an adequate technician but an incompetent administrator. After years of diligent effort, many data processing managers have learned how to manage groups of people. These managers will soon find that "the rules of the game" have been changed by the advent of time sharing systems.

The regional data center that suddenly shrinks to a small machine plus an operator, will not need a data processing manager. The former manager will be faced with two bitter choices. He can either increase his technical skills and remain in data processing work, or take a line manager's job outside the data processing area. Both of these choices will involve agonizing appraisals and hard work to change a career path. The wise data processing manager will begin to think about these decisions now, to give himself as much time as possible to develop skills that will protect his marketability as a job hunter.

J. A. Campise
General Consultant
Houston, Texas

We have witnessed the infancy and early adolescence of data processing during the 1950s and 1960s. The current searching for direction and the evidence that we are "finding ourselves" and establishing an identity indicates that the industry is entering the stage of advanced adolescence. What can we expect in the 1970s?

When one is asked to speculate about the future of a child, he can only attempt to read the signs, inject some opinion, some hope and some concern for its welfare and growth. Data processing is a child of many parents, and each of them influences its development. Many of them differ in motive and degree of concern, but perhaps need is the most influential use of these. It may be of value then to examine the areas of need and explore those which may be fulfilled in the next decade.

In order to support the large data-base systems we conceived and started to develop in the 1960s, we must have extremely large main memories. Main memories on the order of a billion characters of storage should be a practical reality during the early years of the next decade. Coupled with large main memories, we need truly associative secondary storage devices. Hardware in which it is possible to store and retrieve data without concern for its physical location should be out of the experimental stage by the latter part of the decade.

In order to improve efficiency and ease of programming and transition, we need hardware which will execute compiler level statements without intermediate translation. This will necessarily evolve in stages and will influence, and be influenced by, standardization of the procedural components of compiler languages. We should see some implementation of high level hardware commands in the early 1970s, but high cost and lack of acceptable standards will probably delay full implementation until the late 70s.

The input bottleneck must be broken in the next decade. The most promising vehicle is voice recognition. Current experimental devices should be available on a limited basis within a few years, and by the end of the decade, voice input should be readily available if not commonplace.

Software needs will change dramatically during the next 10 years. Because of hardware developments, operating systems will be far less complex and less time consuming than those required by current hardware. Manufacturers will almost certainly begin to price hardware and software separately in the near future. The first step will probably be to separate applications software and reduce "free" support in that area. "Off-the-shelf" applications programs will become more abundant and more competitive. Compilers should be the next major software item to be separately priced, while operating system software will be integrally priced until new hardware features are available. By the end of the decade, hardware and software should be entirely separate in pricing and in character. There will undoubtedly continue to be a proliferation of specialized software and hardware firms. Competition in these areas will become more severe.

As a result, the individual manager will have to weigh many more alternatives in his decisions concerning both hardware and software. His preoccupation with the programmer shortage will lessen as hardware changes relieve the programmers of most of the time consuming tedium of hardware manipulation and permit him to concentrate his efforts on procedure. This, coupled with the availability of usable "packaged" programs and more qualified people emerging from colleges and universities, should relieve the programmer shortage by the end of the next decade.

Space does not permit an exploration of all of the ramifications of these impending changes and the changes are certainly not limited to those mentioned. Developments in communications technology and peripheral devices, coupled with those already cited will undoubtedly make the 1970s the decade of time sharing, but more important to the industry is the fact that these things will permit a concentration on the problems of the user and an opportunity to use our technology to contribute to the growth and well-being of our organizations.

We may see state or federal licensing, we will probably see better measures of performance of all our activities, but above all, we should be able to broaden our perspective of general management and take our place as professionals with a speciality at the hub of all organizational activity. Data processing will then have found direction and purpose; ready to function as a young adult in shaping the future of all other disciplines which are its peers and parents.

Marvin M. Wofsey
Associate Professor of Management
College of General Studies
The George Washington University,
Washington, D.C.

The basic purpose of a computer is to function as an extension of man's mind. To the management it is a tool, a means toward his doing a more effective job. He may or may not have known about the quantitative areas of decision making, but until the computer arrived this was academic. Even if he knew how to use operations research to aid in decision making, by the time he created a model and reached the optimal solution, the time for decision making had passed.

In the use of computers, for at least 15 years it has been understood that operating systems, realtime systems, time sharing, multi-programming, multi -processing and remote inquiry into computers were feasible. The hardware started appearing about 1959, followed by the needed software. In the third-generation computers implementation of these concepts are feasible. Yet, the great majority of computer installations are still operating in the batch mode. Why?

The answer to this lack of progress is education. Are the colleges and universities ready to accept the challenge of the future? Traditionally they have lagged behind developments in government and industry. Frequently, the curriculum reflects changes that already have occurred, rather than leading the way. Future managers graduate with little or no knowledge of computers and quantitative methods. Despite the percentage of large accounting systems on computers, many graduate accountants have never been exposed to the computer. Many young economists, econometricians and statisticians know nothing about programming, and not much more about computers.

If colleges and universities somehow could be stimulated to take the lead in these areas, effective use of the computer would be advanced by at least a decade. With people in the operational areas able to write programs and to use the computer effectively, a shift of applications programming from centralized data processing is anticipated. Overall systems design and coordination, data bank development, standards, systems programming and computer service would be the main function of the centralized group. Remote consoles, real-time systems, time-sharing and quantitative methods would be the rule, rather than the exception. Will colleges and universities be ready to lead the way? I doubt it, but time alone will tell.

S. F. Keating
President
Honeywell, Inc.
Wellesley Hills, Mass.

One of the most famous of the medieval morality plays is called "Everyman." The word "Everyman" sums up Honeywell's view of the future of the computer industry. Until the present, the computer industry has been of and for experts. It took experts to build computers and, more important, it took experts to run them. But in the next decade our industry will reach out and touch "everyman"—and every woman and child—through computer terminals which will take their place in the kitchen or office or school room.

The beginning of the impact of our machines on the broad spectrum of society comes, in my opinion, not a moment too soon. Our machines have shown themselves marvelous tools with which to simplify the complexities of doing business in the latter half of the twentieth century. They have made inventories manageable, files orderly, paperwork tolerable.

It is now time for computers to work their magic on all of society—to become tools to simplify the complexities of just living in the later half of this century. I mean, of course, that computers and the accompanying systems approach to problems are making possible for the first time truly in-depth studies of poverty, ignorance and other social ills. Computers have enabled business men to look systematically upon the problems of their enterprises and to seek systematic solutions. They are beginning now to do the same for society. This trend will continue and, perhaps in this century, enable us to wage at last a successful war on poverty.

But when I talk about the complexities of life I mean more than just social ills. I mean also the complexities that touch all of us. Think of the demands that are made upon our twentieth century "Everyman." He is called on to be lawyer, doctor, mechanic, plumber, tree surgeon, psychologist, theologian, fundraiser, critic—and not necessarily one at a time. With the help of computers, he will learn to take a systems approach to his life and its responsibilities. The computer industry has been compared in its effects on mankind to the automobile industry, and the comparison is valid. I do not expect, at least in this century, that every man will have a two-computer garage. But the time will come when he will have in his home or business one, two or more computer terminals available to him and have the knowledge to use them intelligently for the benefit of his career and of his family.

S. D. Baxter
Chief, Computation Centre
National Research Council of Canada
Ottawa, Canada

The future of EDP, I would predict, is a very secure one. However, the question that concerns me is the future of man, living and working in an EDP environment. Yes, he is going to work, we have seen enough already to predict that man is not going to be displaced by machines. His tasks will be different. In many ways they will be menial tasks, but there will be work.

In the years ahead we are going to have to bring our common sense to bear in order to ensure that the machine is not deified at the cost of a lowered importance of the human personality. Ever since man began his activities on earth he has deified things external to himself and not usually of his own creation. We are now living in a period when man, because of his tremendous technological achievements, has succeeded in creating things which he can, and does, readily deify. Such a creation is the electronic computer. In the years ahead we must be very careful to ensure that computers serve man but do not rule him.

I have recently read a statement to the effect that the survival of the nation is threatened if we do not spend more money on computers. I understand the point that is being made but I maintain that if every last computer in Canada were hauled away the nation would still survive and would survive rather well. I make the point that if we fail to emphasize the importance of the man rather than that of the machine, survival of man as a being who has the capacity to live graciously, is seriously threatened.

In the early 1950's it was felt that the problem of translating natural languages was one that could readily be handled by computers. Now, almost twenty years later, I am told by the experts in this field that it will be fifty to one hundred years, if ever, before a computer will be able to produce a literary translation. In my opinion it will be never. Thus, there are things which machines will never really be able to do very well and man, in spite of his 6,832 failings, will always be able to handle much better.

Let us welcome the cashless society where the tedium of handling change and charging is taken over by a computer but let us never, never rely on computers to pick our childrens' spouses (Victorian parents will always be better at this). Let us leave them the fun of choosing, the excitement and uncertainty that will accompany this, and the joy and pain of making and learning from mistakes.

Render unto the machine those things for which it is best suited but leave to man those things of the spirit and personality which no machine can ever adequately do. And in the use of machines let us guard against an efficient system if a concomitant of this is an agonized, frustrated and unhappy humanity.

Norman F. Kallaus
Chairman, Dept. of
Office Management and Business Education
The University of Iowa,
Iowa City, Iowa

This is an age when people have developed a penchant for predictions—for looking long and longingly into their crystal balls. The future is, of course, important and I shall try to provide some "restrained clairvoyance" about the look of the business data processing programs in colleges and related schools as we enter the second decade of computer education.

In general, our schools will pass from a have and have-not status to one in which all will have access to computers, either on-site or by remote means. With this shift in availability will emerge universal acceptance of the computer (somewhat like the typewriter) as a basic tool. As software developments are refined and expanded, there may be a de-emphasis of programming for programming sake, with an impressive swing to the study of systems and general systems theory. Programming, however, will remain the *sine qua non* of computer education, and a scientific-based discipline of information will emerge. A technology-humanology interstudy will be common as machines-oriented students and social-oriented students will increasingly interact with technical, behavioral and conceptual problems of business as the core focus.

It seems obvious that a great increase can be expected in the use of the computer as a device for facilitating mathematical solutions (i.e., simulation and increasingly more complex model study) to business problems or as "preventives" to the development of present-day type of problems. A great facility and commonality of understanding of coming knowing several computer programming languages) will be found. In larger universities, if not in all colleges, there will be a requirement that all students "be comfortable with" the computer, understand vocabulary and general computer capability.

Each level of education will accept the computer as a commonplace, fundamental tool. The elementary school will make inroads in introducing computer concepts into its math and social studies programs; the secondary school, in a "here's what it can do" way, in its high school business, social studies, and math programs.

But the community colleges and their related vocational-technical branches will, to the greatest extent, expand courses, programs and personnel to offer programs for (1) unit record systems (though to a reduced extent); (2) computer programming; (3) machine operation; and (4) basic systems analysis and design. From this area will emerge the future staff of computer departments, with the colleges and universities, furnishing managerial timber for the functional areas where the computer will then be the reliable "Machine Friday."

Thomas J. Watson, Jr.
Chairman of the Board
IBM Corporation
White Plains, N.Y.

"The full potentialities of the electronic technique," J. Presper Eckert, the co-inventor of ENIAC, wrote in 1955, "are only beginning to unfold."

As all of us know, he was right. Computers in the United States have multiplied from a handful in the early fifties to more than 60,000 today. Additions per second in representative machines have shot upward from 16,000 in the first generation to a million and a half in the third. Day by day, computers are helping to take on more and more jobs for airlines, banks, power plants, law enforcement agencies, oil refineries, steel mills.

And when we look forward we can see these trends continuing: the number of computers in the world, for example, tripling in the 1970s; computers reaching into new tasks—helping us cut air pollution, speeding rush hour traffic, probing deeper than ever into the depth of outer space and the mysteries of the genetic code.

These prospects excite all of us, and they should. But we should not let them dazzle us into blind optimism. For while our technology has progressed, the crises in our society have remained, and in some instances worsened.

"Who can foresee the consequences of such an invention?" a brilliant Italian wrote in 1842 of Babbage's Analytical Engine. "The idea ... is a conception which, being realized, would mark a glorious epoch in the history of the sciences."

It can and I believe will. But as we look ahead today, we must share an even larger resolve: that our industry do its share to unknot the tough problems about us; that it remember not just the big numbers but the small ones—the single child instructed, the single family helped across the poverty line, the single life saved. By so doing we can truly help usher in a brighter epoch for the individual human being, both in our homeland and around the world.

R. Stanley Laing
President
The National Cash Register Company
Dayton, Ohio

Achieving more productive use of the computer's potential is likely to remain the principal challenge of the data processing industry over the next several years. In today's age of advanced communications, man's "data base" is accumulating at a tremendous rate. The data processing industry must lead the way in making it possible for the businessman, the educator, the scientist and the government official to use information more effectively.

We now have computers with enormous memories, vast computational ability and internal speeds measured in billionths of a second. Peripheral equipment of many different types has been developed to move information into and out of the computer itself—magnetic tape units, high-speed printers, cathode ray terminals, optical scanners and a host of other advanced machines.

Yet it is in the area of improving these input and output devices that tomorrow's greatest progress will have to be made. We must narrow the current performance gap that exists between the central processor and its associated I/O equipment. Remote data terminals, sophisticated visual and graphic display units, automatic copying equipment, voice response units and revolutionary computerized indexing systems will, in the future, be linked to huge central data banks. These and other devices, some still in basic research, will allow tomorrow's computer user to establish a closer, more dynamic relationship with the wealth of information now available.

Considering the information processing industry's vast technological capability, there is virtually no limit to the hardware which can be developed as circuitry reaches new thresholds of miniaturization, dependability and economy and as the storage density of memory devices increases beyond the current state of the art.

None of this in itself, however, can enable the data processing industry to reach full maturity in the years ahead. Rather, the manner in which the hardware is used—that is, systems design, programming and other software and supporting services—will be the critical factor in the industry's future development.

To achieve this potential, great emphasis will have to be placed on new teaching techniques. Exposure to new concepts must be carried to the highest management levels. This is because creative computer usage requires considerably more than top management's installing an advanced system and then standing by while someone down the line makes all the decisions on what to do with it.

But such involvement will be worth the time and the effort which management brings to the challenge. A new era of control is within our grasp—an era in which the computer's incredible power to manipulate data, to help us with mathematical modeling and problem simulation, will be increasingly employed. It will be an era which goes beyond any preoccupation with impressive and costly physical systems alone. It will be open to virtually every organization which has the intuition, imagination and intelligence to logically structure problems which need to be solved and then to employ the incredible new tools now evolving toward that end.

Robert E. McDonald
President
UNIVAC
Philadelphia, Penn.

Contributions to computer technology are no longer confined to any one country. They are on a global scale. Yet, despite the obvious increase in knowledge, internationally, much has been said about a so-called "technology gap" existing between America and Europe.

Although there may be some disparities in certain areas, our experience has shown that we have learned a great deal from advances being made in computer technology and applications in Europe and elsewhere in the world.

Opportunities for the computer industry in the international sphere are truly staggering. Living standards are rising in many countries and, as new buying power appears, the avenues for business to help fill the needs of millions of people seeking a better way of life are constantly being broadened.

Application of computer technology to the growing demands of international science, business and industry is extremely challenging for both the user and the manufacturer. As the nature of the work accomplished by the computer becomes more sophisticated, the more we are able to understand the full capabilities of data processors.

Now, more than ever, businessmen throughout the international environment need the ability to analyze thousands of facts and to organize them into reliable information with which management can make vital decisions. Computer technology gives them this ability and enables them to establish proper, solidly based management information systems from which they can obtain meaningful, timely, accurate information for the ultimate benefit of business guidance and administration.

Frank W. Field
Assistant Vice-President
Business Information Systems
Bell Canada
Montreal, Quebec

The future of EDP depends on hardware, communications and people. As a major supplier of telecommunications in Canada, we are vitally involved in this future in two ways: As a supplier of telecommunications links between user and computer, and as a major user of computers for its own needs.

Canadians—long-time holders of the record for being the world's most avid users of the telephone—will perhaps achieve another world record involving use of the telecommunications network for data transmission. New facilities, new service offerings and rating arrangements will be required as the communications industry grows and facilitates the future development of EDP.

There is no doubt that many manufacturers will provide us with ever-improving hardware and software. The challenge will be to resolve the problem of economically harnessing available technology to better do the essential things.

The major key to the future, which at the same time is the major problem, lies with the people involved. Remote job input, on-line terminal ranging from Touch-Tone telephones to improved cathode ray tubes and computers of various sizes, will remove EDP from the computer room and give many people a real on-the-job computer interface. More and more computer and system skills will be required to do almost every job. The "people" problem of today will be magnified many times and will pose a major challenge in the future of EDP.

Questions:

1.   Discuss the future of data processing personnel based upon the varying viewpoints offered in this article.

2. Discuss the possibility of a nationwide computer utility, much like telephone or electric service, based upon the varying viewpoints offered in this article.

3. List the areas in which you feel the computer will have the greatest impact in the next decade.

THE COMPUTER COMES OF AGE

BY NEAL J. DEAN

FOREWORD

The most successful U.S. manufacturers today are making much greater and more sophisticated use of the computer than they were just three years ago. This is one of the findings of a recently completed survey by Booz, Allen & Hamilton Inc. of 108 leading manufacturing companies. The study shows, in addition, that only 11 of all the firms surveyed do not have a top computer executive at the corporate level; that there is a tendency for more senior managers to become involved in computer activities; that the computer is penetrating management functions other than finance and administration; that certain patterns are forming in use of various types of persons in computer activities; and that individual company computer costs range from $200 to $34,000 per $1,000,000 of annual sales, with the average cost being 0.56% of sales.

Mr. Dean, a Vice President of Booz, Allen & Hamilton Inc., is in charge of the firm's management systems group, which includes the computer systems division. Formerly head of electronic data processing consulting activities for the Ramo-Wooldridge Corporation, he has had over 18 years of experience in the design and application of automated information systems.

The survey to be reported on in this article is the second such study made by Booz, Allen & Hamilton Inc.[1] The 108 manufacturing companies covered were selected on the basis of their superior records of sales growth and return on equity compared to the averages for their industries. Every significant manufacturing industry group was included. The companies' experience with the computer ranged from one to eighteen years. Annual sales volumes ranged from under $50 million to more than $10 billion. Both centralized and decentralized companies participated. The manufacturing processes of the companies included "continuous process" companies which convert raw materials into finished products by a flow-through process, "fabrication and assembly" companies which build discrete finished items from component parts, "industrial products" companies which make products that are used largely by other businesses and by the federal government, and "consumer products" companies which make items used by the general public.

---

[1]The first was reported by Neal J. Dean and James W. Taylor in "Managing to Manage the Computer," HBR September-October 1966, p. 98.

EMERGENCE OF THE 'TCE'

A significant finding of the study is the emergence of the top computer executive (TCE). In one way or another, this man is responsible for the company's computer effort. He typically coordinates the activities of other computer managers and is responsible for overall quality, performance, and forward planning in the company's computer effort. In almost all instances, the TCE is found at the corporate level, and most managements seem to feel that it is absolutely necessary that he have considerable power. As one TCE said:

"You must have centralized direction as well as centralized coordination if you expect to manage information systems successfully. Centralized coordination alone without corporate direction wouldn't give us the compatibility of systems that we must have to compete effectively in today's market."

Of the 108 companies covered in this survey, 97 have established such an executive position. As shown in *Exhibit I,* a TCE is found in different reporting relationships in these companies. This relationship tends to be determined by the general pattern of organization in each firm. In about one third of the companies, the TCE reports to corporate controllers; in the remaining two thirds, he reports directly to a president or vice president who, in turn, reports directly to the president.

The TCE performs his role in ways similar to those of other top corporate executives. As shown in *Exhibit II,* he may direct all computer activities on a centralized basis, or provide overall direction to decentralized computer

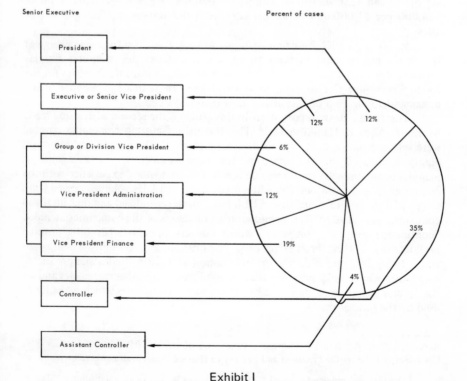

Exhibit I

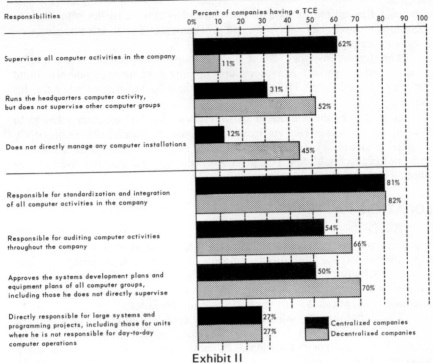

Exhibit II

groups—or do a little of both, if the company organization pattern contains elements of both centralization and decentralization. Whether his management is direct or through other managers, he is expected to be on top of all computer activities in the company program. An oil company executive made this comment:

"Centralized control and decentralized operations of data processing is our present practice. We had a lot of duplication of effort, so we decided to centralize the control of our computer effort. This move runs counter to the basic organizational philosophy of the company. But we are attempting to seek equilibrium by decentralizing control over expenditures and by adding to the autonomy of operations."

A key part of the TCE's job is working with noncomputer executives, who are becoming more and more involved in specifying what the computer is to do for them. This is particularly true because of the increasing trend toward participation of functional, divisional, branch, and plant operating executives in creating short-term systems-development plans. The TCE also works increasingly with the chief executive officer—president or chairman—on the company's overall use of the computer both in current operations and longer-term programs.

ACTIVITIES MANAGED

The TCE, more often than not, is responsible for activities other than the computer activity. In fact, in only 32 companies out of the 108 surveyed are his responsibilities limited to computer activities. His other activities often include operations research, clerical sytems and procedures, and even, in a few instances, broad corporate planning activities.

The study shows that 48% of the TCEs supervise operations research (OR) groups. Clerical systems and procedures are the next most commonly found noncomputer activity of TCEs, with 46% of them having responsibility for this function.

It used to be the practice to assign responsibility for computer activities to a financial executive (or an executive whose responsibilities were largely financial in character). Today, however, only about one tenth of the companies with specifically established TCE positions make financial planning and financial auditing a part of the TCE's responsibility.

LOCATION PATTERNS

Decentralized companies tend to have most or some of their computer operations and systems analysts at division, branch, or plant locations. But in a large number of the centralized companies, too, the responsibility for some computer activities is decentralized (see Part A of *Exhibit III*). There is a clear recognition in these companies that their interests are best served by having the computer where it can directly support company operations.

The dichotomy of having companywide central control and decentralized computer operations has been reconciled in a pattern commonly found in certain other company functions. In both centralized and decentralized companies, there are computer systems planning and development people at the corporate headquarters level. These are the computer systems developers— planning personnel, systems analysts, and programmers. This group assures coordinated development of systems and consistency of hardware and software throughout the organization (see Part B of *Exhibit III*).

The computer systems operating personnel—computer operators, key-punchers, and electronic accounting machine (EAM) operators—working under the direction of this headquarters group, are more commonly found in the divisions, branches, and plants than are the planners and analysts (as shown in Part C of *Exhibit III*). An interesting indication of the importance of on-site computer operations activities is the fact that clerical systems and procedures specialists are less commonly found at branches, divisions, and other decentralized operating locations than are their opposite numbers, the computer systems analysts.

A little more than one third of the companies in this study have computers in foreign countries. The mix of computer people at various locations in these foreign countries generally is similar to that in domestic operations. Those capabilities involved in operating the computer are more commonly found in the operating divisions and plants, while the planners and systems developers are typically located at the foreign headquarters level or at corporate headquarters in the United States.

SPECIALIZED FUNCTIONS

Many companies use computers for specialized purposes—that is, for activities other than processing business information. Often these groups have

Increasing costs for systems planning and programming are consistent with the historical patterns established by companies that have made successful use of data processing capabilities.

When a company initially acquires a computer, its primary need is for programming personnel to convert existing systems to the computer. Later, it obtains systems analysts to improve the already converted systems and to develop new computer-based systems to improve the efficiency and profitability of company operations. However, it is not uncommon for a company to establish a considerable number of systems analysts in separate groups *without coordinating their efforts.*

So, when companies recognize the high cost of duplicate systems, they frequently acquire planning personnel to coordinate the efforts of systems analysts and to ensure standardization of practices and procedures in data processing systems. Professional systems analysts and planning personnel then recognize and move into the more sophisticated systems that need to be developed. For example, operations research personnel may be employed to put mathematical techniques to use as an essential ingredient for capitalizing fully on the benefits of the computer. This sequence accounts for the trends of the figures in *Exhibit VI.*

INCREASING USE

The study clearly indicates a trend away from restricting the computer to finance and administration. It is used more and more often in major operating areas—marketing, production, and distribution. In the next three to five years companies in the survey expect to direct over half of the total computer effort to serving operating areas, and company executives expect to double the proportion of effort given to planning and control (see *Exhibit VII*). This trend toward more emphasis on applications in operating functions is more pronounced as a company's years of computer experience increase.

| | PERCENT OF COMPANIES EMPLOYING SPECIALISTS IN: | | | |
	PROGRAMMING	SYSTEMS ANALYSIS	PLANNING	OPERATIONS RESEARCH
All companies in survey	78%	69%	57%	48%
By years of computer experience				
1-5 years	57	52	43	33
6-10 years	78	66	47	48
11 or more years	90	82	74	54

Exhibit VI

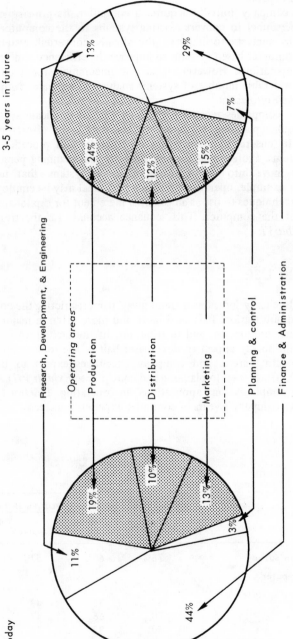

Today

3-5 years in future

Operating areas

Research, Development, & Engineering

Production

Distribution

Marketing

Planning & control

Finance & Administration

Exhibit VII

The study reveals some interesting differences in emphasis among various types of applications within industry groups. These variations directly reflect the characteristics of different types of business and the recognition that different functional areas are critical to a company's success. For example:

☐ In fabricated and assembled products companies, RD&E computer applications represent 18% of the computer effort, and manufacturing or factory applications account for 24% of the computer effort; by contrast, the comparable percentages are 7% and 14% respectively in continuous-process companies. This difference reflects the contrasting requirements of product engineering, production, scheduling, and control in the two types of businesses.

☐ In consumer goods industries, computer applications in marketing account for 16% of total computer effort, as compared to 11% for companies producing industrial products.

SYSTEMS INTEGRATION

The median company in the survey now has some computer systems which are integrated within functional areas; that is, major data processing systems within a function (such as marketing or production) are linked together, coordinated, and run as a unit. In three to five years, the median company expects to have integrated systems which tie together two or more functional areas. And, in the future, all companies in the sample expect their computer systems to be integrated to some significant degree, as shown in *Exhibit VIII.*

Predictably, computer systems in decentralized companies are less integrated now than in centralized companies primarily because of the complexities of multiplant and multiproduct activities. But, the survey shows, in three to five years both centralized and decentralized companies expect to be at about the *same* level of integration of computer systems. In other words, the decentralized companies expect to overcome most of the difficulties of standardizing and integrating diverse and independent product groups.

Most of the companies (82%) also regularly prepare long-range plans to guide their computer activities. The most common time span for long-range plans is three to four years. About a quarter of the long-range plans reported in the survey cover five years or more.

As part of their long-term planning, many companies are investigating the pros and cons of eventual integration of computer activities into total "management information systems." However, most of the companies, including many of those with the longest computer experience, do not intend to go that far in the next three to five years.

PLANNING & CONTROL

Executives of 90% of the companies say they maintain planning and control of their computer operations by the use of a formal short-range plan. Of these companies, over half include in the plan costs and schedules for all projects, while the remaining companies include costs and schedules for major projects only.

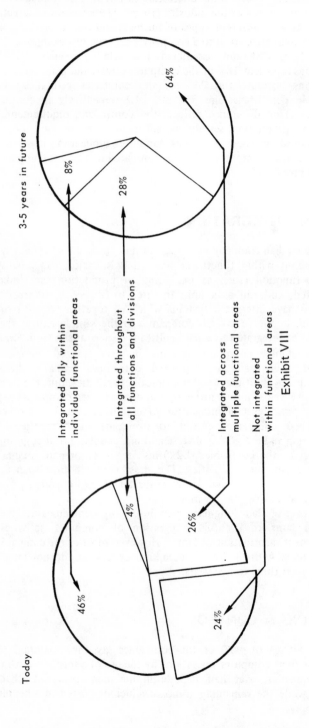

3-5 years in future

64%

8%

28%

Today

46%

4%

26%

24%

Integrated only within
individual functional areas

Integrated throughout
all functions and divisions

Integrated across
multiple functional areas

Not integrated
within functional areas

Exhibit VIII

Short-range computer plans are an important control mechanism in all of the companies in the survey. In more than two thirds of the companies, in fact, short-range plans are the most significant control device for management. In the remaining third, short-range plans are used primarily as guidelines.

Nearly all of the companies in the survey use some measure of relative profit improvement as a means for choosing among different systems projects proposed for consideration. Formal return-on-investment analysis is the major criterion in 24% of the companies, less formal analyses of operating improvement are used in 61% of the cases, and direct cost reduction or other measures of selection are used in the remaining companies.

AUDITING ACTIVITIES

The managements of two thirds of the surveyed companies use regular audits to improve their control of computer activities and performance. The larger the company, the greater the likelihood that management regularly audits computer work. Of increasing significance is the degree to which operating managers are involved in making these audits. The managers typically serve as members of a committee that reviews the findings of the audit and reports to top divisional and corporate executives.

Of the companies that perform regular audits, most (62%) confine the audits to critical computer applications, while the others (38%) cover all areas of computer activity. In the companies performing audits of either type, there is major emphasis on the following activities (numbers in parentheses refer to the portion of the sample engaged in the activity):

☐ Appraisal of budgets for new computer systems developments and new equipment (78%).

☐ Determination of appropriateness of present systems as management and control tools (75%).

☐ Review of the usefulness of present systems to operating people (70%).

☐ Checking on adherence to operating budgets and output deadlines (67%).

☐ Analysis of systems and operations for potential susceptibility to fraud or other financial irregularity (63%).

☐ Evaluation of personnel and management practices affecting computer systems (62%).

☐ Review of adherence to development project budgets and schedules (60%).

CONCLUSION

The computer systems function, not only technologically but also managerially, has come of age. As a result, it has become an extraordinarily important quantitative tool at the disposal of management at all levels in the intense competitive market which manufacturing companies in the United States face today.

The survey clearly shows that the computer increasingly is penetrating and permeating all areas of major manufacturing corporations. Indeed, the computer is becoming an integral part of operations in those companies. Several findings give solid evidence of this. Most of the companies in the survey are expecting to increase their financial commitments for computer services at a rate which is more rapid than their anticipated annual sales growth. In addition, and because of these increasing financial commitments, the chief executive officers are taking a more active role in the computer function of their companies. Increasingly, other levels of management—operating group as well as staff groups—also are participating in planning for computer usage.

Along with this increasing involvement in money and manpower, the computer activity is becoming a more integrated and established part of company operations. Computers are being used more and more for management planning and control as well as for record keeping. More companies are using OR and advanced mathematical techniques in computer operations.

Accepted management techniques typically used in other parts of company operations are being applied to the computer function. Companies are planning, budgeting, and auditing the computer function. More and more often, computer project selection is being made on the basis of overall benefits to the company. Also, the growing number of TCEs at high levels of responsibility in the corporate structure attests to growing recognition of the importance of computer management.

In reporting Booz, Allen & Hamiliton's first study of computer management, an executive was quoted as saying: "Our real goal is to make sure that we achieve more benefits from computers than our competitors do."[2] This kind of aggressive, competitive thinking has doubtless played a large part in speeding the development of computer systems. It also spells a real threat for laggards in such development, for it means that the gap between effective users, on the one hand, and ineffective users and nonusers, on the other, will widen ever more swiftly. The day may not be far distant when those who analyze annual business failures can add another category to their list of causes—failure to exploit the computer.

Questions:

1.   List the functions of the "TCE".

2.   Discuss the concept of systems integration.

3.   Compare the effectiveness of centralized computer systems to decentralized computer systems.

---

[2]Ibid.

A REALISTIC LOOK AT AUTOMATION

BY ROGER W. BOLZ

In today's world it is widely accepted that technology is moving at a dizzying pace but this is mostly an illusion. The real pace of change is far more uniform and gradual than is portrayed in the popular media. This is especially true of automation. Technology is being applied at a rather modest rate *almost exclusively as economic and market needs demand.*

Ignorance and misinformation fostered by reporters and writers have conspired to create a great myth. The great myth is that automation promotes unemployment and is, in fact, antisocial in character. The truth is precisely the opposite. In our advanced economy with its sophisticated markets and products, recourse to automation techniques offers the only practical way to achieve reasonably priced products, mass market satisfaction, and high quality where labor is demanding and expensive.

CONVENIENT MISINFORMATION

In spite of the real story which is and has been available to anyone, the mythmakers prevail. Because the myths make handy weapons during union negotiations across the country, the propaganda is amplified. It is distressing to note that even such an eminent body as the International Labor Organization continues to hold meetings, as they did in May 1967, to discuss "A Plan of Action to Cushion Effects of Automation on Manpower." Sadly enough, all these meetings deal largely with straw men in the supposed form of self-generating technological invasions, while the far-reaching economic effects of their own unenlightened activities are ignored.

The pervasive myth that automation effects must be cushioned in some manner is discussed without ever facing up to reality. The reality is that automation is imperative if: the demand for goods is to be fulfilled; the need for reasonable prices is to be met; a rising wage scale is to be maintained; the number of hours worked is to be reduced; and better working conditions are to be created.

What most of the mythmakers seem to be asking for is a return to mercantilism. Abhoring change, their discussions and recommendations seem to endorse the prospect of no jobs as opposed to the jobs of the automated plant; poorer living conditions rather than better; higher priced goods; limited consumer satisfaction and—as in railroading or newspaper printing—participation in utterly useless work.

How did so practical a manufacturing technology come to be carried to such heights of fancy? Professor Scott T. Poage, head of the department of industrial engineering at Arlington State College, Texas, made the reason quite clear in the Summer 1967 issue of *The University Bookman*. Commented Professor Poage:

"Some of the most learned nonsense in the press has been in the attempts to deal with the problems of the 'impact of automation' and the 'control of the economy' by wonderously educated gentlemen whose comprehension of the processes of control does not extend to the simplest mechanical system, such as a room thermostat, much less the infintely more complex (technical and) economic systems. The root of this sort of scholarly foolishness is the belief that knowledge can be divided into kinds and hierarchies to be maintained 'in balance and proportion.' The only complaint against knowledge in any area must always be that there is not enough."

No single development has been plagued more by these intellectual flights of fancy than the computer. However, it must be agreed that scientists and engineers have helped the condition by giving credence to such fanciful ideas as creating "thinking" computers. Only reluctantly have these undisciplined speculations been tempered. One example of this change is at System Development Corp. The company is now on a new track in attempting to make practical use of computer equipment as a replacement for a long-standing effort to make a computer "think." SDC research director K.W. Yarnold stated in the August 26, 1967 *Business Week* that: "We've fallen off the artificial intelligence soapbox. The subject is in bad intellectual repute; it hasn't lived up to its early promise." Scientists may be on the way toward discovering that the mind operates directly with images in a complex manner that in no way parallels the digital simplicity of the computer as it is presently devised and used.

NEEDED—UNDERSTANDING AND KNOWLEDGE

The main production problems that face both management and labor are far different than those that are ordinarily presented in the popular media. Consequently, few people understand, for example, that ill-timed pressures by labor can and do put an actual end to some businesses with total loss of jobs. The recently defunct newspapers in New York are examples of what can happen. Automation was clearly not the problem in those cases. There is also the big difficulty of not enought knowledge. Highlighting this problem, General Electric's John F. Cronin pointed to the automation failures resulting in wasted funds, countless lost manhours, and plain disenchantment. The causes were inadequate planning and lack of clearly established objectives presented by management.

Entering into the increasingly sophisticated areas of automation technology will *always* be hazardous. It is vital that corporate managers have an attitude of real support and dedication. Genuine understanding must exist. No one can assure success other than the user himself, and management must be ready to risk some funds or there will be no real advance.

A CHALLENGE TO MANAGEMENT

Automation is a practical tool. Used with understanding it can provide major assistance in advancing the economic position of *any* company. The challenge to business management is real and demanding. A forward looking and coherent policy for any management should include the study, consideration, and implementation of these points:

1. *Establish a corporate automation philosophy.* Know and understand the general underlying facts of automation technology, and be ready to accept changes in existing practices. Recognize that automation technology involves an integrated approach to developing and implementing manufacturing and/or services as a total system.

2. *Continually seek to improve productivity and reduce costs.* Recognize that progress will not be painless or automatic. Increasing productivity through automation techniques requires long-range planning supplemented by a manufacturing research and engineering effort.

3. *Create a stable, long-range capital equipment program.* Your competitive position is limited only by imagination and a willingness to use all available resources. Automation is not magic! But carefully nutured and developed over a reasonable time span, it can provide realistic answers to realistic problems.

4. *Know your products and services.* Know their applications and markets. The primary objective of automation is to achieve economic success in new and expanding markets, not to replace people with machines.

5. *Understand the economics of the competitive marketplace.* Lower-cost products and services with improved quality create an increased market demand and increased employment. Correctly applied, automation techniques can lower production costs and increase product quality.

6. *Develop a competently-administered plan or business operating plan.* Regardless of the level of automation, successful operations depend on informed personnel. Well developed lines of communication, as well as a complete understanding of company objectives, are needed to maintain top efficiency in operations.

7. *Actively develop manpower planning to match automation planning.* Develop accurate future requirements, create manpower projections, and apply overall planning techniques to forecasting needs. Also, personnel must be upgraded or retrained to match operational changes.

8. *Set up a good employee relations program.* Such a program should inform and explain the reasons for changing corporate policies. Communicate on a continuing basis. To be an effective member of the total corporate team, every employee must know something about where his company is going and why. Avoid secrecy or the inference of unconcern for your employees.

9. *Establish a continuing, formal or informal education and training program.* Automation demands the retraining or education of all personnel, from management to hourly workers. Expanded horizons offered by such programs relate directly to improvements in efficiency and the variety of talents that must be brought to bear in the use of automation to meet everyday competition.

10. *Finally, remember that what people do not understand, they resist.* Have a continuing information program, either as a formal or informal activity. Promote community and business understanding of your automation policies.

Take every opportunity to communicate and promote your "people planning." Explain your plans for countering outside threats to your business and your employees' jobs.

With this realistic approach to automation, the rewards will be great. It involves the businessman in his *real* social responsibility—education! And, nothing less will be sufficiently effective to reap the real benefits inherent in the ,technology of automation.

————————

Questions:

1. Discuss the controversy of unemployment and the computer.

2. Guidelines for successfully implementing automation are outlined in a ten point program advocated by the author of this article. Comment in detail on each of these points.

A CRITICAL LOOK AT
DATA PROCESSING

BY IRA S. GOTTFRIED

In many corporations throughout the world, top management members are expressing concern about a new problem—the costs and efficiency of the internal data processing organization. With the continual growth and importance of company computer installations, more and more of each company's capital investments and personnel costs are now directly related to data processing. The same seasoned executives capable of carefully evaluating the costs and profit returns of their companies' sales organizations, production facilities and customer service capabilities are finding themselves at a complete loss to apply equal measurement standards to this new and vital function within their corporations. "Just how should we visualize data processing within our company?" "What criteria should we use to measure performance, or strength and weaknesses of our data processing management?" "How do we know that our personnel in the data processing organization are competent and capable of dealing with our major problems?" "What is the relationship of the data processing department to other departments in the organization?" "What will happen if our data processing manager and his immediate supervision were to leave us—could their successors keep our data processing facility going?" These are the types of questions that are frequently being expressed by top management people concerned with survival of firms.

Since data processing has gained a strong influence over policy decisions of the company and has created a dependence upon the information stored within its seemingly unlimited memories, corporate management is justified in worrying about the efficiencies and capabilities of its data processing people and equipment. This article will attempt to provide answers to management's questions, based on experience by our firm in conducting detailed evaluations of many major computer installations throughout the world.

A VIEW OF DATA PROCESSING

The first step in determining a method of evaluation of an existing data processing organization is to recognize its level of impact on company profits, policy, practices, decisions, and organization. Many data processing installations have a significant impact on company budgets due to the cost of equipment, the space and utilities required to house the equipment, the people required to design work for the computer and to operate the equipment, and the large

Reprinted from the August, 1968 issue of the *Journal of Data Management* and copyrighted by the Data Processing Management Association.

amount of supplies required to produce input and output information. If management relates the total budget costs of data processing to the dollar value of product sales necessary to create sufficient profit to cover this budget, the importance of data processing is placed in its correct light. If they further look at its impact on management decision-making and the importance of computer-created information to the daily direct operations of the company, they can then truly recognize that efficient data processing management is essential to the good health of the company.

In years past, management has looked at data processing as an esoteric and sophisticated function, so modern in its techniques that traditional tools could not be used to measure its efficiency or progress. Yet, data processing has within it the same components that a branch factory of a manufacturing concern has. It can be measured similarly. For example, if the more traditional functions of a manufacturing plant are listed opposite those of the data processing function, it can be seen that each component exists in both organizations:

Factory	Data Processing
Research	Systems Analysis
Development	Programming
Prototype	Program Testing
Manufacturing	Computer Operations
Quality Control	Data Controls
Packaging	Decollating & Bursting
Shipping	Delivery Service

Both organizations even have the same problems in scheduling work to meet customer deadlines and in handling problems of customer service and complaints.

If management can accept the concept of data processing as a self-contained factory, they then are in a position to realistically review data processing in the same manner as they would review a separate manufacturing division. The major evaluation elements of such a review can be classified into five categories:

> Organization Arrangement and Capabilities
> Management Controls
> Methods and Quality of Performance
> Equipment Need and Utilization
> Customer Relations.

ORGANIZATION ARRANGEMENT AND CAPABILITIES

Since the organization's structure and the assignment of responsibility and corresponding authority to its members form the basis for its daily operations, management must first establish the environment and policy restraints to be placed on data processing. These may include a review of:

— The importance of engineering data processing service versus commercial applications service;

— Relative priorities placed on the service to be provided to each of the line organizations;

- The degree of initiative expected to be shown by the data processing organization versus its role as a service bureau, reacting only to requests for service;
- The actual commitment of management to modify existing organization, policy and procedures;
- The past history of growth problems and transitions due to new equipment or new data processing management.

The answers to the above inquiries will help to determine the operating climate that has been imposed or developed for data processing.

Questions of structure should then be carefully reviewed to determine existing relationships, assigned responsibilities and authorities, relative status within the management organization, budgeted staffing levels, and promotional opportunities provided to its incumbents. This will help to determine if the organization is structured to meet its role and responsibilities, and if management has provided it with the necessary oganizational status and tools to do its job.

A positive answer to the above then leads us to an evaluation of the people within the organization. We should be able to measure their background for their jobs, the amount of training provided, the organization's ability to communicate internally and externally to the line organizations through meetings, seminars and newsletters; the apparent level of competence of the incumbent management; the steps taken to assure management backup; the apparent attitudes, fears and frustrations expressed through discussion with data processing supervision, and the relationship of the existing salary levels to those within the company and in similar jobs with the industry. A review of these factors frequently indicates an immediate lack in the capabilities of the organization most frequently due to unrealistic salary levels or inadequate training.

The Organization phase should also cover personnel administration techniques within the data processing function. Is management really aware of the capabilities of personnel and have they classified these capabilities to that they can select the right person for each assignment? Is sick time accurately recorded and is it within reasonable limits? Are vacations scheduled to assure adequate shift coverage? Are recruiting techniques competitive with other firms in the community? Are personnel turnover ratios within reasonable limits as compared to the industry instead of the company's probably lower level of turnover in non data-processing functions? Are opportunities for memberships and professional seminars being provided to the staff to assure them continued exposure to new techniques and progress in this fast moving field? Answers to these questions can help indicate causes of low levels of competence or high employee turnover.

Normal salary levels based on years of experience cannot be applied in today's shortage of experienced data processing managers, systems analysts, programmers and operators. Unfortunately, until supply catches up with demand, salary levels will be considerably higher than similar administrative occupations. This also poses the additional problem of assuring high morale and solid management support, since the loss of a competent programmer can easily cost a company thousands of dollars until a replacement is able to pick up the loose strings of a complex system. This factor must be carefully considered in reviewing the needs of the data processing organization.

MANAGEMENT CONTROLS

Our consultants have evaluated many data processing organizations that have competent people but are not performing well. The key factor appears to be the degree of management controls that have been effectively installed by data processing management to assure the most effective utilization of their competent personnel. It is extremely easy to overlook these controls in data processing, especially when management is expending its effort in getting systems and programs completed. But without these controls, costs are bound to skyrocket and the return on investment will be low.

Budget Controls—Data processing management should be expected to exercise budget controls in a similar manner as any other company organization. The key tracking device should be actual costs versus forcasted costs. Many data processing installations perform as a service organization and distribute all costs to their customers, thus zeroing out at the end of each month. For improved control, we prefer that the data processing organization be held fully accountable for all costs and that it be directly budgeted. In this manner, control can be exercised over total company costs for data processing, rather than having to depend upon each organization serviced to provide sufficient funding.

Many companies budget personnel on the basis of money rather than head count. We prefer that both factors be considered since the type of personnel and the payroll are directly related to requests by the customer organizations. Personnel budgets should include the number of programmers, analysts, operators and support personnel by head count and by approximate salary ranges. Both items should be monitored as part of the budget control process.

The review of budget controls should also include a look at how the costs of reruns due to operator or programmer error are charged. Many organizations charge these costs on the customer, yet they are caused internally and should be borne by the data processing organization. This type of budget control will help to reduce errors in programming as well as by computer operators.

Job Procedures and Rules—Data processing analysts are usually astute in assuring that adequate procedures are written for the customers they are assisting. But they do not seem to have the same concern about job procedures and rules for their own organization. An internal data processing procedures manual should cover, though usually doesn't, such subjects as:

— Housekeeping and cleanliness,
— Work performance standards,
— Flow of paper between internal groups,
— The turnover of completed programs to operations,
— The restraint of "moonlighting" work for other companies,
— The assigned responsbility of supervision,
— The authority of supervision including operations shift supervisors.

The above procedures are in addition to those required to assure adequate equipment operation and performance of specific programs and systems.

PERFORMANCE STANDARDS

Most manufacturing organizations have created efficient performance standards as a means of measuring their employees. Yet, few data processing installations have installed similar performance assurance method.

Measurement criteria for data processing should include the following:

— Key punch errors versus ouput quantity,
— Program actual run-times versus programmer estimates,
— Average job set-up time by machine and operator,
— Job turnaround time versus schedule,
— Actual programming costs versus estimate,
— Job reruns and reasons,
— Number of program tests per new program,
— Report outputs late versus on-schedule,
— Program changes versus original specifications.

Each of the above is an indicator for performance measurement. Since each installation operates under different conditions, it is difficult to establish a firm standard applicable to all; however, the above information will quickly permit data processing management to establish new goals and tighter requirements. It is suggested that these measurements be reported monthly to higher management, thus creating an incentive for improved performance.

Advanced Planning—Many data processing organizations operate in a service bureau format—purely responsive to requests from their customers. Others take the initiative in suggesting areas of cost improvement or improved reporting. In either case, it is essential that advanced planning be done to assure adequate equipment and personnel to perform the mission. Yet, many installations exhibit no organized advanced planning and always seem to be in a panic, reactive situation. Master plans should be well documented and submitted for approval by higher management. These plans should cover advance requirements for systems development, equipment, personnel, training, and internal improvement. They should be sufficiently detailed so that all steps necessary to accomplish goals can be determined in advance and that the plans can be monitored to assure timely implementation. Each action should indicate the start and completion dates, and the person assigned responsibility for direction and accomplishment. The system for feedback and evaluation of progress should include measurement against standards and milestones, and should report problems that may cause changes in the advanced planning. Any deviating trends should be easily recognizable and should call for review and possible modification of the plans.

Equipment Controls—Management controls used to monitor equipment usage can be similar to those used in the production factory. Adequate logs should be established to record all equipment downtime with reasons, set-up times necessary for new programs, time allocated to tests of application and utility programs, actual production time, and rerun times with reasons. Each of these elements should be charted for easy evaluation and any trends outside of normal parameters should be immediately investigated. Use of these controls will also permit the data processing manager to periodically review problems with the equipment manufacturer and with operations supervision. These logs also should serve as basis for payment if the equipment has been leased. Many installations have incorporated automatic logging into their Operating Systems and actually print out the time and cost of work on each output report. This also serves to advise the report requestor of the actual cost of his information.

Priority Rules—The interruption of any factory operation in order to run a special priority job causes disruption and schedule changes. Data processing is no exception to this rule. For this reason, the rules permitting special priorities should be carefully documented, and observed. These rules should cover the levels of management that may grant priorities, the criteria and the means of handling work that is delayed due to this special processing.

MUTUAL AID AGREEMENTS

Although present day computer equipment is very reliable, especially when maintained on a regular basis, management nevertheless must plan and provide for the eventuality of extended computer downtime because of failure of one or more of the equipment components. One of the best protections against loss of management information through computer downtime is through a mutual aid agreement with at least two users of similar data processing equipment.

Factors to be considered in establishing such agreements include:

— Compatibility of computer hardware,
— Compatibility of operating system software,
— Protection of company confidential and proprietary data,
— Access to premises during off hours,
— Reasonable method of reimbursement for equipment and supplies usage.

If suitable users are not readily available, equipment manufacturers test centers or commercial service bureaus may satisfy the above requirements, but usually at a much higher cost.

Inventory Control—In a data processing installation of medium to large size, formal inventory control of supplies is a must for efficient production at minimal investment. Without inventory control, it becomes very easy to tie-up a large cash investment in seldom used or even obsolescent printed cards and forms. As an example, in one installation we found over $5,000 worth of new but obsolescent tab wires. In another installation, we found in excess of five years' supply of standard five-part forms paper. In a similar manner to factor techniques, economic order quantities and adequate lead-times should be determined periodically. Standardization of sizes and number of form copies is possible and profitable. In one installation, a comparative analysis reduced 386 different types and sizes of printed paper to 17 standard formats buying via annualized, competitive blanket purchase-orders is another technique that can further reduce costs where large quantities are required.

SUBCONTRACTING

For one-time jobs or peak periods that cannot be performed efficiently by the existing staff, it is wise to consider subcontracting to consulting firms for systems design, to software companies for programming, to service bureaus for keypunching or processing, to equipment vendors for hardware maintenance, or to office service firms for clerical help. Secondary functions such as janitorial services or building maintenance are other types of frequent subcontract.

Costs of subcontracts can easily skyrocket unless they are adequately controlled. One person in the installation should be designated as the subcontracting coordinator. He should assure available budget, certify the need for outside service, review prices for competitiveness, and record obligations and subsequent expenditures.

DATA PROTECTION

Information is the lifeblood of a company. Without historical and current, up-dated information, the company will suffer from"Corporate Amnesia" and be unable to operate. Much if this vital information is stored in a form vulnerable to loss through fire or theft. Protection measures must ensure against complete data loss. Though prime data files can often be reconstructed, the cost is often prohibitive and the effort time-consuming. Adequate storage of data should be provided in fire-proof vaults, and duplicate key data and program files should be stored in remote locations.

Many companies also purchase insurance to cover data re-creation and loss of productivity after a disaster.

STATE-OF-THE-ART RESEARCH

Data processing is a dynamic field. New concepts, methods and techniques are being developed continuously. The company that isn't aware of these new developments may lose its competitive edge or may spend unnecessary time and effort in "Re-inventing the wheel." Some of the means of keeping abreast of the data processing field are through technical magazines, attendance at trade and professional meetings and seminars and visits to other installations. One or more persons in the installation should be assigned responsibility for systematically collecting, reading, abstracting, evaluating and disseminating pertinent and useful information. Association memberships should be centrally coordinated to assure adequate coverage of each organization. Meeting reports should be required and circulated among the professional staff.

Evaluation of the above areas provide insight into how well data processing department management performs its functions of planning, organizing, staffing, directing and controlling.

FUNCTIONAL UNITS

A review of each functional unit within the data processing department provides areas of possible improvement in the day-to-day methods of performance.

Planning and Estimating Unit–Many data processing installations have a back-log of requests for new systems and for changes to existing systems. To be able to plan and schedule these systems effectively, priorities must be established based upon detailed development and operational time and cost estimates prepared according to standard, written estimating procedures. Records should be kept of subsequent actual performance so that the department and its customers can be kept informed of progress and to permit estimating guidelines to be continually improved.

to permit estimating guidelines to be continually improved.

Reception Counter–A great number of existing data processing problems can be directly attributed to lack of adequate control after data has been received by the department. Similarly, poor customer relationship can often be attributed to the inability of service clerks in advising customers on the progress of submitted work. The data reception counter plays a most important role in work flow control; it is the link between the department and its users. The counter should be operated according to standard procedures and be fully aware of current work load schedules and job turnaround times. Specific provisions should be made for faster processing of unscheduled and urgent small jobs. Efficient layout of the counter is important for smooth operations; jobs should be kept separated, in labeled individual containers. The counter should have a system in operation, enabling the tracking of work through the shop and be able to advise programmers of job completion. As appropriate, keypunching of a small number of job cards or program corrections should be readily available.

Input Preparation Section– Source data is normally converted from source records to machine-processable media by keypunch machines. Newer methods such as keyboard to magnetic tape or directly to computer buffer are also coming to the fore. Input preparation work must be scheduled, assigned and controlled to assure smooth flow into operations. For best efficiency, each job should be documented for the keypuncher; program control cards should be standardized; and keyboard layouts should be common. When possible, all fields should be left justified and verification avoided through use of check digits, batch totals and computer edit routines.

Operators should be rotated frequently so that several people are familiar with every job.

EAM Machine Accounting–Many installations still make use of electronic accounting machines, either as an independent data processing unit or as an adjunct to the computer installation. Due to the large volume of punched cards that must be manipulated, considerable discipline is required on the part of the operators. This discipline is reflected through effective work flow from machine to machine, planned and scheduled processing, and use of written processing procedures.

Each machine should be tested at the beginning of each shift and cleaned at the close of the shift. Control panels should be permanently wired when possible and use of panel covers should be mandatory. Formal documentation of wiring diagrams and procedures is as important to this section as it is in the computer room.

Tape and Disk Library–Control of magnetic tapes and disks, carrying data or computer programs, is often overlooked or exercised inadequately, even in the more efficient installations. It is not uncommon to find literally hundreds of tapes devoted to obsolete programs or data. Since tapes are fairly expensive, this represents a sizable but unnecessary investment.

A formal library system, whether manual or computerized, should significantly reduce inventory, indicate when a tape starts deteriorating and needs to be re-certified or replaced, and avoid destruction of recorded information. Access to the library should be restricted to authorized persons. Ideally, the library would be in a fully enclosed location with tapes to be issued only by the librarian. Tapes must be protected against damage from fire, humidity or dust through good library planning, controlled environment and restrictions against smoking. Color coded labels should be used to differentiate permanent program or master files from rotatable tapes or disks.

Computer Room—Most computer rooms are laid out for effective display of the computer equipment, but are inadequately planned for smooth work flow and data storage. A random visit to most installations is frightening: Data cards are found everywhere, tapes lie on chairs, desks and tape drives, supplies are stacked in traffic lanes, or over floor vents, operators lean or sit on typewriter consoles for lack of chairs, and unauthorized people wander in and out.

Efficient, error free and safe data processing operations can only be realized in a businesslike atmosphere with good housekeeping and only authorized, required personnel. There should be standard, written procedures at the console for job flow, stacking and set-up, handling or console error messages, restart methods, re-runs, and priority jobs. A detailed manual or mechanized log should be kept of all jobs runs and of special problems encountered on each computer room shift.

Emergency procedures should be prominently posted and drills held regularly. Operators should know the location of fire-extinguishers and the individual power and air-conditioning system cut-off switches. The computer should be closed down when no personnel is present and jobs should never be run without an operator nearby.

Programming—Programming is the transitional tool between design and implementation. To assure communication between programs, ease of maintenance, speed in coding and accuracy of results, standards should be established for program language, file maintenance routines, initialization, program modularity and data-named definitions. Data input editing, sorting, merging, re-starts, and data output routines should be standardized and pre-punched sub-routine decks used by all programmers. Documentation of every program should be mandatory, and include descriptive narrative, major routine flowcharts, table lookups or decision tables and data definitions. This is the only way to protect the company's investment in programming time when programmers quit their jobs or have to make changes to programs written by another person.

Systems Analysis and Design—The systems group is responsible for efficient translation of the user's requirements into an operational procedure. Systems effort should be held to manageable tasks that can be designed, programmed and implemented within periods under one year. This assures continuity of organization and personnel and provides results in a reasonable period of time. As with programming, documentation is essential as a communication device with both the user and the programmer.

The systems analyst should be responsible for providing detailed input and output formats, processing requirements and test data. Turnover for Programming should be formalized as should review of system specifications by the user and by internal audit.

Necessary user training, written procedures, and coordination of file coversions should also be accomplished by the analyst. A post-installation audit should be conducted within six months after the sytem has become operational to assure realization of anticipated savings and to identify necessary system modifications.

Equipment Utilization—Many data processing installations utilize only a small percentage of available time and do not benefit from the low second and third shift rates. Some data processing managers are not aware of their equipment has too much or too little capacity for the normal workload.

A basic requirement for utilization analysis is a daily detailed log of machine usage by type of operation. (Production, test, maintenance, rerun). Graphing of these logs will indicate necessary corrective actions such as operator re-training, improving scheduling of routine work, smoothing to reduce peakloads or re-design of inefficient applications.

Installed equipment features should be periodically assessed to determine economic justification. It is surprising how many business installations have floating point arithmetic features which are never brought to use.

Customer Relations—The justification for a data processing installation is the work it performs for its organizational customers. Data processing personnel frequently are so involved in the operations of their department that they may neglect the needs of these customers.

Lack of communication and understanding is a frequent problem that can be solved by several proven techniques. Data processing management can hold regular monthly meetings with major customers to cover mutual problems, progress and solutions. The installation can conduct courses in basic concepts of data processing to give customers a better understanding of modern data processing. In some installations, a EDP complaint box is affixed in the computer room and has served to create a feeling that EDP management is sensitive to its customers' problems. Sponsorship of occasional tours of the installation can also allay some of the fears of line personnel and create a more cooperative atmosphere.

SUMMARY

Data processing departments represent a sizable investment of a company's money in personnel, facilities, equipment, supplies, and time. It is therefore essential that top management realize a pay-off from this investment. Data processing managers can be measured in a similar way to all other functional management. Creativity and efficiency can both be accomplished through adequate and continuing controls throughout the data processing organization.

Questions:

1. Compare the traditional functions of a manufacturing plant with those of a data processing activity.

2. The author has five categories of evaluation elements. Discuss each of these categories.

AMERICAN EDP, TODAY AND TOMORROW

BY FRANK GREENWOOD

Since the first commerical U.S. computer installation in the early 1950's, many companies have become EDP users despite its high costs. The hoped-for benefits of EDP often were real and now typically include lower working capital requirements, reduced operating costs, and improved customer service.

Early computers were relatively slow, with small units of internal storage, and they were often awkward to program. Early applications were mostly scientific and engineering. In the business area they were usually isolated jobs such as preparing the payroll, keeping track of inventories, and billing customers. Commercial computers were usually part of the accounting function, and the EDP unit often reported several echelons below the top financial executive.

After a few years of EDP experience with isolated data processing jobs, companies began easing into integrated data processing, taking advantage of the fact that one transaction, such as a customer's order, can create a chain reaction throughout the firm in sales, purchasing, manufacturing, shipping, and accounting—all the way through to the profit and loss statement. The same information can, therefore, often be used by several functional areas, cutting data processing costs and increasing its speed. Accuracy of the input data is then critical, as is its compatibility with data entering from various parts of the system.

While company experience varies widely, from firms with no EDP to companies with sophisticated applications, a recent survey[1] suggests that the data processing function of a typical large U.S. computer user can be partly described as follows:

The total annual budget for all data processing activities (electro-mechanical accounting machines, plus EDP) is about $1 million, split approximately as follows:

Machine rental or purchase	40%
Operations (material, program maintenance, computer operating staff)	35%
Systems (analysis, programming future applications)	25%
	100%

Most of the hardware is rented from manufacturers, but there is a marked trend toward purchase by the user, or purchase/lease-back arrangements with a third party. Computer expenditures are expected to increase significantly over the next five years. Third generation equipment is installed in approximately

---

[1] *Summary Report of a Survey on the Cost Effectiveness of Software and Hardware,* by the Diebold Group, Inc., 1967.

Reprinted from the June, 1968 issue of the *Journal of Data Management* and copyrighted by the Data Processing Management Association.

one-third of the responding companies, and about another one-third has placed firm orders for these computers.

Another recent study[2] of the most successful American manufacturers suggests that the computer is coming into its own. Almost all the manufacturing companies covered by the study have high-ranking computer executives, two-thirds of whom report directly to the president or to a vice president. The computer executive's role typically includes providing overall direction to computer groups and working with top management and line executives to create systems-development plans. In addition to computer activities, he characteristically supervises operations research (OR) and clerical systems and procedures.

The longer these manufacturers have been using computers, the more the company spends on this operation. The median for the 108 companies surveyed is $5,600 per $1 million of sales. Average computer expenditures are:

Systems planning and programming	29%
Equipment rental	38
Other operating expenses	33
	100%

Rather than being restricted to finance and administration, the computer is being used more in marketing, production, and distribution. In the next three to five years, these companies expect to direct over half the total computer effort to serving such operating areas, and company executives expect to double the computer effort devoted to planning and control.

The median company has computer systems integrated within functional areas, so that in any one function the data processing systems may be coordinated and run as a unit. In three to five years the median firm expects integrated systems tying together two or more functional areas.

Most of these companies regularly prepare long-range plans to guide their computer activities. Over 90% use formal short-range plans which deal largely with project costs and schedules. Two-thirds regularly audit computer activities, mostly restricting themselves to critical computer applications.

The survey clearly shows that the computer is penetrating and permeating all areas of major manufacturing corporations. Indeed, the computer is becoming an integral part of operations in those companies. Several findings give solid evidence of this. Most of the companies in the survey expect to increase their financial commitments for computer services at a rate which is more rapid than their anticipated annual sales growth. In addition, and because of these increasing financial commitments, the chief executive officers are taking a more active role in the computer function of their companies. Increasingly, other levels of management—operating groups as well as staff groups—also are participating in planning for computer usage.

Along with this increasing involvement in money and manpower, the computer activity is becoming a more integrated and established part of company operations. Computers are being used more and more for management planning and control as well as for record keeping. More companies are using OR and advanced mathematical techniques in computer operations.

---

[2]Neal A. Jean, "The Computer Comes of Age," *Harvard Business Review,* January/February, 1968, 83.

Accepted management techniques typically used in other parts of company operations are being applied to the computer function. Companies are planning, budgeting, and auditing the computer function. More and more often, computer project selection is being made on the basis of overall benefits to the company. Also, the growing number of TCEs (Top Computer Executives) at high levels of responsibility in the corporate structure attests to growing recognition of the importance of computer management.

THE FUTURE

Perhaps the current American EDP situation is epitomized by the estimate[3] of a group of automation professionals: that existing computer technology is being applied at about 20% of its potential. This suggests ample scope for future developments, the probable courses of which are discussed below.

HARDWARE

Computation is becoming both faster and cheaper. Smaller, faster and cheaper circuits are appearing, as are larger and faster memories. The next big breakthrough in computer technology may be truly cheap, mass random access storage. Communications techniques are advancing rapidly, as illustrated by the spreading use of video units, and remote terminals. Communications between computers is just starting (and may advance until we have a partially cashless society). Manufacturers are striving for compatible equipment, because users oppose the expensive conversions that have normally accompanied equipment acquisitions. There appears to be a trend toward more purchased equipment (including that purchased for resale and lease-back), and perhaps future rental contracts will be on a flat fee basis, allowing unlimited usage. Future hardware may include applications packages that can be "plugged in," much as software packages are now.

Timing is out of alignment in most computerized data processing systems. That is, the computer works electronically in billionths of a second, while another part of the same system operates manually on a time scale calibrated in minutes or even hours. Preparation of input data by keypunching, for example, is among the slowest, most expensive operations in EDP (as well as being subject to human error). Better communications—for both input and output—are needed to get such systems into balance. Consequently, scanning devices will probably eventually eliminate keypunching, converting handwriting directly to tape. Converting voice directly to tape is also a real possibility. As communications improve, EDP systems will be faster, cheaper, smoother and more complete.

One U.S. computer manufacturer describes two of the important trends in equipment design as follows:

First, there is a need for better and less expensive terminals, in addition to the well-known standard teletypes and video displays. Equipment for convenient data acquisition ranges from such trivial devices as badge readers and assembly

---

[3]*The General Electric Forum*, Vol. X, No. 4, Winter, 1967-68, 26.

line counters to such complex ones as signature scramblers and analysers for pass book handling of savings accounts. The need for field encoders to make source data available in machine and humanly readable form is growing extremely fast. Such encoders can be used in every filling station or department store. More specialized, but nevertheless receiving significant interest, are computer connected terminals that can display drawings and by use of a light pen allow modifications of the drawing, allow different perspectives of 3-dimensional objects and other convenient aids to the design engineer or architect. Better and less expensive terminals to be used in schools for computer-aided instruction will be a major market in the next five or ten years.

Second, the extensive use of data gathering and the sharing of computers by many users will increase the need for equipment to store and retrieve large amounts of data. Equipment development for mass storage devices is one of the major concerns of computer manufacturers. Generally, technologies imply that storage devices with fast access are more expensive than the ones for slow access, which means several different types of storage devices will have to be developed. The net result of all these factors will probably be cheaper and more widespread computer usage.

SOFTWARE

Software designers are improving the "engineering" of their product, using macro assemblers, ALGOL-like languages and more efficient compilers. Despite these advances, software has often been available later than scheduled for much third generation hardware, and promised features have sometimes been absent.

Essentially, the software design problem is making the proper trade-offs between what is possible and what is practical. With the power inherent in any good general purpose computer, a great number of things is possible. A much smaller number is practical, economical and reliable. The main software problem is striking the proper balance.

Any given user may find himself helping to pay for characteristics built into his manufacturer-supplied software (i.e., operating systems or executive routine) that he cannot use. He may be helping to meet the needs of other users which he does not share. This may contribute to pushing users to favor tailor-made software in contrast to vendor-supplied operating systems. In due course, software and hardware may be separately priced. Software may go out for bids and then be delivered as a copyrighted package. Computer manufacturers would then compete in the software market as they do in the hardware market. Hardware prices would drop and software firms would grow. These elements suggest that computers soon will be cheaper and easier to acquire and use. Hopefully, this trend will continue to develop naturally, based on sound economic and technological reasons, rather than on a regulated pricing structure.

APPLICATIONS

Presently, computer applications are generally of the "production" type. Commerical examples are: billing by utilities and gasoline marketers and handling of premium processing by insurance companies. Technical illustrations are: simulation of equipment behavior by aerospace firms and solution of equations by weather forecasters.

Which such "production" applications operating reasonably well, and with EDP knowledge beginning to spread, many companies are ready for more advanced applications. Assuming that cheaper random access storage will be available, different "production" applications designed at various times will probably be replaced by more integrated, compatible systems, which will be concerned with the company's most important profit-making areas. This tends to establish a common data base for the firm, so that various users can dip into the same pool of information.

Once a common data base exists, information sharing is a real possibility. Different users at remote locations can simultaneously employ the hardware for computation, data retrieval, and file up-dating. The airline reservation systems are an example of this tendency toward time sharing.

Time sharing applications will probably eventually led to genuine management information systems. Information retrieval, simulation with management science techniques, correlation of facts, predictions, and recognition of trends will all be part of these realtime management information systems.

In general, future applications will tend:

1. to incorporate what were relatively isolated applications into broader systems

2. to integrate more extensively financial and nonfinancial systems

3. to carry out much more work in nonfinancial areas (particularly for manufacturing plants)

4. to consolidate data processing formerly carried out at decentralized points, often using high-speed communications networks as an integral part of the system

5. to provide much faster service to users through real-time systems or systems which, although not "real-time," have some of their characteristics

6. to seek to develop and utilize the concept of the data base and therefore become increasingly concerned with classification, storage and retrieval techniques

7. to integrate OR more effectively into both regular and special data processing operations

8. to require or favor the use of internal (or possibly external) service centers where the EDP equipment and staffs serve a variety of users in a variety of ways and where problems of scheduling and priorities and of administrative and organizational relationships become both more difficult and more important.

9. to seek more and more to serve the needs of top management in planning, controlling and making the major decisions affecting the future of the company.

ORGANIZATION

Information processing activities are widely regarded as one unit, so that computer operations, programming, systems and related functions often all report to the same individual. Cheaper random access storage, better communications and other factors seem to be moving many companies toward having all their information in one place, retrievable as needed. Such corporate data files require centrally controlled data defintions and formats. These data bases support management reporting systems. One can infer from these assumed trends that EDP will become a major function in many companies, on the same level of importance as the traditional line departments. Therefore, EDP will be raised to report higher in many firms. Also, EDP may tend to encourage centralized decision-making, probably leading to some flatter organizations with fewer levels of middle management. On the other hand, lower-unit-cost communications facilities offer the possibility of central data files (for lowest D.P. cost) and decentralized decision-making through lower cost communication networks.

TOP AND MIDDLE MANAGERS

It is becoming clear that EDP raises management's power to make accurate decisions by improving their timely knowledge and factual analysis through devices such as exception reporting and simulation, and that, properly used, EDP can give a competitive advantage because of such results as better decisions and reduced reaction time. Consequently, EDP will have a big impact on the way enterprises are managed.

As the costs of computing and storage come done, retaining and processing historical data becomes economical and a corporate-wide data base is practical. This data base is a fundamental requirement for an integrated management reporting system, which supplies top management with whatever information is wanted when it is required—making EDP a tool that directly supports top management in running the company. The spread of integrated management reporting systems will require mangers to be more analytical and creative.

Middle managers will probably find that, as EDP develops, it takes over much dull, repetitive work and that programmed decision rules automate part of their control function. Computers should give middle managers better tools upon which to base decisions and to take risks. This will improve the quality of the training grounds for top managers. Middle managers whose roles have primarily involved the organization or the retrieval of data will need to extend themselves to find new roles, but computers will thereby offer them the possibility of growth.

COMPUTER UTILITIES

Knowledgeable individuals predict that within a decade much of the data processing in America will be done by computer utilities. Such forecasts usually point to the roughly analagous situations in electricity and communications, noting that it has not been practical for most users to each generate their own electricity, or to maintain their own telephone system. Champions of this idea say that it will be advantageous to many users to employ computer utilities offering large, centralized computers with sophisticated, extensive software to many widely-scattered clients. This concept appears to be particularly promising where the users are interrelated so that common programs could be used.

Using a computer utility instead of having a captive computer would typically offer advantages such as: access to a bigger computer and to better software than users could afford for themselves and reduced initial costs because equipment selection problems would be nonexistent and software would already be available. Among the disadvantages would be: the problem of security for confidential data, the standardization requirements, and the transmission costs.

Overall, it appears that those who forecast early and heavy use of computer utilities are on sound ground, and managers of systems analysis may increasingly recommend this alternative.

THE MANAGER OF SYSTEMS ANALYSIS

That these American developments are also the trends in the U.K. and on the Continent is suggested by a British computer manufacturer who summarizes them and notes their effect on the systems analysis manager as follows:

The future trend in computer usage is towards Management Information, that is, providing the correct information at the correct time and the correct level throughout the whole company structure.

This means that conventional applications such as payrolls, invoicing, stock control, etc., will become of less importance in the overall system than was the case in the past. Each of these types of applications will be used as a source of information for improved management control. In addition, other applications will be used to an increasing extent, such as discounted cash flow techniques, marketing, simulation models, and applications peculiar to the companies concerned, such as engineering, transportation, PERT, linear programming, etc.

Thus a computer system, as least in a medium to large sized organization, will have to handle a very much larger amount of data than in the past, and will be used in many more areas and by more staff within the organization. This means that the leading systems analyst will have a much more complex task in co-ordinating, planning and designing the system. To do this effectively there will have to be a higher degree of specialization at the lower levels in the various applications that are used.

The effect on hardware can be summarized as follows:

1. An increased use of large, fast central processors, with satellite processors in large organizations or organizations that are widely dispersed geographically.

2. An increased use of large random access storage devices.

3. Provision of data capture equipment in greater quantity and variety to feed information direct from its source into the system, and so eliminate or reduce as much as possible the manual processes.

The software requirements will be more complex and cover a much wider field than in the past, and from the cost and effort aspects will become of greater importance than the hardware. In particular, the provision of software for controlling the system will be of major importance. There will also be an increasing need to standardize data identification and file format.

As the EDP function reports higher, the job of the systems analysis manager will be more demanding. He will be expected to operate at or near the policy-making level and to help solve the problems of general management. Therefore, both he and his staff will have to be more capable, able to take part in actually running the company.

Applications packages are taking over the systems analysts' traditional role of designing and implementing "production" systems. Instead of these, the systems staff will work on more challenging projects with technical features such as the following:[5]

1. With on-line systems, programs must often operate within severe time constraints and also within computer memory constraints; data must be protected from damage or tampering; the system reliability requirements may be severe because when the system is down, everyone will know it.

2. With data communications systems, the different remote terminals often will have different transmission rates, data codes, and control codes; errors must be detected and handled without a loss of data, if possible; message routing can be complicated, including multiple destinations in store-and-forward systems and the need to recover messages previously transmitted.

3. File design will be more complex and must meet not only "production" requirements but also the need to answer complex inquiries rapidly; file size may be huge, measured in tens of even hundreds or *billions* of characters for even medium-sized organizations; file growth will be irregular and must be accommodated without reprogramming.

4. Management science techniques will be more widely used, including the use of simulation, linear programming, and general purpose statistical techniques; staff members must be able to work with operations research people on projects where such techniques are used.

5. Other technically complex areas with which the staff must become conversant include multiprogramming and multiprocessing, use of remote consoles, use of optical scanning, use of time-sharing, and data retrieval indexing techniques.

The systems analysis manager will not only have to operate at a higher level, but also probably across a broader spectrum. It seems likely that, internally, he will deal with more different company units, and that externally, he will often handle relations with suppliers and customers (whose computers will be directly connected to his).

People will continue to be the path to success or a big headache. Persuading top management, influencing functional managers, and motivating his subordinates will require much time and attention. Systems analysts will continue to be in short supply, so that education and training will make heavy claims on his energy.

While the computer systems analysis function is too new for a trend to be in evidence, it appears that there is a high probability that systems analysts will advance to important executive jobs outside data processing. The basis of such promotions would be knowledge of how the company operates. Because of the nature of systems analysis and design, systems people usually learn a great deal about the company and its people. Thus, systems work is a good training

---

[5]Richard G. Canning and Roger L. Sisson, *The Management of Data Processing* (New York: John Wiley & Sons, Inc., 1967), 59.

ground, and systems people will "outknowledge" their competitors in the functional areas and therefore will probably earn general management positions more frequently.

In conclusion, EDP in America is just coming of age. As this vigorous young technology matures, it will reach the status of a major business function in many corporations and will have an increasing impact on the management of these concerns.

———————

Questions:

1. Discuss the future of the TCE (Top Computer Executive).

2. The author discusses the future of the computer within an organization in terms of hardware, software, applications, etc. State what the author is predicting and speculate on other advancements that you think must be made.

THE FUTURE OF INFORMATION PROCESSING TECHNOLOGY

BY HERBERT A. SIMON

The day before yesterday, in the beautiful and historic city of Guanajuato, I saw the impressive monuments located there that celebrate Mexico's political revolution—*La Alhondiga* and the statue of *El Pipila*. But while exploring the city, I also saw a monument that celebrates today's technological revolution—an electronic computer, in the offices of the government of the State of Guanajuato. Indeed, in the present age, the presence of electronic computers has become a prime symbol of the explosion of technology.

But I must be careful in my use of terms. We use the words "revolution," "explosion'" and "breakthrough" very freely nowadays. Hardly a day passes without a new "breakthrough" in toothpast manufacture or the design of raincoats. If we are to avoid a Madison-Avenue dilution of meanings, we must employ these terms accurately and sparingly. We must ask whether we are really justified in applying "revolution" to contemporary trends in technology generally, "explosion" to information specifically.

PLUS ÇA CHANGE; PLUS C'EST LA MEME CHOSE

Is there in fact, as is so often claimed, an "information explosion"? Why do we think so? If there is one, what does it signify?

Certainly the daily press has no doubts that information is exploding. A single issue of the Sunday New York *Times* yields the following two items:

In the financial section:

Will a full week of shorter trading hours bring happiness to brokerage firms whose back offices are jammed with paper work?

In the news columns:

George A. Miller, a professor of psychology at Harvard, warned that by 2000, the limit of man's mind to absorb information may be reached. "We may already be nearing some kind of limit for many of the less gifted among us, and those still able to handle the present level of complexity are in ever increasing demand."

These two items are simply a more or less random sample from the very much larger number I could quote—the first two that came to hand. The first conjures up a fascinating picture of the Stock Exchange slowly submerging under a tide of paper; the second promises prosperity to "those still able to handle the present level of complexity"—and I assume that means all of us present here.

Reprinted with permission from the May, 1968 issue (Vol. 14, No. 9) of Management Science Magazine, a publication of the Institute of Management Sciences.

How can we assess these developments, and the others like them? How valid are the predictions of the impending Flood? To answer those questions, we must sort out the elements of stability and the elements of change in human affairs.

Change—extremely rapid change—there certainly is along technological and economic dimensions. We know that technology is advancing with great speed. We know that it is *beginning* to make possible for the first time in human history the elimination of acute poverty. We know that it is even providing means for combatting the over-rapid growth of population—the most serious threat to that prospect of banishing poverty.

But (there is always a "but" at this point in the argument), if we measure the world by Man, by his values and his goals, we have good reason to doubt whether it is changing very much at all. Lesson 21 in the Spanish grammer I brought along to this meeting, provides me with a splendid commentary on the stability of human affairs. In translation, the lesson reads:

> News! I finish reading the paper. I have learned that prices have gone up. The weather continues to be bad and there may be a storm tonight. No solution has been reached in the dispute between the union and the factory management; it is probable that there will be another strike. It appears doubtful that the political parties will reach an agreement. The international situation is not improving. The other news is the same: accidents, crimes, deaths, births, and weddings.

I am sure the author of that passage intended it as no more than a lesson in Spanish vocabulary. It turns out to be a good description of the human condition—a condition that has not changed much since Greek times. Or since the time of Cervantes—for the adventures of Don Quixote are highly suggestive of events in the world today—even including tilting at windmills.

We must not suppose that with the progress of technology, or even with the progress of our economies, mankind will become deliriously happy. For Man's aspirations have a way of adjusting to his opportunities. We must not expect that technological progress will produce Utopia; it is reasonable to hope that it will bring relief to acute hardship and acute pain.

AN ESSAY INTO PREDICTION

With these cautions and reservations, let us turn back to the technology itself and examine the changes that are taking place in information production and processing. Ten years ago, at an ORSA meeting in Pittsburgh, Allen Newell and I made some very specific ten-year predictions. I wish I could tell you now—since the deadline for the predictions is almost here—that each one had been exactly fulfilled. Unfortunately, that isn't the case. But rather than take much time here either to defend or to explain away our past predictions, I will simply make a few general comments about them, and then exercise proper caution by eschewing predictions for the future.

If I were to defend our predictions, my defense would take these lines: All of the predictions were wrong in detail, but they were correct in their general import: the trend they foresaw and the rate of change. We did not guess correctly how research efforts would be allocated to specific areas, and we did not guess correctly the rank order by difficulty of specific problem areas. Hence, although musical composition, chess playing, and theorem proving by computer have made important progress, they have not yet reached our ten-year targets.

On the other side of the account, fundamental understanding of natural language and progress in construction of high-level computer languages have advanced more rapidly than we would have dared predict a decade ago, as have automatic design by computers, visual displays for man-computer on-line interaction, and automatic character recognition.

Hence, in the light of the decade's progress, we remain unrepentant. We see no reason to revise our basic thesis: that electronic computers are general-purpose information-processing devices; that we will step-by-step learn to do with them any kind of thinking that Man can do; that with the help of computer simulation techniques, we will learn (and are learning) how Man thinks, and we will learn how to help him to think better.

ATTENDING TO THE INFORMATION THAT IS THERE

Grant me the premise for the moment that the technology of information processing is progressing as rapidly as these claims would imply—and the TIMS program at this meeting provides much additional evidence for that premise. If this is in fact occurring, why *won't* there be an information explosion? Let me propose a metaphor to explain why there won't—or needn't—be.

The mountain climber, Mallory, when asked why he wanted to climb Everest, gave his famous reply: "Because it is there." Not all of us accept that reply, at least for ourselves. Not all of us aspire to climb Everest, or would look forward to the prospect with any relish or sense of purpose.

Now it is possible to be just as skeptical about processing information as about climbing mountains. Specifically, *information doesn't have to be processed just because it is there.* The telephone doesn't have to be answered just because it is ringing; the newspaper doesn't have to be read just because it has been tossed on our doorstep.

I hasten to acknowledge that information is sometimes ignored at our own peril. The inexhaustible Sunday *New York Times* again provides an example:

Tag Petersen, a traffic controller at a railway signal station told a court Friday that he permitted a train to go on Thursday although signals indicated the track was not clear. Since he had not heard from another train on the same tracks, he assumed it was in Nyborg, 20 miles to the East, according to schedule, and that the signals on his control board were in error.

In spite of this example, and others of the same genre that could be produced, we are more often guilty of the opposite error—of supposing that all would be well "if we just had more information." I turn once more to the *Times* for an apt illustration:

A Nobel Price winner at Stanford University thinks it is time for the polls to go to the people instead of the people going to the polls. "I believe that our engineers are in an advanced enough state to put a simple electronic voting device in all homes," said Professor Robert Hofstadter, a 1961 prize winner in physics.

A qualified citizen could vote, say, in his own living room. Professor Hofstadter said "modern computers can assemble the data almost instantaneously and flawlessly to give a definite result on the issue."

We recognize this as an example of a pathetically naive belief in the "technological fix." The following is a more frightening example (for, after all, we do not take physicists too seriously when they sound off on politics):

The U.S. State Department, drowning in a river of words estimated at 15 million a month to and from 278 diplomatic outposts around the world, has turned to the computer for help. Final testing is under way on a $3.5 million combination of computers, high-speed printers and other electronic devices. Officials say these will eliminate bottlenecks in the system, especially during crises when torrents of cabled messages flow in from world trouble spots.

When the new system goes into full operation this Fall, computers will be able to absorb cable messages electronically at a rate of 1,200 lines a minute. The old teletypes can receive messages at a rate of only 100 words a minute."

A touching faith in more water as an antidote to drowning! Let us hope that Foreign Ministers will not feel themselves obliged to process those 1,200 lines of messages per minute just because they are there.

ATTENDING SELECTIVELY

It is ridiculous to suppose that we can save ourselves from drowning in information by installing faster printing devices. *Lack* of information is not the typical problem in our decision processes. The world is constantly drenching us with information through eyes and ears—millions of bits per second, of which, according to the best evidence, we can handle only about 50.

Saturation and information is no new thing. The movements of the stars, visible to Man throughout the tens of thousands of years of his history, contain all the information that is needed for Newton's Laws of Motions or the Law of Gravitation. The information was there all along. What was lacking, until a few hundred years ago, was the basis for selecting the tiny fraction of it that could be used to establish powerful generalizations.

We cannot avoid living in a world that drenches us with information—whether made by Man or nature—but we *can* select for our processing the information that is likely to be useful to us, and ignore the rest. Gertrude Stein, in the opening pages of *The Autobiography of Alice B. Toklas,* said: "I like a view, but I like to sit with my back turned to it." We can follow Miss Stein's example of independence from the environment of information. Our scientific and technological knowledge, our decision-making and information-processing systems are means for permitting us to turn our back to the view—or to gaze on it very selectively, extracting from it just the parts we want.

In the same vein, most of the contemporary concern about the information explosion in science is misconceived, because it is based on an invalid model of the nature of scientific progress. Science does not advance by piling up information—it organizes information and compresses it. A generation ago, for example, organic chemistry was a mass of particulars only weakly organized by known theoretical generalizations. Today, although knowledge of organic chemistry has grown vastly, the principles of quantum mechanics provide powerful organizing means for that knowledge. As a result, it is undoubtedly easier today to gain a mastery of organic chemistry adequate for doing significant original work than it was in an earlier era when there was very much less known.

The example I have chosen is a spectacular, but not an isolated one. In the scientific endeavor, "knowing" has always meant "knowing parsimoniously." The information that nature presents to us is unimaginably redundant. When we find the right way to summarize and characterize that information—when we find the pattern hidden in it—its vast bulk compresses into succinct equations, each one enormously informative.

A SCIENCE OF INFORMATION PROCESSING

Herein lies the real significance of today's information revolution. Information and the processing of information are themselves for the first time becoming the objects of systematic scientific investigation. We are laying the foundations for a science of information processing that we can expect will greatly increase our effectiveness in handling the information around us.

Thus, at a time when we are acquiring devices that will both transmit and process symbols at unprecedented rates, the most important change that is occurring is not the growth of these devices but the growth of an information science or computer science that will help us understand them. It is the growth in our understanding of how information can be transmitted, how it can be organized for storage and retrieval, how it can be used (and how it is used) in thinking, in problem solving, in decision making.

This growing understanding of information processing returns to us the decision of whether information must overflow and we must drown in it. It returns to us that decision, just as advances in medicine return to mankind the decision whether population must overflow, and we must drown in our own numbers.

A major task ahead for science and technology is to design effective information-processing systems for making decisions in business and in government. It is important that we talk about designing "information-processing sytems" and not just designing "computers." This choice of terms is not meant simply to emphasize that the computer programming system—"software"—is at least as important as hardware. That is true, but it is only part of the story. The design of such systems must encompass far more than the computer hardware and software; it must handle with equal care the information-processing characteristics and capabilities of the human members of organization who constitute the other half of the system.

For generations to come, although the systems we call organizations will have some mechanized components, their most numerous and most crucial elements will continue to be men. The effectiveness of these systems in handling problems will depend more heavily on the effectiveness of thinking, problem solving, and decision making that men do than upon the operation of the computers and their programs. Hence, in the period ahead of us, more important than advances in computer design will be the advances we can make in our understanding of human information processing—of thinking, problem solving, and decision making.

A TASK FOR MANAGEMENT SCIENCE

Management scientists will play a major role in these developments. They will carry a heavy responsibility for raising the level of rationality in the organizational decisions that will affect the fate of millions, sometimes even billions, of men.

Perhaps, if they are effective and fortunate, they will be able to raise the quality of decision making in executive offices and chanceries to the point where the disasters that inept problem solving all too frequently bring on us will become rare events.

Don Quixote symbolizes forcefully Man's frequent and pathetic incapacity to understand the world in which he lives. But Don Quixote, in the end, recognized his own madness and gained his freedom from it.

And so, in a world that sorely needs balance and clarity of thought, in a world where Man sometimes appears dangerously mad, we may be able, with out growing understanding of the technology of information processing, to restore a measure of reason.

Questions:

1.   What is an "information explosion"?

2.   Illustrate the characteristics you would expect in an information processing system.

THE COMPUTER INDUSTRIES GREAT EXPECTATIONS

BY GILBERT BURCK*

Never before has the stock market shown quite so much enthusiasm about an industry as it has lately about the computer industry. Recent prices of computer stocks represent some of the highest price-earnings ratios ever recorded. Even the shares of giant I.B.M., which increased sixfold between 1957 and late 1966, have doubled since. In July the market valued I.B.M., whose physical assets amount to less than $6 billion, at more than $40 billion—more than any other company in the world, actually as much as the gross national product of Italy. And the market value of smaller and newer companies in the industry has gone up even more steeply than I.B.M.'s. In less than three years the price of the University Computing Co. of Dallas rose from $1.50 a share (adjusted for splits) to $155. The stock market valued this newcomer, whose sales last year were less than $17 million, at more than $600 million.

Wall Street's bullishness is not shared by everyone inside the industry, but it matches the dominant industry mood. Except for a minority of skeptics, computer men believe their business is entering an era in which all but the incompetent or the inordinately unlucky are destined to fare handsomely. Hardly a decade old, the electronic data-processing industry has already waxed faster than any other major industry, any time. During each of the past two years it has grown a stupendous 40 to 50 percent, depending on how growth is measured. Although the annual production of computers and related hardware is expected to flatten out a $4 billion to $5 billion during the next three years or so, the value of the nation's general-purpose computer installations, now about $15 billion, is conservatively expected to more than double by the end of 1972.

By then, U.S. business, government, and science, which are now spending at least $8 billion a year buying, renting, programming, and operating general-purpose computer systems, may well be laying out upwards of $18 billion a year. According to the generally accepted forecast, what's more, this growth will be accompanied by total profitability. Most of I.B.M.'s larger competitors have been forced time and again to postpone realizing their profits. Now some are at last beginning to make money, and before long practically all will be in the black. And over the next decade, as the total market doubles and triples and even quintuples, it should provide profitable opportunities for many other companies. So, at least, runs the prevailing view in the computer industry.

Some optimists, indeed, see no clear end to the increase in demand for computers and all that goes with them. A computer installation is a piece of

*Gilbert Burck is an editor of FORTUNE Magazine.

Reprinted by permission of FORTUNE © Time, Inc. August, 1968 capital goods, but it differs from other kinds of capital goods in that its potentialities cannot be gauged with even rough precision. A company buys a drill press or a lathe for a well-defined purpose, expecting to realize a calculable return. Within narrow limits, it can use only so many new drill presses or lathes. But once it buys of leases a computer for a specific purpose, it discovers this machine can be put to numerous other uses. More and more of these uses, such as improving the quality of management decisions, are quite unmeasurable. The computer is becoming a device for enlarging brain power, which cannot be costed like machine power, and the electronic data-processing industry is becoming the knowledge-expansion industry, whose limits are indefinable. Thus the market for computers, the argument goes, is limited only by the industry's own ability to sell customers on new uses for the machines.

THE HIGH COST OF SUCCESS

This exhilarating prospect, however, may be overdrawn. I.B.M.'s major competitors may find the struggle harder than they now anticipate. So may many newcomers that have achieved success overnight with the temporary advantage of a technical innovation or a special marketing skill. And the whole industry may be running into difficult, if transitory, problems because the profit-making potential of computer systems, though increasing all the time, may take longer to realize than is now generally supposed.

What I.B.M.'s competitors may yet be up against is well illustrated by what they have experienced in the past. I.B.M., which still accounts for about 70 percent of the nation's total computer-manufacturing business, accounted until recently for more than 90 percent of the industry's profits. Far behind, in roughly the following order, marched Sperry Rand, Honeywell, Control Data, R.C.A., Burroughs, N.C.R. (National Cash Register), Scientific Data Systems, General Electric, and Digital Equipment Corp.

All entered an industry whose profitability they correctly appraised as extraordinary, not to say stupendous. Profit margins, as profit margins are ordinarily reckoned, can run to more than 35 percent of the cost of making the hardware and confecting the basic "software," the detailed instructions involved in using the hardware. The only catch is that it takes time to realize such a return. More than 85 percent of the new machines are leased at rates calculated to return their list price, which itself includes a generous profit, within four to five years. But installation costs, "support" activities, and marketing expenses are particularly heavy in the first two or three years. Most companies, moreover, use accelerated depreciation, which means they charge off a large percentage of costs in those early years. So revenues do not overtake costs for at least three years; and even then a company cannot realize a profit unless it rests on its oars. For, curiously enough, if it sells aggressively and successfully, it has to keep laying out huge sums to develop and build new machines and to compose software for them; the more successful it is, the more expensive its success becomes. Not until rental revenues build up to the point where they cover research and development and start-up costs on new machines does a company make money.

A few companies, notably Control Data of Minneapolis, Scientific Data Systems of Santa Monica, and Digital Equipment Corp. of Maynard,

Massachusettes, got around this bind from the start by turning out big computers for universities and scientific institutions, which often bought the machines outright. But the rest of I.B.M.'s competitors had to struggle with delayed revenues and mounting capital expenses and wait for the day when their rental money would begin to pile up the way I.B.M.'s did. Moreover, I.B.M. had been dominant in punch-card tabulating machines since the early 1920's. This headstart endowed it with not only a ready-made market for computers but also a continuous profit that still probably runs into nine figures a year. Competitors, however, were not discouraged by I.M.B.'s built-in advantage; sooner or later, they were sure, their rewards would also come rolling in. By the late 1950's, as a matter of fact, many were confident they would soon be making money.

Then came an unpleasant shock. The "first generation" of computers, such as the Univac I and the I.B.M. 701, both vacuum-tube models, had been introduced in the early 1950's. So swiftly had computer technology advanced that within three years these relatively slow machines were growing obsolete. I.B.M. called the turn, late in 1958, by introducing its second-generation 1400 and 7000 series, utilizing solid-state components. Rivals had no choice but to begin marketing their own second-generation machines. By 1960 most of them were so occupied in making and selling new machines and building up their sales and service organizations that their expenses increased much faster than their rental revenues. The day of profitability again receded into the future.

Meanwhile everybody was developing third-generation computers, featuring integrated circuits and higher output at less cost. Early in 1964, just about the time I.B.M.'s rivals were once more beginning to talk about making money, I.B.M. again called the turn by introducing its third-generation family of computers, System/360, on which it had literally staked billions. (See "I.B.M.'s $5,000,000,000 Gamble," FORTUNE, Steptember, 1966.) Once again I.B.M.'s competitors found themselves eating their predictions of just-around-the-corner profits. System/360 hardware was less advanced than many competing machines, and early versions contained many bugs. But I.B.M. corrected the system's faults and pushed it into the market with its usual no-expense-barred aggressiveness. Today System/360 accounts for more than 50 percent of the dollar value of all computers installed and on order.

GOING FOR THE WEAK SPOTS

Some of I.B.M.'s rivals, however, have also been fairly successful with their own new machines, particularly when they concentrated on gaps or weaknesses in the I.B.M. line. Control Data, Scientific Data Systems, and Digital Equipment have been consistently profitable mainly because they did just that. Now three more companies have reached, or almost reached, the happy state of making money on their computers.

Sperry Rand's Univac Division has managed to stay in a strong second place, putting its advanced hardware and wide military experience to good use in special, complex applications such as airline management information systems. Univac has been profitable for two years, and last year actually contributed more to the increase in Sperry Rand's earnings than any other division.

In 1964-65 Honeywell achieved considerable success with its 200 series, which it deliberately built to be compatible with I.B.M. machines; and recently it brought out a whole new line of machines. Since its previous models could not provide enough rentals for an early payout, it achieved profitability swiftly by setting up an equipment-leasing subsidiary, which buys Honeywell computers outright. So Honeywell began to make money in 1967.

Burroughs, strong in the banking market, recently landed $90 million worth of contracts to install remote-terminal systems in three leading British banking chains. Having pioneered in multiprocessor machines, which can handle many programs concurrently, Burroughs also has a strong position in very large computers and supercomputers. It recently sold an advanced supercomputer system to U.S. Steel, which will use it for scientific and engineering work and as a management information system. For the Defense Department and the University of Illinois, Burroughs is building the Illiac, which will contain no fewer than 256 processing (or computing) units, and will push multiple processing "to its practical limit." It is expected, among other things, to revolutionize weather forecasting. Burroughs has been showing steeply rising earnings on its office-equipment business: the company expects its computer operations to be profitable next year, and looks forward to expanding its total earnings handsomely from then on. "We are prepared," purrs President Ray Macdonald, "to live with success."

THOSE DEEP RENTAL POOLS

So among I.B.M.'s major competitors, only General Electric, R.C.A., and N.C.R. have no immediate prospect of making money on hardware. Nevertheless, all three companies are optimistic. N.C.R. has brought out a new line and G.E. says it is making money on time sharing. Wall Street analysts also believe the three will turn a profit on computers sooner or later and will eventually find the business increasingly lucrative. There are, in the main, two reasons for this optimism. One is that the industry's so-called rental pools or backlogs are increasing enormously. An idea of the magnitudes here can be gathered from a study of computer-industry profitability recently prepared by M. James Arachtingi of the Wall Street firm of Auerbach, Pollak & Richardson, which does research for institutional investors. Rental pools of companies other than I.B.M., the study shows, have doubled since 1964, and by 1970 will amount to five times their 1964 size. Since it is already huge, I.B.M.'s pool will, of course, grow less rapidly.

The other reason for optimism is that the industry's growth and profitability do not depend, to the extent they did in 1964, on the introduction of a new generation of computers. The third generation has been remarkably adaptable. It not only does routine jobs such as billing and making out payrolls; fortified with all manner of peripheral equipment—random-access files, auxiliary memories, improved input-output devices—it is being used for advanced applications such as market analysis. So it seems likely that there will be a few radical changes in the fourth generation. It will probably be introduced gradually, perhaps in 1970; its peripheral units and software will probably be compatible with the "architectural structure" of the third generation.

Everything, of course, depends on what I.B.M. does and when. But the industry is inclined to think I.B.M. will adopt the evolutionary rationale—if for no other reason than that, in the words of the Arachtingi report, it does not want to repeat the "horrendous, complicated, and expensive process of implementing a whole new system of programming."

A minority in the industry, nevertheless, doubts that I.B.M.'s competitors will find their new profitability so easy to maintain as they like to believe. Merely to keep their place in this precarious business, they must constantly come up with something better and newer than I.B.M. But it takes both money and scarce technical manpower to innovate, either in hardware or in software. Any resolute, well-planned attempt to beat I.B.M. can chew up the revenues for quite a large rental pool. Thus, in the pattern of the past, competitors constantly find themselves in a net investor position—a position where they must lay out so much money in the hope of attaining their inherent profitability that they are likely to keep on postponing that profitability.

Look at R.C.A., the skeptics say. It was making money on computer manufacturing two years ago. But the costs of developing and introducing its Spectra line, which embodies several technical advances, put it back in the red, where it will remain until at least 1970. Look at G.E., which pumped millions into ambitious projects, only to be forced to retrench by hardware and software failures; gabble in the trade has it that half of G.E.'s technically oriented work force left the company.

According to a common assumption in the computer industry, business is growing so fast that I.B.M.'s competitors need only maintain their share of it to grow sizable and profitable. Rental pools, in other words, will grow to the point where they will be more than sufficient to cover development costs. The skeptics say this isn't always so. As your business increases, one computer executive explains, you may have to expand disproportionately the resources you need to maintain that increase. And despite the general confidence that the fourth generation will make no trouble, there are those who feel that I.B.M. will come up with a fourth-generation product, in either hardware or software or both, that will force competitors to funnel much or all of their rental-pool income into further development.

RAIN UNDER THE UMBRELLA

There is some doubt, indeed, that I.B.M.'s competitors can even be sure of maintaining their combined share of the business. Estimates worked up by Frederic Withington of Arthur D. Little Inc. indicate that I.B.M. accounted for 73 percent of the dollar value of general-purpose hardware shipments in the U.S. last year, against 71 percent the year before. I.B.M.'s world position vis-a-vis that of its U.S. competitors apparently has improved even more. According to a set of figures compiled by one computer-industry specialist (there are no official industry data), total world shipments by U.S. companies increased from $3.8 billion in 1966 to $5.7 billion in 1967, up roughly 50 percent in one year. But I.B.M. expanded its share from $2.7 billion, or 71 percent, in 1966 to $4.25 billion, or 74 percent, in 1967. In other words, I.B.M. copped 81 percent of the total increase. These figures suggest that keeping up with I.B.M. will be harder than it sounds.

Keeping up with I.B.M., some feel, would be easier if the Justice Department forced that company to price its software and hardware separately. Just last May, indeed, this perennial proposal was discussed vehemently at the

Joint Computer Conference, a semi-annual affair sponsored by the whole industry. I.B.M.'s profits on hardware are so great, the argument goes, that it can afford to give its customers free service and software its competitors cannot afford. If hardware, software, and services were priced separately, competition would be fairer.

The trouble with the argument, as the trade paper *EDP Industry Report* has pointed out, is that separate pricing would surely make life tougher for the other hardware manufacturers, which could not hope to cope with I.B.M.'s economies of scale in a more price-competitive market. For the same reason the proposal might also work against independent software companies, whose resources are only a fraction of I.B.M.'s. Separate pricing might also block the development of the new "software in hardware" approach, which involves building basic programming into hardware at the factory. In effect, the *EDP Report* said, the industry is flourishing under the price umbrella of I.B.M., and has more to lose than gain by getting out from under. But it is clear that an I.B.M. rival wanting to make money has to do more than tag along under the umbrella.

One branch of the industry that has been able to make money tagging along is computer leasing. The companies in it buy computers and lease them to users at discounts of as much as 20 percent below the manufacturers' rentals. Manufacturers depreciate their machines over four or five years, but most leasing companies gamble that the useful life will run to ten years. So their books, despite the discounts, show very nice profits. Their big problem is to keep the equipment leased long enough to make it profitable. To reduce the risk of being left with an unwanted machine before it is fully depreciated, nearly all deal only in I.B.M. computers; most, indeed, will not buy and lease other makes unless the customer shares the risk. Quite a few leasing companies are strengthening their positions by moving into software and services. Currently the leasers buy only 5 percent of computer shipments, but this figure will doubtless rise considerably.

Last May the leasing companies scored a point on I.B.M. Until then I.B.M.'s policy was to deny its systems-engineering assistance and educational courses to second-round customers—i.e., to users who acquired I.B.M. machines that had been previously leased to others. This policy, the leasing companies argued, made it hard for them to keep their equipment in use long enough to make money. After Harvey Goodman, president of Data Processing Financial & General Corp., a leasing company, threatened to sue, I.B.M. decided to provide more help for second-round customers. The stock market promptly bid up leasing-company shares.

DATA-PROCESSING LAUNDROMATS

Hundreds of companies are counting on basic changes in the structure of the computer industry to help them latch on to shares of its future volume and earnings. One of these changes is the growing importance of software, whose dollar volume is even greater than the dollar volume of hardware. According to estimates by the *EDP Industry Report,* software outlays in the U.S. this year will come to nearly $6 billion. Of this, some $4.5 billion is being spent directly by computer users, $250 million by independent suppliers, and $1,250,000 by computer makers, whose software outlays are of course included in the price of their hardware. By 1972 the total figure will come to $11 billion. One reason software outlays are rising faster than hardware outlays is that the price of hardware, in terms of work done, is declining steadily. A more important reason is that the third-generation computer systems are being used in increasingly complex jobs, such as capital-investment analysis, resource allocation, sales forecasting, and research and development. Software for this kind of work is complex and expensive. The customer must analyze his problem and structure a model of it before he can write his program. Installing even a relatively simple credit-information system, for example, can use up something like 30,000 man-hours of systems analysis and programming, at about $15 per man-hour.

Although the big hardware companies are continually building up their own software potential, a growing number of independents have established themselves in the field. Among the important ones are Computer Sciences, Computer Usage, Computer Applications, Planning Research, and Computing & Software. Largest and perhaps most aggressive is Computer Science of Los Angeles, founded in 1959 by Fletcher Jones, a North American Aviation computer executive, together with Roy Nutt, a systems analyst at United Aircraft. Chairman Jones, now thirty-seven, has built up Computer Sciences' revenues to an estimated $80 million this year. What's more, he has obtained stockholder approval on both sides to acquire Western Union, whose wire network he intends to use in converting Computer Sciences Corp. into a worldwide service agency.

Jones's ambition is riding with another salient change in the industry—the rapid growth of the so-called service-bureau business. Some 800 service bureaus now gross more than $650 million, and are increasing their take at about 40 percent a year. Although large companies like I.B.M., I.T.T., Control Data, and N.C.R. get much of the trade, many smaller firms are prospering.

In their simplest form, service bureaus offer batch processing. They may be loosely described as data-processing laundromats, to which customers bring batches of calculating and computing work and either wait or come back for the solutions. More advanced are batch service bureaus that provide direct lines to customers, who can feed the data to the computer from their own offices. Many bureaus go further and offer direct access to computers, with immediate response; customers use them for a wide variety of processing jobs, and for retrieving up-to-date data on file in the computer's memory, such as credit ratings, stock prices, and statistics.

WHERE THE FUTURE IS

Relatively new are the bureaus offering *complete* data-processing services to companies or industries that can be accommodated with identical or fairly similar programs. These bureaus are already immensely successful; hundreds of retailers, distributors, auto dealers, grocery chains, and hospitals are subscribing to them. An important and fast-growing sector of the service-bureau business is time sharing, which reduces costs and speeds up service by enabling a number of customers to "converse" directly and simultaneously with a computer from their own offices. Time sharing has run into some technical problems (see "Computer Time-Sharing—Everyman at the Console," FORTUNE, August, 1967), but it is overcoming them.

Some computer-industry prophets regard the service bureaus as the key to the industry's future. The computer business, they say, will evolve into a problem-solving service. What they envision is a kind of computer utility that will serve anybody and everydoby, big and small, with thousands of remote terminals connected to the appropriate central processors. The central processors, sharing a common memory, will often be enormous and highly efficient, with the ability to execute dozens of programs concurrently. Basic software will be built into the hardware ("software in hardware"). Components of large-scale systems will tend to become standardized, and will be largely bought off the shelf. A computer utility will integrate diverse activities now scattered around in the industry—systems engineering, applications engineering, programming, time sharing, on-line data processing, financing, leasing, and even the manufacture of special peripheral hardware. One company heading in that direction is University Computing Co. of Dallas.

The big hardware companies themselves are making sure that they will be in a position to take advantage of the trend, when and if it comes. Univac, strong in multiprocessing and peripherals, has set up an Information Services Division to capitalize on any trend toward the utility concept. "The future of business is in service," says Robert E. McDonald, head of Univac. And I.B.M. is in a strong position to expand its service operations; its Service Bureau Corp. subsidiary is actually the largest service organization in the country.

KEEPING UP WITH THE CENTERS

Whatever happens to the computer utility concept, the hardware business is bound to change. The dollar volume of peripheral equipment, which already exceeds that of central processor units, will continue to grow much faster. The central unit, whatever its capacity, can process data only as fast as the peripheral equipment can put it in and take it out. Without adequate input-output devices, time sharing, for example, is impossible.

So far, however, the speed of central units has increased faster than the capacity of peripheral units. One result has been an explosion of technical and sales activity among makers of peripheral equipment. Punch-card devices and other kinds of equipment that require a lot of clerical attention are giving way to a wide range of speedier innovations. Many of the hundreds of small companies now in the field have already hit the jackpot with a proprietary product. There are more than fifty independent makers of remote terminals and improved input devices, including Mohawk Data Sciences, Sanders Associates, Digitronics, University Computing, and Tally. There are makers of optical character-recognition machines, such as Recognition Equipment, Farrington, Optica Scanning, and Cognitronics. There are makers of magnetic tapes, disk packs, and peripheral memories bearing brave names like Memorex, Caelus, and Consolidated Electrodynamics.

Despite the proliferation of independents in the field—from about 100 companies in 1960 to more than 250 today—most of the peripheral equipment is turned out by the big computer makers. Since they do not report separate figures for this equipment, it is difficult to estimate total peripheral sales. A good guess is around $2.5 billion. By 1972 the figure will probably be at least $4 billion, so there will be plenty of room for inventive independents to grow. But the independents' combined share of the peripheral-equipment market has probably declined from 35 percent or so in 1960 to less than 15 percent today. Although the market is growing so fast that the independents' volume is still expanding, it seems inevitable that the independents generally will find the going harder. The weaker ones will fall by the wayside, and the stronger ones will be candidates for acquisition by the big companies.

In another segment of the computer business with excellent growth prospects, small independents will not be able to compete at all. This is the market for very powerful central computers—the very large machines such as the Control Data 6400 and the Univac 1108, and the so-called supercomputers such as the Burroughs 8500 and the Control Data 6600. Only big computers are able to handle large scientific jobs and extensive information systems for corporations or computer utilities. Moreover, because software is getting more expensive while hardware is getting cheaper relative to capacity, there will be a tendency to use plenty of hardware rather than spend a good deal of money creating software that will maximize hardware efficiency.

M. James Arachtingi, the Wall Street analyst whose estimates of rental-pool growth were referred to earlier, has worked out projections of the big-computer market five years hence. There are now about $2.5 billion worth of very large computers and supercomputers in existence; by 1972, Arachtingi predicts, their gross value will come to more than $8 billion. I.B.M., which has never been strong "on the upper end," will be able to sell only 41 percent of this market. Second place will be held by Control Data, with 28 percent. Univac will be third, with 14 percent, and Burroughs fourth, with a bit more than 12 percent. That leaves only 5 percent for G.E. and others. In terms of dollars, I.B.M. can look forward to turning out $730 million worth of very large and supercomputers in 1972, compared to $410 million for Control Data and about half that for Univac. This forecast, however, does not mean I.B.M. will lose ground in the industry as a whole. What its competitors gain at the upper end, Arachtingi predicts, will be offset by I.B.M.'s sales of smaller equipment and software.

"A GIANT ELECTRONIC WEED"

Every now and then some observer of the computer industry points to a cloud—small yet vaguely threatening—that sometimes appears to hang over its future. The costs of computer systems keep climbing but the returns keep getting harder to calculate. Until fairly recently, most business computer applications were devoted to relatively routine, well-structured jobs such as billing and invoicing, in which they paid off measurably and handsomely. As computers grew more complex and expensive and were assigned more sophisticated tasks, the payoff became less easy to achieve and more difficult to measure.

A. Carl Kotchian, president of Lockheed Aircraft, recently ventilated some of his thoughts on the subject in the *Financial Executive*. Lockheed, he had learned, was spending a total of $60 million a year renting and operating its computers, up from $48 million two years ago. "When I heard that figure," he wrote, "I had a vision of these machines taking over all of our plant and office space like a giant electronic weed, squeezing and choking everything that got in its way until the only thing Lockheed could produce would be the loud, steady humming sound of its integrated computer system!" He would like to leave a challenge with financial executives, he went on: "Find out everything you can about computers. Not just how to live with them or how to use them in your work, but other things, such as why costs keep going up so fast, how can we be sure we're getting the proper use out of them, and at what point does the corporation become the tool of the computer instead of the other way around? When you get the answers to these questions, lay them before your management—but be prepared to see grown men break down and cry with gratitude!"

Not long after this appeared in print, David B. Hertz of McKinsey & Co., the management consultant, published a study of computer use in thirty-six large U.S. and European companies. Hertz found that mounting computer expenses are no longer matched by rising economic returns. "From a profit standpoint," the study said, "computer efforts in all but a few exceptional companies are in real, if often unacknowledged, trouble."

Fortunately for makers of computers, this is not the whole story. "As yet," the study went on, "the real profit potential of the computer has barely begun to be tapped." Hertz's conclusion was that too many companies are still leaving the application of computers up to technicans rather than managers. Only when top managers pitch in, cooperate with computer staffs, and relate their problems to the potentialities of the machine can they realize those potentialities. Some companies have done that. One maker of heavy construction equipment, for example, learned to put computers to many new uses—consolidating sales forecasts from thirty-one countries, working out manufacturing plans for thirteen plants, deciding whether to "make or buy" in all plants, maintaining cumulative records of labor efficiency. All such uses paid off measurably and handsomely.

Neal J. Dean of Booz, Allen & Hamilton, management consultants, took a somewhat different approach but arrived at a very similar conclusion. Dean picked 108 large manufacturing companies that had used computers successfully and tried to find out why they were successful. His study, printed in the *Harvard Business Review* under the title "The Computer Comes of Age," showed that these companies—all of which had superior records of growth in sales and earnings—had discovered ways to apply computers to all major areas of their activities. The main reason for their success was that top management had taken charge. Nearly all had appointed top computer executives who participate in the companies' highest councils. These companies' aggressive use of computers was in large part a response to competitive pressure. Dean concluded that companies that fail to get the most out of their computers will do so at their own risk.

TO DEFINE PROBLEMS CLEARLY ENOUGH

There is evidence that the computer industry is not going to wait for competitive pressures to push the laggards into realizing the computer's potentialities. I.B.M., for example, is finally installing an integrated management-information system in its own organization. In the past, I.B.M. has made abundant use of computers at the plant or division level, but its new $100-million Management Information System will encompass the whole company. When complete, it will consist of some 3,700 terminals connected to dozens of central computers. I.B.M.'s announced aim is to improve its own internal efficiency, but if successful the system will manifestly improve I.B.M.'s ability to show others how to use computers profitably in ways few are yet using them.

Precisely because the potentialities of the computer have been only partly realized so far, the industry is sure that the business market for its computer systems will grow faster than business itself. But that growth will not be automatic. It will depend to a large degree on how well the industry can show customers and prospective customers how to define their problems clearly enought to make use of the computer's marvelous capacity to provide solutions.

Questions:

1. Contrast the growth of IBM to other computer manufacturers.

2. List the various specialty areas of computing firms.

3. Discuss the future of the service bureau concept of operations.

. . .AND NOW A WORD FROM NO. 1

BY ALAN DRATTELL

"I'm terribly proud of where we've gotten to at IBM," says Thomas J. Watson Jr., chairman of the board of the company that is the undisputed leader worldwide in terms of sales and installations in the data processing field. "When I went to work for IBM," he continues, "we had a $32 million gross." It is expected to be well above $5 billion for 1968.

It is difficult for both its boosters and detractors to think of International Business Machines Corp. in terms other than bigness. Everything the company does is big—even if it is only in the minds of others.

How the manufacturer reached its present pinnacle is now almost legend. Every dp entrepreneur knows of the classic management decision made by Thomas J. Watson Sr., which led to the establishment of IBM as one of the biggest companies income-wise in the world.

During the depression of the 1930's, Watson elected to keep his trained talent employed rather than dismiss or lay them off. In fact, IBM increased employment, trained more salesmen and upped engineering efforts. As a result, the company was able to provide machines and services for a huge unit record contract from the Social Security Admin.

From unit record, it was a natural jump to computer technology in the early 1950's, and despite Univac being there first, IBM's numbers made the eventual difference.

The remainder of this historic recitation even the uninitiated can guess: IBM parlayed its people and marketing savvy into making it No. 1 in the data processing industry. It was able to keep potential competitors off-balance by adhering to a strict policy of deferred income by renting its machines rather than selling them. The Justice Dept., however, stepped in and issued a consent decree in 1956 which, among other things, forced IBM to sell some of its equipment.

Since then, though, IBM has been forging ahead despite the Dept. of Justice's constraint. But it has done its sprinting with a continual cautious peek over its shoulder.

This almost paranoiac nervousness concerning the Federal Government's reactions to its deeds has often been frustrating for IBM-watchers, and in the past IBM's reluctance to "tell it like it is" has led upon occasion to misinterpretations arising from the company's acts.

Through our correspondents in strategic European capitals, for example, we have been keeping abreast of sales of computers to Eastern European countries. We have also questioned manufacturers in the U.S. when we learned about these sales from our men abroad. IBM World Trade Corp., a subsidiary, invariably issued the standard dodge to a confirmation of shipment query: "We neither confirm nor deny."

BIGNESS OFTEN BREEDS CONTEMPT

During our interview with Watson, the corporate chairman was visibly disturbed when told about World Trade's consistent response. He explained that such a comment was not in accord with company policy—that IBM, like other manufacturers, had in fact sold computers to the Communists. He then dashed off a note, presumably to World Trade, and put it in his "out" basket.

Bigness, while sometimes causing a breakdown in internal communications, often breeds contempt—many times unfairly because of jealousy on the part of the disdainers. "The bigger you get in the eyes of other people," says Watson, "the more you may inadvertently bother them."

But with all the barbs, IBM continues to get healthier—even despite the recent antitrust suit filing by Control Data Corp. It can probably be said that the slings and arrows have helped rather than hindered.

And the competition has been assisted too. When Honeywell moved into the computer field, it was the first "other computer company" to tell everyone that its chief competitor was, in fact, IBM. Other manufacturers had been ludicrously cautious, fearful that by mentioning IBM they were helping to build No. 1 up even more.

Honeywell dammed the torpedoes and zeroed in on IBM's hottest seller, the 1401 computer. Its 200 system, Honeywell said, would do a better job for less money. This approach aided the Honeywell people in establishing the 200 as one of the successful computers in the industry.

CAUTIOUS ABOUT PREMATURE CLAIMS

Others, like Control Data, began carving out segments of the industry IBM was not strong in—like super scale computers. General Electric took the lead in time sharing and process control.

IBM, though, unwilling to be second in anything, began to make inroads into these areas. The company's initial incursions into super scale computers and time sharing, however, were not successful. But its financial strength and manpower—thanks to Tom Watson Sr.'s foresight back in the '30's—enabled it to overcome the setbacks. "I think that everyone who got into time sharing," says Watson Jr., "underestimated the difficulty in making a true time sharing computer. Our errors have made us much more cautious about making premature claims about what we can produce in advanced areas."

Although the company will not officially discuss its troubles in super scale computers, the fact is that its Mod 90 addition to the System/360 line is only being produced in a limited quantity.

Francis G. Rodgers, president of the Data Processing Div., says that the 90 was to be a limited production model; the Mod 85 added in 1968 was not meant to replace it. However, these facts were never fully disclosed by IBM prior to the plug being pulled on the 90, and doubters must conclude that some technical and perhaps other problems forced the final decision. To date, seven 90's have been shipped, and the remainder will be dispatched this spring. In all, the total number to be installed is expected to be under 20.

Jerrier A. Haddad, vice president-engineering, programing and technology, says: "Everyone, IBM and others, completely underestimated the computing time and overhead of the time sharing systems. The degree to which the computer had to operate and keep threads separate in the number of terminals that were to be hooked into the central system was underestimated. The trouble is computing is not an exact science." Haddad directed the development of IBM's first large scale EDP system, the 701, introduced in 1952.

IBM's setbacks, however, have had a humanizing effect on a company that has become, because of its size, the epitome of Big Brother. But, ironically, what has made IBM tick has been its concern for people, according to Watson. "We have that position of leadership because we have demonstrated a great desire to serve our customers, stockholders and employes."

Watson openly espouses his late father's people philosophy. The elder Watson, who died in 1966 at the age of 82, was considered a humanitarian by his peers, and his employe programs were ahead of their time. For example, in 1928, IBM established a suggestion program for employes; in 1937, although paid holidays were fairly unknown in major industries, the company announced a policy of paying employes for six holidays a year; a paid vacation plan was also introduced in the same year; and in 1946, a hospitalization program was announced and family dinners were launched.

It is interesting to note that in an industry in which at least the production workers are unionized at some companies, no union has been able to gain a foothold at IBM.

In addition to its concern for its employes, the manufacturer has been in the forefront of the nation's fight for job equality for all Americans. Last summer, the company moved into the Bedford-Stuyvesant section of Brooklyn, N.Y.—one of the hard-core Negro ghetto areas in the country. There IBM built a plant and employed black help.

PEOPLE ARE THE CLUE

"We were not prompted solely by economic factors," Watson explains. "We moved into Bedford-Stuyvesant because we're a large company and have some power to help solve the major problems of the ghetto that a small company does not have. We don't expect to run the plant at a loss. It may not be, theoretically, the most ideal place for a plant, but we intend to end up with the plant being profitable.

"I think it is incumbent upon a business which is financially able to do this to do so."

Another charge leveled at IBM in the past is that its success can be laid to its marketing acumen rather than its technical expertise. Says Watson: "I just don't think you can sell a second class product with a super sales force."

Rodgers says that the company's strength lies in its decentralization. "Our branch offices are the key to our marketing success. Specialization within the Data Processing Div. is another plus. There is no question but that's the best way to market."

This factor has, of course, been an ace for IBM, which when competing with other computer companies can usually bring in a salesman who is knowledgeable about a specific application area. Thus, in banking, the IBM-er is a banking expert. Some competitors complain that if the application were widgets, IBM would come up with a specialist in that area too. Here again, numbers pay off.

Watson admits that people are the clue to the company's success, and he says it would be easy "to get mesmerized with big machines and not people."

Internal structure has also played a role in keeping the firm in the top spot. The organization has been fairly fluid; no moss has been allowed to accumulate. IBM was "very centralized," says Watson, until the early 1950's. By 1958, it went to two divisions—data systems and general products. There was no attempt to centralize.

A system family, explains the chairman, forces a certain amount of centralization; thus, the discipline of centralization is forced by a product. "Now that we are out of the 360 bind, we're studying methods of decentralizing further." Watson's remark alludes to the company's software problems and initial shipment concerns of its System/360 family of computers. Haddad sums up the software snafu simply: "Boy, did we underestimate the programing." But by applying its manpower resources, IBM overcame the potential dangers that other companies—less secure in men and money—might have been prey to.

Although computers can be said to be the bulk of its business and the commercial area its biggest customer source (space and defense contracts with the Federal Government amount to only 4 percent of IBM's total revenues), the company has been eyeing other areas for some time. One of these is copying machines.

There have been unsuccessful attempts to link up with other companies, such as Harris Intertype, to develop and market a copy machine. One caution, of course, always had to be observed: avoiding the legal wrath of the Federal Government.

All sorts of exotic markets are ahead for the company, the chairman says, including the "whole philosophy of reservations, medicine, teaching. Matching the text to the teaching mechanism has been difficult. The problem is more in the state of the art."

Adds Rodgers: "Management information systems is the area of greatest growth. We see the marketplace rapidly leaving the batch processing world and entering the world of real time. However, no system in the future will be successful unless the top executives of a company will set the ground rules and objectives in MIS. The greatest effect, thus, will really be on the role of management."

CONJURING UP EMOTIONS

Haddad explains that so far the data processing business has gone after one application at a time—payroll, production scheduling, inventory control, etc. "Now, people are beginning to integrate all these into an operational data system. Then they will be in a position to put MIS on top of that."

One significant area of future growth is the computer utility, although Haddad regards this terminology as bad. He says it conjures up emotions since a utility really refers to a regulated government monopoly. However, individual users will find it cheaper not to hook into a central computer. "Shared and non-shared use," he adds, "will coexist."

Another of IBM's strong points in the past has been its ability to move into areas that others have pioneered. For example, it was not until the success of Mohawk Data Sciences' data recorders opened a lucrative market that IBM stepped in with its direct-to-tape input devices. Some observers reason that this move has serious portents for the manufacturer's lucrative keypunch business which, as has been shown, was the base for its success in the information field.

Rodgers, though, sees IBM's sally into the direct-to-tape field as "one more entry directed at solving our customers' problems. The keypunch will be there for a long time." Customers, he adds, will choose one or the other on the basis of individual need. Haddad calls data entry a very exciting development area—and includes tape input, keypunch, optical scanning and data display, which are all strong IBM product areas.

And while IBM has gotten stronger, competition has tried to sap some of this strength.

As a result, IBM became the center of a multi-million dollar dispute more than a year ago that involved a U.S. Air Force computer order for its Phase II Base Level Automation Standardization Program. One of four bidders, IBM originally garnered the award, but complaints by Honeywell and Burroughs prompted Congressional and Federal watchdog agency investigations. The original award was subsequently negated, and Burroughs eventually got the $60 million prize.

FLIP-FLOP ON TIME SHARING

The Justice Dept. also initiated an inquiry last year into the antitrust implications of IBM's estimated 70 percent share of the computer manufacturing field.

And, admittedly, the consent decree along with fear of antitrust action, have acted as containments, toning down IBM's moves in certain areas. For example, the threat of Justice's action caused IBM to do a flip-flop several months ago on its time sharing subscriber services. Originally, the services were being marketed by the Data Processing Div. There were outcries of "unfair competition" with competitors claiming that the direct sale of time sharing services by IBM violated the consent decree. Under the pact, IBM had agreed to break out its service bureau operation under a separate company that did not use the IBM name.

At first, the company stood by its thesis that it was not violating the decree; however, after reconsidering the consequences, it transferred the services to its wholly owned subsidiary, Service Bureau Corp.

In another turnaround, within the span of a week in October, IBM adjusted its maintenance charges for data processing equipment and then withdrew the adjustments. Howls had come from the leasing companies, which would have been most affected by the original price adjustments.

It is interesting that the leasing business, an industry that exists today largely because of IBM's preeminence in the dp field, is having some strange effects upon No. 1. By purchasing large numbers of System/360 machines, the third party lessors have caused IBM's income to soar. However, they may adversely affect the manufacturer's future income, since the current level of outright sales to rentals is abnormally high for a company whose financial strength has been built on rentals.

In addition, the lessors, by threatening action by the Justice Dept., have forced IBM to make certain concessions to them—such as the maintenance price brouhaha—that, in effect, have aided the competitive nature of the leasing companies against the manufacturer.

Late last month IBM announced another move, which has led to a great deal of industry speculation concerning what the announcement really means. The manufacturer said that it expects to make changes in the way it charges for and supports its data processing equipment, and these changes will probably be disclosed on or before July 1.

The announcement could mean a separation of hardware and software pricing in some areas. However, two months prior to the disclosure, Rodgers said that the interdependence of hardware and software would make it difficult to separate them. Haddad added: "If the industry develops into a bunch of hardware merchants, that puts a requirement on all customers to be really expert in in-depth programing and systems requirements."

Other possibilities could be new maintenance policies which could open up the field for non-manufacturer maintenance companies; non-IBM equipment interface support; relief for leasing companies faced with relocating equipment that has been turned back; new charges for certain types of systems support; or possible new hardware pricing structures. However, it is still too early to really tell what the announcement means.

Of late, there has been some quiet talk in the industry concerning the possibility of a new consent decree, and although nothing official has been uttered, the 1956 manifesto could conceivably be in line for remodeling or replacing. Obviously, the industry today is much different from the one that existed in 1956. For one thing, it is more diverse; for another, the competition is much healthier, and it is beginning to pressure for a more equal share of the business. The antitrust suit against IBM by CDC and the possible suit (at press time) by another organization within the computer community attest to the restlessness within the business automation field and give credence to the theory that the consent decree may come in for some overhauling.

Meanwhile, the programing area has perhaps been IBM's—and everyone else's—most volatile. The initial problems with 360 software did much to damage the company's image with its customers, and many manufacturing competitors freely admit that IBM's programing woes helped them to sell users who they formerly couldn't reach because they were locked into No. 1.

One area of contention has been the Cobol-PL/1 controversy.

IBM says that it developed PL/1 not to replace Cobol but out of an original effort to make Fortran look like Cobol. This was done so that users could have one language to perform both scientific and business applications.

For the record, the company says that it supports both Cobol and PL/1. But many users have complained that IBM is only "paying lip service" to the support of Cobol.

PL/1 has had its boosters too, but it is in the area of standardization that it comes under the most fervent fire. It is a language limited in use to one company's machines and its users—although this one company has by far the largest number of users. This threat of a *de facto* standard emerging frightens other computer manufacturers. But Rodgers assures: "We're working with the Federal Government, the Business Equipment Manufacturers Assn. and others. We will not look at standards on a purely self-interest basis, but for the good of the industry. We are going to cooperate and work in that area."

WHAT COMES AFTER THE 360?

At the root of many of the arguments surrounding IBM's dominance of the computer market is what the company will do next—particularly in regard to the announcement of a new generation of equipment. Obviously, the company is quite cautious, from a competitive angle, of "tipping its hand." It is apparent that IBM, like other manufacturers, is stressing peripherals at the moment—particularly graphics and displays. New application techniques are also in for a greater push in the months ahead. However, the hot questions remain: what comes after the 360, and when?

Among the latest developments in the 360 area that have led to increasing conjecture and concern is the fact that the Mods 30, 40, 50, 75 and some models of the 20 are now in "limited new production." This means that previously used machines may be retrofitted for resale as new machines.

Says Watson: "We'll continue to develop the 360 line. I think there are significant improvements that can be made in software."

What the company's board chairman and others in top posts appear to be saying is that the changes in technology will come within the 360 umbrella. These changes could include large scale integrated circuitry. There will not be an entirely new family *per se;* there will be new members within the 360 line.

The big revolution in the computer industry came in the change from the first generation (tubes) to the second (transistors) and less into the third (integrated circuits).

Some third generation systems, however, could be operated like second generation machines, but at a lower price/performance cost to the user. For instance, a 360 could be used in 1401 emulating mode at less cost than it was to have a 1401 second generation machine.

The big change in the fourth generation will be in programing technology and in cost/performance. Large scale integrated circuits and other technological advances will enable manufacturers of computer equipment to give the user more power for less money.

"The basic 360 concept," assures Haddad, "will live for a long, long time."

There has also been some talk of IBM trying to open up the lucrative East European market to sell its second generation machines and its 360's too. Watson estimates this market to have a $2 to $3 billion potential.

BUSINESS BEHIND THE CURTAIN

IBM's business behind the Iron Curtain has been curtailed by U.S. edict, as all computers shipped to the East by IBM and other manufacturers are subject to rigid Dept. of Commerce controls under the Export Control Act of 1949.

"There are arguments on both sides of the East-West trade issue, but I think non-strategic trade with the East has many advantages for our nation," says Watson. "I believe the fact that the Russians felt they had to invade Czechoslovakia last summer may have resulted in part from the fact that the Czech market had become more West-oriented by trade." The Czechs have been important customers for IBM computers.

When asked about a possible licensing agreement with an Eastern country, Watson says that there are a number of detriments. Foremost is IBM's remembrance of an agreement with the Russians prior to World War II when the USSR did not respect IBM's patents.

As for the future, Watson looks at the U.S. and Western Europe as holding the greatest growth promise for IBM for the next five years. Japan is another area, despite Japanese government moves to prevent U.S.-owned companies from gaining strength there.

The excitement of the EDP business has been a tonic for the board chairman, who says, "We are not in a static situation or involved in some kind of mundane business; we're in something very exciting." And tomorrow, in terms of management's role, is also on his mind. He sees the job of management "much more precise and less visceral. There will be less and less opportunity for people who do not have advanced degrees and high intellectual ability."

Questions:

1. Discuss some of the technically oriented reasons why IBM has earned and maintained its position in the data processing industry.

2. Discuss the latest legal suits against IBM. What might the impact be on other firms in the data processing industry?

FUNDAMENTAL CONCEPTS OF PROGRAMMING LANGUAGES

by JEAN E. SAMMET

In order to use a digital computer it is necessary to write a program to accomplish the desired task. Thus, a computer without a program is about as useful as an automobile without an engine. If programming is necessary to make a computer "go," then the language in which the program is written is the key to effective use of the computer. Hence, it seems fair to say that the communication between person and computer is fundamental — both as a problem and as a technique. Since the advent of the computer, the endeavors of many people have been — and continue to be — devoted to trying to ease this communication problem. Probably the single most important tool is what has become known as a "programming language," sometimes called a "higher level language" (to distinguish it from the normal machine codes or assembly languages which are more closely related to the hardware).

Unfortunately, there does not appear to be any universally accepted definition of a programming language, and it is therefore easier to provide characteristics rather than a specific definition. It is of course taken for granted that a programming language is some set of characters and rules for combining them by which the user can communicate with the computer to cause useful work to be done; this communication takes place through another program which is normally called a compiler, and whose purpose is to translate the user's program (called the source program) into machine code (called the object program) which can then be executed by the computer. This contrasts with the use of a language which is the same as, or very similar to, the direct language used by the computer, namely an assembly language.

This article seeks to characterize programming languages, point out their advantages and disadvantages, provide some classifications of programming languages with proposed definitions, and discuss the major issues in programming languages. The latter are subdivided into nontechnical and technical characteristics of programming languages. Although much of the material in this paper may be familiar or even well known, it is hoped that the various classifications and ways of grouping concepts will prove useful.

Jean E. Sammet, PROGRAMMING LANGUAGES: History and Fundamentals © 1969. Reprinted by permission of Prentice-Hall, Inc., Englewood Cliffs, New Jersey. This condensation of chapters I thru III of Miss Sammet's excellent book appeared in Computers and Automation.

CHARACTERISTICS THAT DEFINE PROGRAMMING LANGUAGES

A programming language is a set of characters and rules for combining them which has the following four characteristics:

It requires no knowledge of machine code by the user. In other words, the user need only learn the particular programming language and can use this quite independently of his (perhaps non-existent) knowledge of any particular machine code. This does not mean that the user can completely ignore the actual computer. For example, he may wish to take advantage of certain machine facilities which are known to him and which provide more efficient programs, and in particular he obviously cannot use input/output equipment which does not exist on a particular computer configuration. However, the fundamental point is that he does not need to know the basic machine code for the given computer.

A programming language must have some significant amount of machine independence. This means that there must be some reasonable potential of having a source program run two computers with different machine codes without completely rewriting the source program.

When a source program is translated to machine language, there is normally more than one machine instruction per executable unit created. For example, an executable unit in a programming language might be something of the form "A = B + C*D" or "MOVE A TO B." Normally each of these executable units would be translated into more than one machine instruction.

A programming language normally employs a notation which is somewhat closer to the specific problem being solved than is normal machine code. Thus, for example, the example "A = B + C*D" might be translated into a sequence of instructions such as:

$$
\begin{array}{ll}
\text{CLA} & \text{C} \\
\text{MPY} & \text{D} \\
\text{ADD} & \text{B} \\
\text{STO} & \text{A}
\end{array}
$$

which is clearly less understandable than the programming language form.

ADVANTAGES OF PROGRAMMING LANGUAGES

As always, one cannot obtain something for nothing, and therefore there are both advantages and disadvantages to programming languages, where the alternative is some type of assembly language. Let us consider the advantages first.

The primary advantage of a programming language is that it is easier to learn than a machine language. It must be emphasized that there is a relative aspect involved in this advantage. An extremely powerful programming language might be harder to learn than an assembly language on a computer with only a dozen instructions. However, given programming and assembly languages of approximately the same complexity in their relative classes, the programming language will be easier to learn. This actually has two facets to it. The programming language may itself be extremely complex, but its ease of learning often comes because the notation is somewhat more related to the problem usage than is the machine code; furthermore, more attention can be paid to the language itself rather than to the idiosyncrasies of the physical hardware which are necessary when one deals in machine code.

A problem written in a programming language is generally easier to debug for two major reasons. First, there is actually less material which needs to be written, because of the explosion factor indicated as the third characteristic of a programming language. Thus, in comparison with a program written in assembly language, the source program will be physically shorter. Since the number of errors is roughly proportional to the length of the program, obviously there will be fewer errors. A second reason for the program being easier to debug is that the notation itself is somewhat more natural and therefore more attention can be paid to the logic of the program with less attention paid to details of the machine code.

A program coded in a programming language is generally easier to understand and to transfer to someone other than the originator because of the notational advantages and relative conciseness already mentioned.

Fourth, the notation of a programming language automatically provides certain documentation because the notation is easier to understand and the logic is easier to follow.

Finally, the above advantages tend to accumulate into one general advantage which is that the total calendar time required for the problem solution is generally reduced significantly.

DISADVANTAGES OF PROGRAMMING LANGUAGES

The primary disadvantage is that the advantages do not always exist in specific cases, and the person might be worse off than with a very simple assembly language, as was indicated under the first advantage. Thus, the programming language must be extremely difficult to learn, and unless proper attention is paid to the compiler and other facets of the overall system, the other advantages may not themselves accrue. Fortunately, this seldom occurs.

Second, the additional process of compilation obviously requires machine time, and this may require more than the machine time saved from easier debugging.

Third, the compiler might produce very inefficient object code. This would significantly affect production runs, i.e. programs which are run repeatedly and whose machine time requirements are increased significantly by any inefficiencies. (The counter argument to this of course is the fact that compilers nowadays generally produce code that is at least as good as the average programmer can produce and there are only a few really expert programmers who can write the most efficient machine code.)

Finally, the program may be much harder to debug than an assembly language program if the user does not know machine code and the compiler does not provide the proper type of diagnostics and debugging tools. A user who must look at a memory dump in octal, which he does not understand, is going to have more trouble than debugging an assembly language program in which he understands what is happening.

CLASSIFICATIONS OF PROGRAMMING LANGUAGES AND PROPOSED DEFINITIONS

As indicated earlier, it is very difficult to define a programming language. However, it is a bit easier to propose definitions for classes of programming languages. The terms to be defined are the following: procedure oriented, nonprocedural, problem oriented, application oriented, special purpose, problem defining, problem describing, problem solving. Note that some of these are overlapping and that a particular language may fall into more than one of these categories.

A *procedure oriented* language is one in which the user specifies a set of executable operations which are to be performed in sequence; the key factor here is that these are definitely executable operations, and the sequencing is already specified by the user.

The term *non-procedural* has been bandied about for years without any attempt to define it. It is my firm contention that a definition is not really possible, because non-procedural is really a relative term in which decreasing numbers of specific steps need to be provided by the user as the state of the art improves. Thus, before such languages as FORTRAN existed, the statement Y = A + B*C − F/G could be considered non-procedural, because it could not be written as one executable unit and translated by any system. Right now, the sentences "calculate the square root of the prime numbers from 7 to 91 and print in three columns" and "print all the salary checks" are non-procedural because there is no compiler available that can accept these statements and translate them; the user must supply the specific steps required. As compilers are developed to cope with increasingly complex sentences, then the nature of the term changes. Thus, what is considered non-procedural today maybe definitely procedural tomorrow. One of the best examples of a currently available non-procedural language is a report generator in which the individual supplies essentially the input and the output without any specific indication as to the procedures needed.

The term *problem oriented* has been used in many ways by different people, but it seems that the most effective use of this term is to encompass any language which is easier for solving a particular problem than machine code would be. Any current programming language illustrates this, and thus the term "problem oriented" is a kind of catchall.

The term *application oriented* seems to apply best to a language which has facilities and/or notation which are useful primarily for a single application area. The best illustrations of this are such languages as APT for machine tool control, and COGO for civil engineering applications. Notice that both of these are of course problem-oriented languages. On the other hand, FORTRAN and COBOL are problem oriented but much less application oriented than APT or COGO. Here again, the term is somewhat relative because FORTRAN is suitable for applications involving numerical mathematics, whereas COBOL is obviously suited for business data processing and the overlap between these is relatively small. The wider the application area, the more general the language must be.

A *special purpose* language is one which is designed to satisfy a single objective. The objective might involve the application area, or the ease of use for a particular application, or pertain to efficiency of the compiler or the object code.

A *problem defining* language is one which literally defines the problem, and may particularly define the desired input and output, but does *not* define the method of transformation. Here, the best illustration is a report generator. A somewhat secondary example is sorting routines, except that the input to sort routines usually is not in the form of a language per se.

A much more general type of language classification is that referred to as *problem describing* in which the objective is described only in very general terms, e.g. "calculate payroll". All such a statement does is describe, in the most general way, the problem which is to be solved but gives no indication whatsoever as to how to solve it. We are an extremely long way from this type of language.

Finally, a *problem solving* language is one which specifies a complete solution to a problem. Like the term non-procedural, this is a relative term which changes as the state of the art changes.

NON-TECHNICAL, i.e., FUNCTIONAL, CHARACTERISTICS

Most articles and talks about programming languages tend to throw in a great many concepts and characteristics without any very careful delineation of their relationships to one another. Thus when people try to decide which language to select for a given task, they often run into difficulty because of a lack of clearcut factors against which to make their evaluation. In particular, insufficient attention is usually paid to the difference between non-technical and specific technical, characteristics. While it is *not* the purpose of this paper to tell readers how to select a particular programming language, it is hoped that some of the fundamental background material contained herein might be useful in such a situation.

PURPOSE OF A PROGRAMMING LANGUAGE

Three different types of purposes must be determined in defining any programming language. The first and most important is the particular application area for which the language is designed. Thus, it must be determined whether this is to handle such things as numerical scientific work, or graphic displays, or business data processing, or engineering design, etc.

The second purpose is to specify the type of language, where in this context the following things are meant. First: into which one or more of the classifications previously cited does the language fall? Secondly: what is the form of the language relative to succinct and/or formal notation, versus naturalness? Third: is the language meant for direct input to a computer or primarily as a publication or reference language? Finally: what type of user the language is intended to assist? Generally speaking, programming languages tend to aid the application programmer who is not necessarily a full-time professional programmer, or in other words, most programming languages tend to help the individual who has a specific problem to solve rather than somebody whose major interest is in computer programming.

CONVERSION AND COMPATIBILITY

There has probably been more talk and discussion about conversion and compatibility than almost any other aspect of programming languages. It would be impossible to discuss these topics in any great detail here; so the main thing is to point out some of the varying types of compatibility that exist. The first is compatibility across individual machines, i.e. how machine-independent is a particular language? The second type of compatibility relates to the compiler; unfortunately, the same language is not always implemented the same way even for the same machine; there exist cases in which compilers for the same language, on the same machine, do not produce the same results. A third type of compatibility is related to the problem of dialects, where major and minor changes and/or subsets and extensions are all made in the name of the same language.

With regard to ease of conversion, the first and easiest ways of converting is based on compatibility which hopefully exists. Two other ways are direct translation into another language, and semi-translation whereby the user does some of the work.

STANDARDIZATION

The purposes of standardization are fairly well known. Basically, standardization of programming languages eases conversion problems, permits compatibility across machines, eases the training problem, and generally reduces economic costs from many points of view. The problems in standardization are a little less obvious. They actually fall into three classes — conceptual, technical, and procedural.

In the conceptual category falls the major difficulty of determining when it is time to establish a standard, and how one establishes a standard and at the same time permits new developments to proceed. This type of conceptual problem is not unique to programming languages, and exists in many fields.

The technical problems in standardizing programming languages are enormous. For example, in the more than five years of existence of Committee X3.4 (which is the subcommittee on standardizing programming languages), only one language has been standardized and that only recently — namely FORTRAN; this was by far the best known and most widely available language. In essence, it is very difficult to write down the definition of a language in unambiguous terms.

The third problem in standardization is the method of establishing standards and the procedures associated therewith. These are long and laborious, and have the advantage of requiring a consensus, so that when a standard actually does come into existence, it is one which will really be obeyed, even though compliance with USASI (formerly ASA) standards is completely voluntary.

TYPES AND METHODS OF LANGUAGE DEFINITION

When one thinks of language definition, one almost invariably thinks of various technical ways in which languages can be defined. However, although it is often overlooked, the administrative framework within which a language is defined tends to have a significant effect on the language. For example, the question of who designed the language and in what organizational framework, is of paramount importance. Unfortunately, language design is still an art and not a science, and different people often have very strong personal views which can't be defended on any other grounds than "I (don't) like it". The organizational framework is also of major importance, because a language which is designed by an intercompany group will have many more compromises than that designed by a single organizational unit.

However, I wish to state very strongly that those who oppose language design by committee are putting their heads in the sand, because I do not know of any major fully implemented language which was actually designed by a single person. The moment that several people become involved, there is in fact a committee, even though it may be a single organizational unit with a person designated as being in charge. Thus, the mere fact that a language is designed by an intercompany committee is not bad in and of itself. The more significant problem in a situation like that is that the people usually have other job assignments and thus their time is limited. Furthermore, the interconnection between the language designers, the implementers, and those who maintain the language (i.e, settle tricky points of interpretation and perhaps try to extend it) is a crucial part of the administrative framework. If the people who implement the language are not the ones who designed it, or conversely, there is always trouble. Similarly, if the people who maintain the language are not those who designed it then there is difficulty arising from the fact that the newcomers always have (or think they have) better ways of doing things. Sometimes the language is redesigned each time a new group of people becomes involved, and chaos results. The interconnection between the language maintainers and those who do the implementation plays a key role in the orderly development—or lack thereof—of a language.

A number of technical problems are associated with language definition. First and foremost is that we do not yet know how to give a completely formal definition of a programming language. The three components of a language definition are: (1) syntax, which specifies the legal strings of characters (e.g., A + B, not + AB); (2) semantics, which specifies the meaning (e.g., add, not subtract); and (3) pragmatics, which specifies the interaction between the user and the system. We have fairly good ways of defining the syntax, but ways of defining the semantics are only now being developed, and we have made no progress on the pragmatics except to recognize that it is a problem.

EVALUATION BASED ON USE

Very often languages are evaluated on the basis of manuals, speculation, and offhand opinion, rather than on the basis of use. It may be logical for somebody to evaluate a language manual in this way — but he should not evaluate the language itself until it has undergone some usage. Part of usage is training, learning, writing programs, debugging them, etc., and each is fair game for objective evaluation. However, one must be very careful to distinguish between evaluating the language and evaluating the compilers which translate it. The language may be good and the compilers very bad; in cases like this, it is almost always the language which is blamed, although it simply may be a matter of ineffective compiler writing.

*TECHNICAL CHARACTERISTICS

Technical characteristics of a language, mean the sum total of what actually constitutes the language. The main technical characteristics of a language are the form of the language, the structure of the program, the data types and units, the executable statement types, the declarations and nonexecutable statements, and the structure of the language and the compiler interaction.

FORM OF LANGUAGE

The form of the language involves many facets. The first is the actual character set which is used, and the second is the ways in which the characters are combined to form names (e.g., TEMP), operators (PLUS, AND), executable commands (COMPUTE, GO TO), and non-executable declarations (DIMENSION, INTEGER). The third facet of language form is the specific rules for forming names and words. The rules for names involve such things as the formation of data names and statement labels, the handling of subscripts and qualification, the use of reserved words, and the definition of literals. The methods of combining words involve the significance of blanks, the use and meaning of punctuation, the presence or absence of noise words, and ways of combining operands and operators. Finally, the form of language obviously involves the physical input which is used, as well as the conceptual form (e.g., fixed format versus a string of characters, English-like versus highly symbolic, etc.). Although a language is really independent of the input medium, when punch cards are meant to be the prime input source, the language tends to be defined as a partially fixed format. Similarly, if paper tape or direct typewriter input is involved, the language is usually designed as a string of characters.

STRUCTURE OF PROGRAM

The structure of the program is based on the types of subunits that are permitted, their characteristics, and the ways of intermingling them. The types of subunits that are normally allowed are declarations (including data descriptions); executable units; loops; functions, subroutines and procedures; the complete program; and the method of interacting with the operating system and the environment. The characteristics of subunits involve the methods of delimiting them, whether they are recursive and/or reentrant, the types of parameter passage required, what types of executable statements and declarations can be combined, and what other languages, including possibly machine language, can be included.

---

* Some of the terms used here may not be self-explanatory, and lack of space prevents adequate definition. It is hoped that the reader will get the general concepts even if a few specific words are not understood.

DATA TYPES AND UNITS

The different types of data variables include the following: arithmetic, Boolean, alpha-numeric, formal (=algebraic), strings, lists, vectors and arrays, hierarchical. A key characteristic is what types of data units can be accessed by the commands in the language. Thus one needs to know what data units of the hardware, as well as what variable types, can be obtained through the use of a particular command. Many different types of arithmetic can be performed, e.g. fixed and floating point, rational arithmetic, multiple precision, complex number, etc. Along with all these different types of arithmetic and different types of data go various rules on modes such as rules on which data types can be combined, and conversion and precision rules for computation.

EXECUTABLE STATEMENT TYPES

Many people feel that a programming language is completely determined by the executable statements it contains. Certainly, the executable commands play a very significant role, but they are not the only parts of a language. This is rather a narrow view.

The major classes of executable statements are assignment statements, those for handling alpha-numeric data, and those for sequence control and decision making. Almost all programming languages have all of these in some form or other. An increasing number of languages include executable statements for handling various types of symbolic data, e.g. algebraic expression manipulation statements, and statements to handle lists, strings, and/or patterns. Finally, with the increasing complexity of hardware and operating systems, the programming language itself must include a number of statements to provide interaction among these. Specifically, there are apt to be statements dealing with input/output library references, debugging, storage allocation and segmentation, and finally statements which deal directly with the operating system and/or machine features.

DECLARATIONS AND NON-EXECUTABLE STATEMENTS

Although the executable statements are obviously essential in order to accomplish anything, in general they cannot operate without knowing something about the data on which they are to act. For this reason, most programming languages have either primitive or complicated declarations to cover such things as data and/or file descriptions, format descriptions for input/output data, and storage allocation.

STRUCTURE OF LANGUAGE AND COMPILER INTERACTION

Among the characteristics of programming languages are the abilities for self-modification of programs, or self-extension of the language. Many languages contain directives to provide the compiler with useful information. Consideration must be given to the effect of the language design on compiler efficiency, and to the inclusion of debugging aids and error checking. A key characteristic of more theoretical than practical interest is whether the language can be used to write a compiler for the language. Finally, an interesting characteristic of the language is whether or not it is useful outside of its primary application area.

CONCLUSIONS

The widespread use of programming languages has given tangible proof that in most cases the advantages far outweigh the disadvantages. While obviously there are specific instances in which no existing higher level language will serve an existing need and therefore an assembly language must be used, these situations are becoming fewer. Careful examination of languages with respect to their non-technical as well as technical characteristics should help avoid incorrect choices by users.

Questions:

1.   Compare the advantages and disadvantages of programming languages.

2.   List the three major problems in standardizing a programming language.

3.   What would be the benefits of "standard" programming languages?

TRENDS IN THE
PROGRAMING PROFESSION

BY ROY M. SALZMAN

Any profession dedicated to a relatively new field goes through a progressive development as the field itself matures. In some cases this has taken decades; in others, centuries. Now we are witnessing the ripening of a profession in a matter of a few short years; and as it ripens, we can observe the increasing tendency toward specialization in separate, but related disciplines.

Programing, as a profession, has quite naturally followed the development of the digital computer, and only recently has it become the principal factor in the use of this new tool rather than merely serving as a support function to the computer. It is now accepted as fact by both hardware manufacturers and users that they will spend as much if not more money on software as on hardware, and that the success of their venture into the computing field will depend far more on competent analysis and programing than on a sophisticated instruction set or memory cycle time. Articles dealing with computing devote more attention to the mounting requirement for programers than to the need for new hardware techniques to compress space or increase logic speed.

Beyond the simple fact of the dominance of software over hardware, however, is the more complex consideration of what *kinds* of programers and analysts are being sought. In the early days of the industry, this question had no significance, a programer was simply a programer who would fill the memory of the machine with whatever code was necessary to get the job done. Input-output routines were written by the same man who coded the matrix inversion algorithm or calculated the Social Security tax. Common routines that could be used were regarded as windfalls rather than as expected tools for the programer. Basically the same programing techniques were used for the development of an assembler or a one-shot solution to a numerical analysis problem.

We have gone a long way since then. The distinction between *scientific* and *business* programers is obvious. So, too, is the split between general-purpose software developers and applications programers. Not so obvious are the more subtle divisions within each of these categories and the many other more specialized categories that exist. The need for recognizing these distinctions becomes more apparent as each field develops its own theoretical bases, techniques and common practices, terminology, machine characteristics, market place, etc. The question of whether such distinctions are advantageous to the individual or to his employer must also be considered in order to guide educational programs, hiring practices, career plans and organizational structures.

Reprinted from the November 1968 issue of DATA PROCESSING MAGAZINE, The Authoritative Publication of Computers and Information Technology.

DIRECTIONS OF SPECIALIZATION

The concept of specialization in the programing field means different things to different people. One might consider one's own professional strengths in terms of a multidimensional matrix where the dimensions refer to 1) function within the organization, 2) programing application area, and 3) machine type. We will examine each of these dimensions in turn and observe the relationships among them.

Within a programing organization there tend to be three basic functional lines of progression, as shown in figure 1. In general, the one which leads to the highest potential salary is the administrative/technical avenue in which the individual must be not only technically competent but also able to perform administrative functions such as hiring and evaluating people, writing proposals for new work, allocating resources and scheduling, coordinating with other groups, and arranging for support functions.

Ideally, this type of person should have some business acumen and a sensitivity to personnel problems along with, hopefully, superior technical

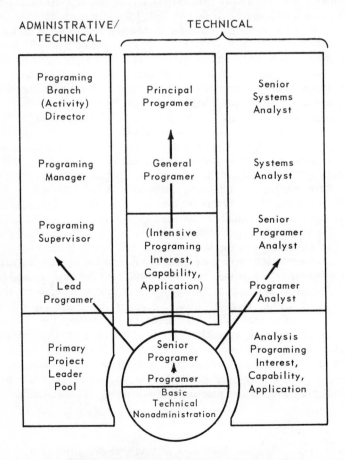

Figure 1. Typical Programing Organization

abilities. There are schools of thought which claim that effective managers can manage anything without too much technical knowledge of the product. In the programing field, however, where the product is the brainpower of intelligent and sensitive people, many (including the author) are convinced that a thorough understanding of the problems and practices of these people is essential to good management.

OTHER ADVANCEMENT PATHS

Recognizing that not all, indeed relatively few programers have the temperament for the more administrative aspects of the field, other lines of advancement must exist to recognize these with technical superiority. A person having gone through the basic *apprenticeship* of being a programer for a couple of years either may remain in that same environment, becoming more and more skilled in coding and debugging techniques and steadily improving his own output efficiency, or he may move into the analysis end of the business, where he is concerned less and less with details of implementation and more and more with problem-oriented parts of the project.

Traditionally, the systems analysts can potentially attain a higher salary than the *hot-shot programers*. This is due to the belief, probably well-founded but never proven, that there is an inherent limit to the output rate of a *pure* programer which is not that much greater than the rate of a relatively inexperienced programer; i.e., two mediocre programers at $10,000 per year are worth more than one hot-shot at $20,000.

The analyst, on the other hand, tends to increase in value at a rate greater than his salary based simply on years of service, since each problem he solves gives a broader foundation from which to attack the next, as well as increased skill at the analysis process itself. This type of individual frequently assumes the administrative roles mentioned previously. It should be recognized, though, that a skillful systems analyst and designer can often be of far greater value to a programing organization if he is permitted to devote his talents to the difficult and creative process of design and not diverted into managerial functions for which he may not be well suited.

SECOND PATH,
APPLICATION AREAS

The more commonly considered direction of specialization among programers relates to the type of applications or problems on which they customarily work. Their particular area of specialty usually derives from their organization; but occasionally as in the case of truly diversified software houses, their educational background, personality, recent experience or other more subtle factors dispose them to concentrate in a particular area. It is worth enumerating some of these with the associated characteristics required of those who specialize in them.

Business data processing is probably the largest group due to the continuing need for talent in this area and the relative ease of getting into the field. Backgrounds traditionally include business administration, accounting and liberal arts, and a fairly short professional education (several months of COBOL and AUTOCODER or BAL) before the individual can become productive. This is not to say that the problems are correspondingly easy.

To the contrary, they are often very complex logically, subject to constant change, required to interface with existing incompatible systems, and heavily dependent on deadlines. For this reason, really good analysts and programers, especially those with some administrative ability, are in great demand and rightfully command impressive salaries. Beginning and mediocre people in this area, however, are a dime a dozen. The problem is telling them apart.

The so-called scientific computation area is generally too vaguely defined to be called a specialty; but it has been used to include that large group of programers and analysts who talk almost exclusively in FORTRAN. Problems consist of data reduction, orbit computations, numerical analysis, engineering calculations, and a myriad of other problems requiring relatively little dependence on the characteristics of the machine on which the problem is to be solved, relatively little structuring of the data, and virtually no time dependence.

Most members of this group have degrees in mathematics, physics or engineering and tend to regard themselves superior to their COBOL'ing cousins even though their problems are often more straightforward and their tools better developed.

OTHER SPECIALTIES

Within this group, as in any of the groups mentioned, there naturally are even finer breakdowns of specialties. The mathematicians, who publish, confirm and repudiate algorithms, usually in ALGOL, are one little subgroup; statisticians are another, mechanical engineers another, and so on. In case of extreme specialization, members of these subgroups within the FORTRAN-ALGOL milieu cannot even communicate with each other, much less with groups in different spheres of the computing profession.

They may, of course, be so problem-oriented that they consider themselves more a part of the profession in which the problem originates than of the programming profession; but a surprising number expect the salary of a general-purpose programer while comprehending only a small segment of what programing really is.

The next largest class, by the author's estimate, is the software development group, primarily those working for hardware manufacturers. These divide even more distinctly into subgroups comprising the compiler writers, the operating system people, the assembler and utility routine programers, and the application package developers.

The compiler writers tend to be the most snobbish since their somewhat esoteric area was, until recently touted as the means of salvation of automation, i.e., an effective language and compiler could allow the business manager or scientist to dash off his own program without the need for professional programmers. This has turned out to be untrue, and people have learned that compilers are not so mysterious after all; therefore, the star of this group is on the wane.

OPERATING SYSTEM PROGRAMERS

Replacing them as the current darlings of the software world are the operating system people who have managed to make a science out of a difficult but nonesoteric area. Techniques for storage allocation, time-slice scheduling, memory protection, interrupt handling, etc., provide material for many papers and symposia, and the group has achieved notoriety through such efforts as Project MAC, TSS-67, General Electric's time-sharing developments, and many others.

The assembler and utility routine programers are basically cut from the same cloth as the two preceding groups, but are not as identifiable. Like their betterknown brethren, they are heavily machine-oriented, and greatly concerned with coding efficiency, generality, stability, and maintainability of their product, and compatibility with other elements of software being developed.

Backgrounds tend to be quite diverse with mathematics leading the field. This area is a particularly good one for the high-level programer who has no bent toward systems analysis or administration but simply likes to generate good programs. Here he may validly *play around* with several approaches to the same programing problem in order to cut out a few microseconds or core locations.

The applications package developer for a manufacturer tends to fall into separate specialty areas depending on the type of package he develops, e.g., PERT, simulation, numerical control, linear programing. Each of these areas involves a fairly even split between the machine orientation of the software developer and the problem orientation of the applications programer. Each has its own *in-group,* symposia, conference sessions, etc., and an aspiring programer could well direct his efforts toward becoming an expert in a specific field; such as one of these.

OTHER SPECIALTIES

Other specialty areas are less associated with manufacturers than the subgroups just described. One such group now coming into prominence is the graphics group, concerned with problems of communication between man or machine or, more properly, between the user and his data-base through visual means. This field touches on many applications areas and requires expertise in data-base management techniques, real-time programing, data communications, matrix manipulation, projective geometry, human factors analysis, crt hardware technology, and many other disciplines.

Another field with its own terminology, experts, publications, conventions, societies and other trappings of a discrete science is information retrieval. Although the problems to be solved are fundamentally interdisciplinary in nature, there is a certain mystique about this field, like many other specialty fields, which makes for a sort of clubbiness that is pleasant for those who are in it but frustrating for those outside it.

The listing of such areas of specialization could go on almost indefinitely. Process control people could deservedly claim equal time for their unique interests, as could the hardware diagnostic programers, the artificial intelligence boys, the computer-aided instruction group, the medical instrumentation field, the military command and control systems people, the symbolic and algebraic manipulation aficionados, etc.

The conclusions can only be that specialization into computer usage is a fact of the industry and the enterprising young programer must consider carefully the implications of each job change or new project on the basis of whether the favors or rejects specialization in his own case. Each course has its own merits which will be discussed shortly.

The third dimension of programing specialization, though by no means as significant as the first two, is worth mentioning. The specific computer on which a programer has had experience may matter much or not at all for the next task he is to do. A highly valued programer who is the world's leading authority on the X-123 computer may not be worth a beginning programer's salary on an unfamiliar machine where he must actually fool around with bits and masks and logical operations instead of just characters and decimal numbers. The fixed-word-length man who cannot comprehend word marks had better have a quick learning ability or all of his expertise may go for naught. To a large extent, of course, the machine type is related to the applications are in which the individual is working, but it is a separate consideration.

WHY SPECIALIZE?

There is obviously no single answer to the question of whether or not one should specialize or the degree to which this should be carried. The question imposes itself in every profession and the considerations are fundamentally the same.

An individual may specialize because he is genuinely more interested in a specific area than in peripheral or unrelated fields. Conversely, he may specialize because he is aware that he does not have the capacity to master many fields, and that to make his mark in the world he must concentrate on a single area compatible with his capability. It is true, after all, that the narrower the field on which one focuses, the easier it is to become expert in the history, theory, practice and personnel involved in that field.

One gets seen at the appropriate symposia, publishes papers, hobnobs with the select group, and is soon selected to sit on panels, review other people's papers, and participate in society activities. From a position of leadership in a field, one may then move laterally into related fields and extend his horizons at a comfortable pace. Naturally, this progression is far from automatic or easy, and genuine talent is as essential as simple dedication to a specific field.

The generalist, on the other hand, has the advantage of being able to relate separate experiences to broaden the background base from which to approach a new problem. He has at least a smattering of knowledge about many fields so that he can probably converse more or less intelligently on virtually any subject. He can more easily exploit opportunities that arise since, being more flexible, he can jump in wherever the need for his services develop.

If his capacity for originality is weak, he need not go into great depth in an area because his value to a project presumably lies in his ability to interface with different areas and bring to bear a breadth of experience. He may also be far more valuable in a completely new area than a specialist in some adjacent area in that his thinking is not constrained by a pattern which may not apply to this situation.

SPECIALIST SELLS REPUTATION

From the organization's point of view, the specialist is valuable because he is sometimes easier *to sell* on the basis of his reputation in a given field. He has well-established and reputable contacts in his chosen field, and if need exists at all for his services, there is high likelihood of his being happily and profitably occupied. Frequently, an organization can justify getting into a new technical area solely on the basis of acquiring an *expert* in that field who can lead them safely into it, thus increasing their own diversification.

Most programing organizations, of course, are themselves specialized; hence, they not only attract similarly oriented specialists but also value them for both their technical contributions and their expected contentment with a rather stable environment. The programer or analyst looking for variety will spend most of his time in a new ogranization learning the discipline on which that organization concentrates. Then, after becoming most valuahle as a result of this experience, he will decide to move on to new pastures.

Certain types of organizations, however, should place greater value on the generalist. He may be easier to sell because of his adaptibility to many diverse situations. He may tend to bring fresher ideas to bear on a problem from his multidisciplined background and stimulate new avenues of thought. He is most valuable, obviously, in those areas where many disciplines interact, such as the graphics and information retrieval areas mentioned previously. He is also vital to consulting and programing services organizations where great versatility is needed to allow exploitation of opportunities by whomever is available at the moment.

Lest it be inferred that there are only two kinds of people in the programing world, it should be emphasized that there is a continuous spectrum ranging from those who know almost nothing about everything to the other extreme (those who know everything about almost nothing). This could be represented by a family of curves suggesting the professional profiles of different types of individuals (figure 2).

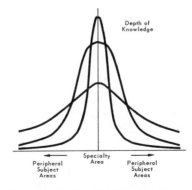

Figure 2. Professional Profile Curves

The higher the value of the curve, the more the individual tends toward specialization around a given discipline and the narrower his viewpoint becomes toward neighboring disciplines. An organization must analyze its own characteristics, determine which range of this spectrum is most applicable, and slant its staffing practices toward that goal. The individual must have insight into his own technical and personal traits to find the type of environment that will be most rewarding to him. This achievement could well be the most fundamental and vital step in achieving professional growth and lasting career fulfillment.

_____

Questions:

1. Trace the development of the programmer.

2. Discuss the pros and cons of programmer specialization.

SIMULATION, EMULATION
AND TRANSLATION

By RICHARD H. HILL

Simulation, emulations, and translation are techniques for making programs written for one digital computer useful in connection with another, but they are not equivalent in terms of end use. Simulation is primarily useful for program production and test, usually for computers that exist only in design form or for which programming and checkout are inconvenient for one or another reason. Emulation, being a machine-aided simulation, is a production computing tool intended to ease the transition from one computer to another. Translation is a technique for program conversion only, and has no direct part in production computing.

The three techniques described here are very important tools in the digital computer systems designer's kit, but none offers any sort of panacea in making the transition from one generation of computers to the next. Simulation is generally too costly to apply, except in very special circumstances. Emulation is better, but at best is a crutch, and, if it is too effective, it will generate the temptation to avoid the transition altogether. Finally, no completely satisfactory and painless method of program translation has yet been demonstrated in a production situation, although translators are getting better as the industry gains experience.

Analog computer users tend to think of simulation as a tool of prediction, rather than production. In the world of digital computer programming, however, simulation of a special sort is an integral part of program production and testing. Further, what has come to be called emulation—really a special form of simulation is a tool for production computing.

This article defines simulation and emulation in these special contexts and expands on the definitions by providing some discussion of the techniques and some examples of usage. Because the translation is an alternative to simulation in program conversion, the article also defines and discusses program translation.

DEFINITIONS

Simulation, in the sense it is discussed here, is the simulation of the machine-level operations of one digital computer on another computer with a different order code and internal structure, without special hardware provision to facilitate the task. The object of the simulation is to be able to execute the

Reprinted with permission from the February 1968 issue of SIMULATION MAGAZINE, a publication of SIMULATION COUNCILS, INC., copyright 1968.

machine code of the simulated computer, or a significant subset of the code, on a machine of a different type. Note the emphasis on the fact that the simulated and simulating machines are of a different type. Some "families" of computers (e.g., IBM 1401-1410-7010, Univac 490-492-494, SDS Sigma 5-7, IBM 360) have varying degrees of machine-level commonality such that larger machines can accept and execute machine-level programs of the smaller members of the family. This "upward compatibility" feature is outside the scope of this definition.

Emulation has the same objective as simulation, but is achieved with some assistance of special hardware features, ranging from interrupts to detect and signal the presence of conditions to be interpreted to special control-function decoders to handle instructions alien to the emulating computer. Generally speaking also, an emulator cannot fail to handle acceptably every possible function of the emulated machine. The emulator concept probably developed from the IBM 704 compatibility-mode feature for the IBM 709 computer. The IBM 360 product line provides emulators for a number of older IBM computers, and RCA emulates the RCA 301 on its Spectra 70 equipment. One of the most interesting recent developments in the emulator line is the Standard Computers IC 6000, which emulates IBM 7090/7094/7094 II and 7044 at very favorable cost/capability ratios. These emulators are, for all practical purposes, Standard's product line. Like the Standard machines, modern emulators rely heavily on micro-programming techniques, discussed later in this article.

Some terms used in discussing simulation, emulation, and translation:

SOURCE COMPUTER—The computer from which the code to be simulated, emulated, or translated is derived.

TARGET COMPUTER—The computer that will execute translated code.

HOST COMPUTER—The computer on which a simulation or emulation is run.

OBJECT COMPUTER—The computer being simulated or emulated.

SOURCE LANGUAGE—Code written by a programmer. May be either machine-level or higher-level language.

OBJECT LANGUAGE—The code executed directly by a computer, or executed by simulation or emulation.

MACHINE CODE—Object language.

MACHINE-LEVEL LANGUAGE—A source language that includes a direct representation of the machine code.

HIGHER-LEVEL LANGUAGE—Any programming language that is independent of the characteristics of a praticular computer.

Translation attempts to bypass the problem of executing "alien" machine language by translating the program codes into the machine language of the host computer. The codes to be translated may be either source or machine level, depending on the skill or technical philosophy of the translation routine. Translation is a difficult art, largely because the unpredictability of the human coder frequently defects the mapping algorithms used in the process. The most successful translators have been those that translate from one version of a higher-level source language into another, such as the LIFT and SIFT routines that translate from FORTRAN II to FORTRAN IV. However, the LIBERATOR package of Honeywell EDP translates 1401 source code to

Honeywell 200 language successfully, and IBM's newly released ACCAP program is said to be 75-80% effective in translating 1410-7010 Autocoder routines to System 360 COBOL. Celestron, Inc. of New York claims to have developed techniques for machine-code to machine-code translation applicable to any machine pair, but evidence of their success to date is sparse. The Celestron approach (called X-ACT by its authors) is the most elaborate and ambitious available so far. With this approach the translation begins with the machine-level ("object") code for the program being translated, constructs a source code version of the program, then makes a source-to-source translation, and finally an assembly into the target-machine object code.

APPLICATIONS

There are three major applications for the techniques under discussion:
- Program production and testing
- Production computing
- Program conversion

In general, the three application areas stated above correspond directly to simulation, emulation, and translation.

Developing a new digital computer system is a complex activity, particularly today, when software plays such an important role in this effort. Ideally a computer for test of the software should be available at the same time that the hardware is under development. This is, of course, impossible. Simulation offers at least a partial solution, since the new computer design can be simulated on an older computer, and both hardware and software concepts can be texted in this manner.

Development of a new computer may not be the only justification for a simulation system. Many computers, particularly machines such as those used in airborne applications, are inconvenient to use for program production and test for various reasons. There may not be an adequate complement of input-output equipment available to make the program test efficient. It may prove more efficient, also, to take advantage of program test tools developed for a more generally used system than to write dumps, traces, etc., for a special-purpose computer. The simulated computer may also have insufficient memory space available for all of the functions desired in program production.

Simulation is rarely used for production computing. The reason is purely economic; typically simulation, involving as it does an interpretive program, is too costly in processor time to compete with the computer being simulated in economic terms. It is also typical that the simulation does not include the complete computer. Simulation of input-output functions is difficult at best; if these functions time-share the memory of the object computer, or are time-dependent, it may be very difficult or impossible to provide a completely accurate simulation. The MASS system that simulated the AN/UYK-1 computer on the IBM 7090, for example, did not even attempt to simulate input-output for those reasons. Nevertheless the simulator was an effective program test tool. Data elements were provided in the simulated memory by external means.

Emulation, in contrast, is entirely a production computing tool. It is intended as a stop-gap measure to tide over an installation that acquires a new computer until programs can be converted to the newer source languages and checked out for production use. For this reason emulators must be more efficient in their operation than the simulators. They also must be complete, since the ground rules for emulation do not permit modification of the source machine code. Ideally, an emulator will accept any program written for the source machine and will execute it at least as economically as the source machine. This goal is achieved in some systems, notably the Standard Computers machines and the IBM 360/65 emulator for the 7090, at least in the latter case if the computer is fully loaded. There are many pitfalls in the economic analysis of emulation, however; so the potential user is cautioned to examine the situation with a great deal of care and possibly to seek expert and impartial advice.

Translation is an aid to program conversion when moving from one computer to another. The easiest programs to translate are those written in higher-level language, since by definition such languages are (or should be, in the writer's opinion) machine-independent in nature and hence less complex to translate from one system to another. In at least one instance (RCA Spectra 70 COBOL and IBM 360 COBOL), the programming languages are so close in nature that it is feasible to write programs in either language and check them out on either machine for use on the other. In most instances, however, code translation is a laborious, although possibly machine-aided, process. It is often and tragically complicated by installation mismanagement that permitted undocumented programs to contaminate the library, failed to insist upon maintaining clean decks, patchfree production programs, and allowed other poor practices to impede the translation process.

In the final analysis, translation is the only satisfactory solution to obtaining the economic benefits of new computing equipment. However, it is an interesting problem for installation management, again, to select those programs to be translated, decide which shall be emulated (and eventually be replaced), and which, if any will be emulated indefinitely.

IMPLEMENTATION TECHNIQUES

The basis for both simulation and emulation is a programming technique called interpretation. Figure 1 is a simplified flow diagram of the interpretation process as it might be assumed to take place for a simple hypothetical computer. An interpretive control routine fetches the items to be interpreted, in this case the instructions of the simulated computer as they reside in simulated memory.

The control routine must assume the functions of, or have available to it, a simulated program counter, in order to determine which item to select. When the selected item has been fetched, the control routine performs an initial decode in order to invoke the appropriate interpreter, actually a subroutine that has built into it the functions that the item would normally perform through hardware in the source computer. When the interpreter has completed its function, certain general functions must be handled, such as updating program counters, checking for interrupts, etc. In the machine being simulated here, it is assumed that after this step the control of the simulated computer checks for input-output activity. If any is present, then it is done at this time. Otherwise, the cycle begins again. Figure 2 shows how memory would be organized in the host computer.

START

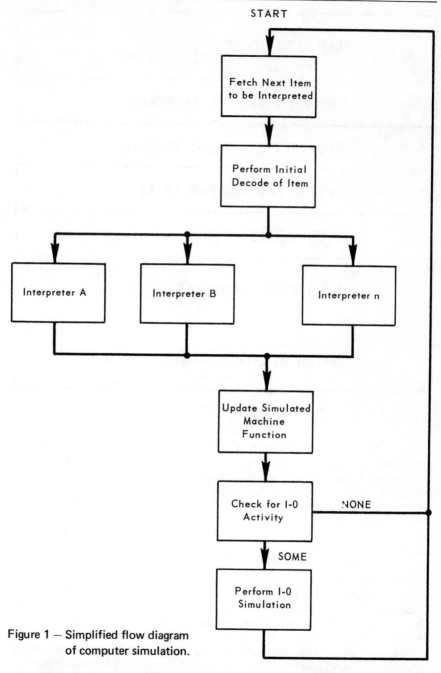

Figure 1 — Simplified flow diagram
of computer simulation.

The same functional flow may be assumed either for simulation or emulation. The difference resides in the hardware assistance given to the interpretive process. Most emulators rely on the technique of micro-programming, in which a small, fast miniature computer is embedded within the

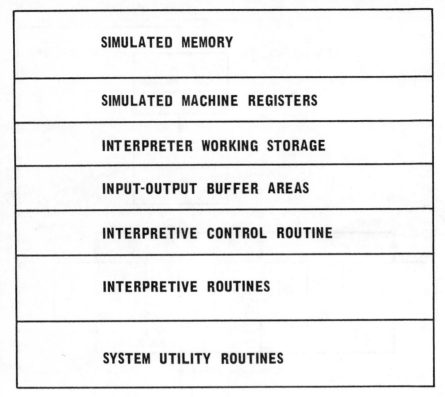

Figure 2 — Storage allocation in simulation.

computer that appears to the external user. The lower end of the IBM 360 line consists of microprogrammed computers; Spectra 70 computers follow the same organizational pattern, and the Standard Computers IC 6000 machines are completely microprogrammed. The AN/UYK-1, TRW 130, and similar machines were designed along the same lines, but did not have available the hierarchy of memory speeds and the concept of read-only storage that characterize the later machines. In a microprogrammed computer the processing capability of the machine is concentrated in a small, fast computer designed especially for interpretive execution of small modules of code. By use of this technique the actual machine code of one computer can be efficiently executed interpretively by the microprogrammed machine. It is this design concept that the Standard Computers IC 6000 product line incorporates very successfully. The benefits are: (1) smaller component count, and hence lower cost, (2) high degree of flexibility, and (3) ability to expand or extend the system without major hardware changes. The disadvantages are few, but significant for many applications. There is, beyond question, a speed handicap that limits throughout in any microprogrammed computer. Thus the lower end of the IBM 360 line is microprogrammed, but the upper end machines revert to more conventional organization. Further, programming a microprogrammed computer is an arcane activity rarely practiced outside the manufacturer's shop, which fact currently makes the inherent flexibility somewhat less than widely available. Some manufacturers, like IBM and Standard, make the microprogramming technique virtually unavailable to users by requiring special information or equipment in order to do microprogramming.*

Implementation of translation techniques is a problem more akin to writing a compiler than to simulation of a computer. The same problems of deriving information from the input and mapping it into an output syntax exist in translation as in compilation. Typically the translation routine will utilize the symbolic information contained in the program to be translated. If the program to be translated exists only in object form, the problem is complicated further not only because the symbolic information is missing (in some cases much of it can be reconstructed), but more seriously because the machine code form of a program is ambiguous. After all, in the computer memory there are only numbers; their meaning is established dynamically as the program is executed.

Questions:

1. Define emulation, simulation, and translation as used in this article.

2. Discuss the major applications for the three techniques.

3. Explain the various economic tradeoffs when considering the use of simulation, emulation, and translation, assuming the proper source/target/host/object computer relationship exists.

4. Define interpretation as the term pertains to these techniques.

---

*IBM's announcement of the 360/25, in which micro programming is made available to the user, came too late to be considered in this article.

MULTI-PROGRAMMING:
WHO NEEDS IT?

By BROOKE W. BOERING

Numerous papers have dealt with the admittedly significant successes of large scale multi-programmed installations of recent date. As a result there seems to be developing a cult whose credo is that "If it isn't multi-programmed, it's out of date". It is perfectly true that both time-sharing systems and the behemoths of batch-processing can and are benefiting mightily from the maturing of multi-programming (henceforth called "m-p"). In the case of time-sharing m-p is, of course, central to the very concept. Devotion to expanding the understanding and use of m-p in such installations is virtually a "must". With these remarks, I have now made the appropriate reservations, set forth the more obvious exceptions, and generally rendered unto Caesar that which is Caesar's.

POTENTIAL DANGERS

But now I must point out that there are potential dangers in assuming that m-p applies in *all* installations. Manufacturers of computers today are promoting m-p for medium-scale (half megabuck) systems, especially where there are plans for both real-time and batch processing. So let's re-examine the fundamentals of systems design and of return on costs, in the light of not only the advent of m-p but also current changes in equipment, prices and capacities.

First, let us look closely at what m-p does for time-sharing and for very large-scale users. In time-sharing, each request for processing by a remote (or local) terminal results in a "job" to be handled by the system in the manner most efficient to the total environment based on the demands of the moment and the condition of previously commenced "jobs" from other terminals. Neither the timing nor structure of such jobs can be determined at the time of systems design, so it makes good sense to provide an extensive set of gear, and an "executive" program which can adapt on a dynamic basis to rapidly changing demands of the system. The technique of "slicing" a job into sub-jobs which has received much attention is secondary to this prime purpose of "gear sharing" which, of course, preceded time-sharing in development.

TIME SLICING

The "time-slicing" technique is necessary where jobs can use a sizable chunk of time of the central processor unit. In the commercial counterpart to time-sharing, namely, real-time business systems, the individual job demands on the CPU are seldom extensive enough to require temporary abandonment unless there is "wait" time for an I/O operation. Nearly all real-time systems are multi-programmed to permit overlap of various real-time "jobs" emanating from many terminals within the system. However it is not *this* definition of m-p that concerns us but rather the broader concept that involves both real-time (whether time-shared or not) and "batch" processing within the same CPU. This concept is, in effect, the most complex yet; for it purports to handle in a sensitive on-line system "batch" programs written without concern for the continuity requirements of real-time. Such systems exist, of course, and do the job as advertised. What is not quite so apparent is the real costs to the medium-scale user looking at such a system as compared to a more conventional approach.

MYTH OF PRECIOUS CENTRAL PROCESSOR TIME

The myth of "precious" CPU time requires almost immediate examination, or it will continue to distort more practical considerations throughout our appraisal. With the advent of "unlimited use" leases and the increasing portion of total gear cost being borne by the peripherals in the latest systems, it is becoming apparent that CPU "pulsing" costs are no longer the dominant consideration.

REQUIREMENTS FOR MULTI-PROGRAMMING

The elements required to operate a m-p environment for simultaneous real-time and batch processing are:

● Enough core to contain the resident real-time system, the batch program, and the m-p executive. Trade-offs are possible to reduce core requirements, which generally involve penalties of increased secondary memory, reduced efficiency of response times and/or need for increased processor speeds, all of which cost money, as does core.

● Sufficient dual-purpose peripherals to enable both systems to overlap and to minimize "idle" units. In actual practice, few real-time and batch multi-programmed systems utilize either common input/output devices or a common data base except for the m-p executive itself. From this it can be seen that the m-p advantage of dynamically allocating such equipment is of little value here.

● Possibly increased CPU speeds to absorb the housekeeping operations of m-p. (Check the price differences between a mod-30 and mod-40 or a 415 compared to a 425 mainframe.)

● The latest hardware "goodies" in the form of base register modification, memory protect, interval timers, non-stop mode, etc. Again, nothing's free, nor should it be.

● The "complexity" introduced to the user's installation. This is probably the most difficult element to assess properly. Although promised (and even delivered) by the manufacturer, the m-p executive for an installation of the size under consideration here must be just as complicated as that required for the most sophisticated (and expensive) installations going. Typically, medium-scale users have limited staffs who are close enough to the user problems to do a good systems job but seldom have extensive background in software design or system maintenance. This would not be a factor if all software were delivered letter-perfect by the manufacturer and/or his subsequent support of said software was consistently beyond reproach. Experience however indicates otherwise.

UNRELIABILITY AND HEADACHES

The factor of complexity brings us to the element of reliability. A software failure of the m-p system that stops the real-time system from operating must be viewed differently from our batch-oriented headaches of bygone days — when we had all night to find the bug.

To our hypothetical medium-scale commercial user who is going real-time, the issue of reliability takes on a dimension quite different from that encountered previously. If something goes wrong with the data-processing environment (software or hardware) which cuts off real-time service, he has extended his troubles *right this minute* to the front line of the enterprise. In the case of an airline, it's the reservation system that does not work; for a bank, it's probably the savings accounts which are now inaccessible; a large wholesale distributor finds he no longer can determine his inventory condition. The data processing manager in such situations has simply *got* to suffer some degree of anguish, embarrassment, or worse, as a result of such occurrences. Naturally, manual "back-up" systems are devised — but, like all such unpractised systems, they are all but forgotten at the time they are most needed. Even when usable, the manual systems are only barely tolerable for only the very shortest times. This entire sensitive matter of reliability takes on a degree of importance not easily equated directly to the costs of the system alone.

DIVIDING THE DAY

Let's now turn to the obvious alternatives to m-p for the medium-scale user who needs both real-time and batch capability. If the data processing demands are modest enough and there are no time conflicts, he might devote the system to real-time processing during regular business hours, and leave the batch processing to the night shifts. Such an approach has some disadvantages. There is the psychological one of requiring operating and programming personnel to work undesirable shifts on a regular and continuing basis. There is the possibility of losing the best people to other installations not having such problems. Another limitation is that the real-time system cannot operate 24 hours per day and also do batch work in a non m-p mode. Such round-the-clock applications for real-time leave no time for after hours "batching." Even when some time remains, say 6 or 8 hours per night, it might prove insufficient to accomplish the off-line processing needed to support the next day's operations.

THE DUPLEX INSTALLATION

One configuration that deserves serious consideration as an alternative to m-p is commonly referred to as a "duplex" installation. Here the principal feature is the presence of two main frames, one normally devoted to the real-time operation while the other normally does "batch" processing. Each can operate independently of the other under normal circumstances; and yet the "batch" CPU stands ready to abandon its non-time-critical work to take on the real-time operation should the other processor fail. For this back-up function to operate properly requires equal mainframes in core size, communication capability, etc. Once such a concept of separation, simplicity and back-up is given serious consideration, what seemed to be impossibly costly configurations often come into focus as the cheapest in view of *total* costs.

So we assert that a 2% usage of CPU time just might be economical under certain conditions, and thereby we incur the wrath of the entire Association for Computing Machinery. But we will now attempt to make peace with the manufacturers, who have perhaps been treated rather shabbily, by recommending to medium-scale users contemplating new real-time, commercial systems to "take two, they're small".

Questions:

1.   What is I/O? Time Slicing? How do they relate to each other?

2.   List the elements required to perform multi-programming.

3.   Define the terms (1) real-time, (2) batch processing, (3) duplex installation, and (4) "Executive" program.

COUNTING GENERATIONS

By R. L. PATRICK

My favorite consulting client is having a bit of trouble converting to System/360. (I always start a magazine article with an understatement.) Why is it that the equipment announced in 1964 and installed in 1966 just refuses to settle down? For a while, IBM's difficulties masked a formidable problem of our own—*we* weren't ready!

In trying to explain the stretched out schedules and distended budgets to a corporate vice president, I became aware that I had been counting my generations wrong. The hardware community, which is about as vague with their word meanings as we are, is agreed (almost) that the first generation was the vacuum tube generation. Machines of this generation used discreet components, their hardware packing density was low, and they were manually wired and soldered. They first became available to customers about 1953.

Hardware historians would describe the second generation as the transistor generation. It, too, used discreet components, achieved medium density packaging, and the machines were pretty much machine wired and machine soldered. The first commercial machines were available in quantity to customers about 1957.

The third generation was heralded by IBM's 1964 announcement of System/360. The smaller models started to become available in quantity in 1965. They feature small integrated circuits, rather high packaging density, and a computer which was pretty much designed and produced by automated processes.

So much for the hardware historians's view of the computing profession. These definitions are not very handy when trying to explain to the vice president of finance why another million dollars is necessary to complete the conversion next year that we promised last year.

Out of a series of rather unpleasant sessions with lieutenants of industry, I have devised a series of explanations which, while they don't condone our troubles and mal-performance, at least assist me in explaining them to the men who control the budgets and pay my fees.

Back in 1953, when the first commerical machines were being made available, we users had no training, skill, knowledge, or other attributes of a profession. The profession was not yet born. There were only a few UNIVAC-Is, IBM 701s and 702s available for exploitation. The staffs of these early computer facilities were made up of accountants, bookkeepers, engineers, mathematicians,

Reprinted from the June, 1968 issue of the Journal of Data Management and copyrighted by the Data Processing Management Association.

and other employees skilled in some field other than computing; but interested in learning the new techniques for one of several personal reasons.

ORGANIZED CHAOS

The computer was delivered bare. A training course consisted of a manual and some time to study it. If you were in the field early enough, subroutines had not yet become popular. Libraries were unknown. The only programs supplied with the machine by the manufacturer were hardware diagnostics. These were the primitive days and I believe can be properly labeled the "first software generation—organized chaos." We had nothing, expected nothing, and knew nothing.

Out of this chaos, some good resulted despite ourselves. In addition to repeatedly reinventing everything, a pattern began to emerge. Some of the early leaders of the field fostered the concept of the cooperative user's group so that we might band together and reduce the needless duplication of effort in producing the fundamental computer programs necessary for the routine operation of a computer shop. We sought out those computer programs or computer program fragments which were universally needed and desired in every installation, and a voluntary effort was organized so that these programs could be produced through cooperative action only once, and shared by all.

A little known, but fundamentally important aspect of this cooperative undertaking, was the establishment of the first programming standards. Subroutines were generically defined, the linkage associated with the subroutine call was specifically defined, and the beginnings of a standard subroutine writeup were promulgated.

At the same time, as part of this same cooperative effort, the first operating systems were born. These provided for an imput stream which consisted of a batch of jobs and their data, a resident monitor program within the CPU, and an output stream which consisted of the results of the execution of the jobs contained in the input stream. These systems sported compilers and assemblers, contained automatic accounting, controlled online subroutine libraries, communicated with professional operators in a standard way, and allowed routine operations to be accomplished without the programmer being present or operating the console.

COMPUTER MANAGEMENT AND OPERATION

These first monitor programs further extended the trend toward cooperative developments by users themselves and established additional standards for interfacing an entire computer program with the resident monitor system which controlled the machine itself. The monitor program and the compilers it controlled and the libraries it accessed heralded the beginning of the "second software generation—computer management and operation." The second generation introduced the professional computer operator to the staff, left the programmers free for programming and analysis, and allowed the computers to be run three shifts a day to gain better efficiency and economy of operation.

As the second generation dawned, a reduction in programmer training and sophistication was realized. Every programmer no longer had to learn how to operate the machine, program its input/output devices (usually tab machines welded to the electronics to form a kludge), or devise all of his own routines. The programmer was freed from some of these extraneous interests and allowed to concentrate on his assigned application and how to produce the reports desired.

Also, at this time, the first FORTRAN compilers became available and it was possible, through a combination of the FORTRAN language; and a machine room inhabited by a computer, an operating system, and a professional operator; to allow non-computer professionals to submit work and receive answers. Thus, "open-shop" operations were born.

EFFICIENCY AND RESPONSE

Sometime in the first half of 1964 dawned the "third software generation—efficiency and response." In late '62 and '63, two or three programming development groups, working quite independently from each other, started developing the first practical commercial multi-processor computer configurations. These received considerable popularity in the latter 7094 days as "direct couple" configurations. In these configurations, the 7094 hardware was scaled down and all primary input/output, scheduling, and file control functions were assigned to a connected computer, usually an IBM 7044. Thus, just about the time the third generation hardware was *announced,* the third generation software was operating.

The third generation software allowed the programmer to submit work destined for any one of several language processors. The operating system maintained priority queues for work awaiting setup, awaiting processing, or awaiting output. The macro-scheduling was performed by the operator feeding cards into the reader. The machine performed the micro-scheduling according to one of several priority algorithms available to the chief operator. Job accounting was kept, restart was possible, on-line libraries were allowed and encouraged. Some of the direct couple systems even had distant card readers and printers for performing service now known as "remote job entry." Thus, the third software generation was heralded on second generation hardware.

The direct couple systems were economic and successful because they maintained strict compatibility with their predecessor systems. Except for very minor changes, the applications programs would run on either a direct couple or a stand alone.

ENTER 360

Lulled into complacency based on the success of a few direct couple systems, the *country* plunged headlong into third generation software. *Never were so many so surprised by so much so suddenly.*

Although we had some experience in running third generation software in actual user installations, there were some not so subtle differences in the software which came with the third generation equipment. It had the appearance of being function rich. While the direct couples were designed for a limited market with limited needs, the design of OS/360 was dumbfounding. We had masses of programmers to teach a new machine—generally this training was rushed, ad hoc, and lacked thoroughness. Many installations failed to recognize that 70% of their manpower was used up in maintenance and this had to continue if the related commercial enterprise was to continue to operate. The new software was not initially stable and this caused additional problems by impacting schedules heavily. But, after all of these reasons were exposed, the fact could not be ignored: we simply were not ready!

Few installations had bothered to set up more than minimal programming standards during second generation operation. Minor attempts were made to get programmers to put comments in their code and to request that flow charts be drawn sometime. The installation which had an active on-going program aimed at keeping documentation current-to-the-code was rare indeed. Some installations were so hopelessly ill-disciplined that file format definitions could not be produced when requested.

I wish I had a dollar for every programmer who started to convert his source language only to find out that the source language, the last listing, and the code were not in consonance with one another.

Back in the second generation, we were delighted when we found that we could lower the required level of training, teach a new employee either FORTRAN or COBOL, and get him productive earlier. However, we made almost no attempt to raise the level of these masses of programming technicians so that they *understood* what they were doing. Further, they lacked appreciation for the fundamentals behind the software they were using. When faced with third generation software, our legions of coders succumbed to the onslaught. For a while we were virtually decimated. Nothing would work. No progress was being made. The machines were being extensively used for checkout. Thank goodness for the 10% extra shift rental provisions or our budgets would never have weathered the storm.

WHAT'S BEEN LEARNED

Those who made it through the transition have treated conversion to the third generation as a serious undertaking. They have trained their programmers in the fundamentals of the new software and drilled them in the practice. They have cleaned up the second generation jobs before any attempt was made at conversion. They have sent pathfinder teams forward into the third generation to convert and leave a trail for the legions to follow. They have recognized the risks and expenses of pioneering. Finally, armed with a lot of faith and big budgets, they have made the transition.

In my consulting calls, I find computing practice is as diverse as it ever was. Although many installations have third generation equipment, some are using first generation software, some are using second generation software, and some, third generation software. The installation that has a programmer present and operating a 1620 emulator on a System/360 Model 30 is still in the dark ages of the first generation. Another installation may be using a tape operating system and batching its input and output in the light of the second generation.

Others may be using EXEC-8 or the MVT option of OS/360 to press forward into third generation operation and sophistication.

Out of all this, one would think that we have learned some lessons, but it does not appear to be the case. Each of us should critically evaluate his own operation to be sure that he is using third generation equipment well—there is no need to overdo just because the potential is there. If the requirements of the environment and the capabilities of the staff are compatible with third generation software, then by all means, "press on." However, if your needs to not require that sophistication, don't adopt third generation software until your staff is trained for it and your house is in order.

When discussing operations with your peers, find out what kind of software he is using before the discussion goes too far. This will allow you to calibrate his remarks and determine how many of his observations are applicable to your own shop. When hiring experienced staff members, best find out what kind of expereince they have. Programmers experienced in emulating first generation programs on a Spectra-70 are in need of much additional education and training before they can use third generation software well. It even works the other way—if a potential employee grew up in an installation which has pioneered all of these new features into the field, he has a lot of valuable experience (provided you are going that way) but he may have a lot of bad habits to go along with it.

PREPARE FOR THE FOURTH

One thing is very clear. While many of us are now enjoying both third generation hardware and software, we must not again become complacent. There *will* be a fourth generation, and a fifth, etc. The fourth generation will encompass terminals for on-line inquiry, large resident data bases stored on disk, and other forms of remote input/output to handle priority jobs. These operations will require that we reach yet a higher level of training and sophistication. The conversion we have just lived through has been horrendous. Let us learn from the past and prepare for the future. Let us actively establish and maintain standards for programs, documentation, and data files to allow us to face the fourth generation with less temerity. Invest today, prepare for tomorrow and enjoy better operation and easier maintenance in the meantime.

Questions:

1.   List the attributes of first, second and third generation hardware.

2.   Discuss the major problems of implementing third generation hardware.

3.   Why does the author feel direct couple systems were generally successful? How did third generation hardware systems differ?

4.   List the major changes that have occurred in the types of personnel programming computers.

FORECASTS FOR THE FOURTH EDP GENERATION

Sometime in the early 1970's, the fourth generation of computers will have established itself, with far-reaching effects for administrative managers. Computer users and specialists are already making predictions about advances to be expected. What are they saying?

New developments in technology will make computers more versatile and capable of handling a greater amount of procedural steps automatically. Storage capacities will increase to vast proportions, while costs and cycle times will drop. Some experts say computer architecture will undergo radical changes. Large-scale integration, time-sharing, adaptive dissemination, polymorphism, image processing and firmware will become common fourth generation terms, and they will be described in some detail below.

STRUCTURE

One prediction says that fourth generation computers will have no order sets or data structure. Instead, the computers will be able to handle specialized functions through replaceable microprogramming.

Microprogramming is already in use today in third generation installations. It is a system in which the programmer uses the basic, built-in instructions of a computer to construct other instructions. Some present computers are equipped with a built-in microporgram, and a second one is optionally available to users, enabling the computers to achieve compatibility with older computers.

In the fourth generation however, according to this predicition, there will be many microprograms available; users and software specialists will also be able to prepare their own microprograms.

The replaceable feature of microprograms will further increase computer versatility. Instead of having a new microprogram structured for each new function, the computer will be able to utilize its existing microprograms to perform a variety of tasks.

FIRMWARE

A new development called firmware, in which microprogramming plays a vital role, has been predicted for the fourth generation. One expert has defined firmware as "microprograms resident in the computer's control memory, which

Reprinted with permission from the July, 1967 issue of ADMINISTRATIVE MANAGEMENT.

specialize the logical design for a specific purpose." Firmware would require new, special hardware to prepare and process it for input.

Most specialists and experts making predictions about the fourth generation agree that it will be achieved during the first half of the 1970's. The specific developments they discuss are also expected to appear during this five or six year span.

The past three generations have been marked by advances in circuitry among other developments, and the fourth generation will be no exception. Large-scale integration (LSI) is expected to be one of its outstanding characteristics. With LSI, highly complex arrangements of circuits will be batch fabricated onto economical silicon chips. The batch fabrication process permits many different items to be fabricated onto a chip concurrently.

Integrated logic chips will provide, among other advantages, a greatly increased density and greater speed. Another predicted development in this area is the advent of cryogenic technology. Cryogenics, a branch of physics relating to the production and effects of very low temperatures, would be applied to the computer memory. Cycle times would be drastically reduced with this approach because, as temperatures near absolute zero, large current charges can be obtained with relatively small magnetic charges.

Other predicted developments in circuitry and memory include gigantic memories utilizing laser beams but costing less than present systems, and a characteristic called *polymorphism*.

Polymorphism will enable the computer to keep going even if one of the circuits is broken. Instead of an instant collapse when this happens, there will be a series of progressive failures over a period of time, with the most vital circuits functioning longest.

DRAWINGS

Image files and image processing will become economical and practical in the computers of the 1970's. New kinds of materials, plus advanced technology, will enable the computers to handle graphic, non-digital information such as engineering drawings, design concepts or legal documents. The computer will be able to receive, store, process and print images as such, rather than having them translated into machine language first, when this is even possible. Developments in thermoplastic media will permit stored image data to be altered as well as erased or reused, according to one prediction.

Time-sharing on a vast scale will become possible with the emergence of the "public utility" computer concept. Here, immense installations will be set up for use by hundreds of businesses, on a basis similar to the present electricity and telephone systems. Some experts feel that these giant computers will be little more than data banks, although others feel processing capabilities will be available too.

SIMPLIFICATION

One surprising result in these developments may indicate a trend toward simplified machine operation to meet the limitations of the user.

Man-machine interface, in this instance, will be improved as machines adapt to their real end-users. This trend will gradually lessen the importance of such intermediate personnel as programmers, because managers will be able to write their own simple programs as developments are refined.

Systems will also be developed that give the manager information particularly relevant to his work, without any initiative on his part. This system, known as "adaptive dissemination," is already being used in the Federal government. It involves providing the machine with an outline of the manager and his information needs. As the computer processes data, it comes across some that is related to the manager's needs, and will automatically forward it to the appropriate manager.

Almost paradoxically, as man-machine interface improves, men will have less and less to do with the machine. In generations beyond the fourth, machines will be able to handle increasing amounts of their work automatically. Vast amounts of personnel time, formerly spent in working out programs, will be freed for more creative purposes.

Questions:

1. List and briefly describe the characteristics of fourth generation hardware systems the author foresees.

2. Discuss the possible benefits of "selective dissemination".

IBM'S NEW GENERATION

I. & U. PRAKASH

IBM'S NEW GENERATION

This is a report on IBM's "new generation" (NG) computers and other peripheral data processing equipment. The report is divided into three main parts. Part 1 covers the strategy and background behind the new equipment, Part 2 lists the characteristics of the new equipment, and Part 3 discusses the possible effect of the new equipment on the data processing marketplace and on other aspects of the data processing industry. The data for this report was compiled from various announcements and other announced developments about new data processing systems and peripheral equipment. Of course many other developments not included in this summary can be expected from IBM during the coming year.

PART I: STRATEGY AND BACKGROUND

It appears likely that some new equipment announcements regarding small card systems which incorporate a new input card may still possibly come in the second quarter of 1969. It is also likely that announcements dealing with large systems in the new generation computers will be scheduled near the start of the second half of 1969. One cannot discount the fact that IBM may change these expected announcement dates, as it has on previous occasions in the past five years. However, it is believed that the marketing strategy behind these announcements is unlikely to undergo any major changes.

We have named these expected machines new generation (NG) equipment, in preference to the term fourth generation, which may not be completely suitable. It is expected that the new equipment will use Metal-oxide-semiconductor (MOS) integrated circuits with several hundred elements. This new technology will assure the NG computers of several important advantages, including: substantially longer component life, far greater reliability, increased ease of diagnosis of reasons for equipment breakdowns, and repair in a fraction of the time it takes today. It is expected that ferrite-core memories will continue to be used, even though they will be made of smaller and smaller cores. These reductions in core size combined with other buffering

Reprinted with permission from Computers and Automation (May, 1969) copyright (1969) by and published by Berkeley Enterprises, Inc. 815 Washington Street, Newtonville, Massachusetts,)2160.

technique innovations used on IBM's large computers (System 360/model 85) will assure substantially increased memory operating speeds.

UPWARDS COMPATIBILITY

The new generation systems will have between two to three times the capability (for example in terms of speed) for almost the current price. These computers will be as new in some respects as the system 360 line was when it was introduced in 1964. There will be important differences between the existing line of data processing systems and those to come in 1969. Certainly, it will not be possible to compare some of these new generation machines with any existing equipment. However, no matter how the new equipment is labelled, it will be able to use current programs and other software developed by users for System 360. It is believed that it will not be possible to use software specially produced for the new generation equipment on current IBM equipment. Most of the machines and systems will be upwards compatible. It is highly likely that the initial machines of the NG line will be one or more of the large systems in the line, and will be comparable to the IBM System 360/models 75 or 65 in price.

Initial deliveries of this new generation equipment are expected to be about nine to twelve months from the date of the 1969 announcement. This will be in line with the delivery schedules of other data processing equipment manufacturers, and will hopefully eliminate any problems with long delivery quotation as stated by some of IBM's competitors in their complaints to the anti-trust division of the Dept. of Justice.

PRICE

It is likely that although the prices of new systems equipment will be comparable to the existing machines, the relationships of rental charges to purchase prices and applicable maintenance agreement service rates will differ from existing IBM equipment. There are many reasons for this conclusion, some of these based on studies of the data processing marketplace conducted by DP Data Corp. during 1967 and 1968.

SYSTEM 360

Far from making current system 360 equipment obsolete, the NG equipment will extend its life in many ways, so that current system 360 and other IBM users will be able to take advantage of the performance of the new equipment when they have outgrown their present equipment. It is likely that it will not be uncommon to mix the new generation equipment with the current system 360 and other equipment in a single system at a single location. In this sense, life of the system 360 machines will be extended into the 1970's.

Since the initial deliveries of a limited number of types of new generation equipment can be expected during the second quarter of 1970, 1971 and 1972 will be the years of volume deliveries to data processing users.

It is expected that the 1969 announcements (and later ones) by IBM will include a large number of machines and devices which go with the central processor. These peripheral units will proliferate over a period of time, making each computer installation virtually a custom-tailored job. This would be in line with increasing specialization at IBM in dealing with the needs of customers from different industries and even of those having different data processing needs and applications in the same industry.

Since the system 360 and new generation equipment life will extend into the mid-1970's, it is not unreasonable to expect a relaxation of IBM's past conservative depreciation practices, in line with the increasing maturity of the data processing industry. The evidence of this maturity, if not based on changes in technology, is based on the increased size that this industry will have attained in the 1970's.

BUSINESS STRATEGY

In coming out with the NG line of computers, IBM's business strategy is expected to undergo a drastic change from that of the past several years. Since it is expected that IBM will start its announcements of its NG line of computers with one of the large systems, the battle between IBM and Control Data Corp. for dominance of the large and very large sectors of the computer field will start with the NG announcements. The battle will be fought on Control Data's home grounds, the very large scale computer systems.

During the past several years, IBM has had trouble living up to the outmoded consent decree provisions which forced it to offer its equipment for sale, in addition to renting it as the corporation had done for over four decades. The consent decree was appropriate at a time when competition was almost nonexistent. Now, however, no one can realistically ignore the existence of competition in the data processing industry. Several large companies—General Electric, Honeywell, RCA, NCR, Burroughs, and Control Data—have entered the industry since that time. There is little doubt that there has been a dramatic increase in competition in this industry since the mid-1950's, almost fifteen years ago.

GROWTH OF LEASING COMPANIES

Over the years, many leasing companies have been established. These leasing companies did not sell any equipment to a user. They just took over the ownership of the data processing equipment from IBM with the consent of the equipment user in return for lower rental payments for the user than charged by IBM. In general, IBM took these leasing company actions gracefully. It looked forward to the day it could learn to live with these leasing companies so that both could cooperate in offering the equipment and services to the computer user. However, this independent leasing idea spread and really caught fire in the second half of 1967. In 1967 and 1968 several hundred million dollars worth of equipment was purchased each year by these financial intermediaries. It appears that from IBM's point of view all of these leasing companies took full advantage of IBM's inability to take any concrete actions, in view of the consent decree provisions. It seems that IBM would have liked to stop the disruption of its relationships with its customers caused by the independent leasing companies.

The leasing companies did not service any of the purchased equipment or provide the data processing user with anything additional except the "lower than IBM rental," which was their initial appeal.

The leasing company side of the story, however, reads differently. They claim to have come to the rescue of the IBM equipment user. The companies lowered the cost of computer usage for their clients and at the same time kept some of the same conditions for the user, such as maintenance service by IBM. In addition, they claim to have created a more favorable climate for the user so that IBM would "treat them more fairly in the future".

PROBLEMS FOR LEASING COMPANIES?

It seems likely that IBM's technological advances will cause severe problems for some, if not all, of these leasing companies. Innovation is the life blood of the current industrial scene; innovation will leave some indelible marks on those leasing companies not prepared for these changes, and on all others who do not attend to their homework in the little time that remains. We believe that IBM's strategy is to introduce large NG systems so as to offer its system 360/model 65 and 75 customers with far more power than they currently have for little, if any, more money. This will be a good bargain for these large system users. An analysis by DP Data Corporation of our file of Installed Data Processing Equipment shows that some of the leasing companies have concentrated their purchases of data processing systems in this part of the equipment spectrum. When current users desire to release their system 360/model 65 and 75 systems and go for the new IBM NG line of computers, there will be some problems in finding new customers for the released equipment belonging to the leasing houses.

It appears to us that in one move, IBM will try to compete with Control Data and regain its customers lost to the independent leasing companies. It is likely that IBM will experience some success in coming to terms with two of its recent problems—the competitive battle for the large system market, and a realistic adjustment of relations with the independent leasing companies.

PART 2: EQUIPMENT CHARACTERISTICS

Some of the main characteristics of IBM's new generation (NG) equipment are new to the data processing marketplace. Others bring to the general computer user the equipment and techniques which have so far been used only by the so-called "advanced customers," all of them users of the large (and very large) computers.

The main characteristics of IBM's new generation equipment include:

1. Stress on use of terminals. These will enable the user to interact with the data, obtain data as needed from a data base, and assist in the updating of the data. In brief, these terminals will be used in several modes, some of these being time sharing and conversation, remote job entry, and entry and retrieval of data.

2. Use of direct access storage devices. Thus one can deal with data based systems on a random basis. Increased density disc drives and disc packs are

a distinct possibility. Drums and mass storages should be an increasingly important part of a computer system, with stress on the improvement of access times. Newer technologies, such as the electron beam, may possibly be marketed at some point in the evolution of these new generation systems.

3. Increased use of multiprogramming – the concurrent operation of programs. This mode of operation will become progressively more important. Batch operations and batch and spool operations only will show a decline, while those including teleprocessing will increase.

4. Differentiation between a uniprocessor, a multiprocessor, and a variation of the two. A uniprocessor is a single processor system. A multiprocessor is a combination of two or more processors which share storage facilities, but which operate under a single control program. It is expected that for a multiprocessing two-process system, throughout would be, as far as possible, equal to twice that of a uniprocessor system.

5. Greater stress on increased availability of the system. This feature will emphasize reduction in the number and duration of interruptions to system functions, whether a uniprocessor or a multiprocessor.

6. A design permitting changes in configuration of a system. Thus it may be possible to include or eliminate control units, input and output devices, processors, memories and channels through either program control or manual operations.

7. Increased performance and throughput. This will be achieved through hardware capabilities which limit the negative effect of special features on total system performance, including those special features which are a part of shared storage systems.

8. Many new CPU (central processing unit) characteristics. Among these characteristics will be the possibility of operating the CPU in more than one mode. For example, two such modes could be "interruptable" and "non-interruptable". In the former mode, a supervisor would be able to interrupt CPU operation for use on some other job. Another new CPU characteristic might be the provision of a console printer with keyboard for each system processor, so that any malfunctioning unit (a console or CPU) will not also cause the loss of the properly operating units in the system. In our opinion, some of these and other new features will make obsolete, in varying degrees, the existing CPU's in the hands of users.

9. Many changes in the memory area, with the emergence of multi-processor units. For example, two memories may be asymmetrically combined. Shared memory storage may be provided which will enable more than one CPU to address one or more memory units. Detection and automatic correction of memory errors are also a possibility. It is likely that the system supervisor will be given the capability of assuming memory units for the use of a specific CPU. Although some of these changes may appear small, they will offer many alternatives to the user which are presently not available, in order to make possible a greater degree of utilization of the computer system's capabilities.

10. A change in the multiplex and selector channel characteristics. This will probably permit a reassignment of a specific job on one CPU to another CPU. In addition, to eliminate some of the problems with failing channels, alternate paths to any input-output control unit of the computer

system may be provided. Also some provision for input-output load balancing may be available through the new (multiplex and selector) channel setup.

11. Provision for the use of current and forthcoming new input-output devices. This will extend the usefulness of existing devices and enable the new systems to operate with combinations of input and output equipment not presently possible.

12. Equipment changes whereby a control unit will be accessible from any channel in the system. This will permit easy switching of input-output devices and control units from one channel to another of the same or some other processor.

13. Newly developed software will be used to introduce many new features. One example is the on-line recording of error indications so that maintenance personnel can obtain a history of events in order to locate a trouble or assist in preventing breakdowns in the future. Other examples are verification of all information written on the input-output storage devices, and the duplicate storage of certain critical control information by the supervisor. In essence, the emphasis in some of these software innovations is expected to be an effort to increase the reliability of the system and produce greater uptime of the computer (even though parts of it may be in the state of requiring corrective adjustments and maintenance).

PART 3: CHANGES IN THE DATA PROCESSING MARKETPLACE

The changes expected in the DP marketplace in the U.S. and their effects on the data processing industry with the marketing of the new generation systems from IBM can be briefly stated as follows:

1. Increased Competition for all Existing Companies. The main battle will be for the business-oriented user of systems presently in the IBM range of 360/30 to 360/50, the largest segment of the current market. At this time, IBM holds the lion's share of this segment which we term the "intermediate range" systems.

2. Imitation of IBM. In order to reduce IBM's share of the total market, all the other companies will tend to imitate IBM. This apparent likeness will extend to their computer systems makeup, the stress on suitable software, the terms and conditions of doing business, and all the sales knowhow. In past years there has been some spreading of IBM sales knowhow (an example is sales presentations) by the hiring of IBM salesmen and other personnel by its competitors. More of it will come in the days ahead.

3. Increased Emphasis on Sales Efforts Directed Toward Specific Industries. Although some of the other major manufacturers have recognized the benefits of selling by industry, they have to date not fully implemented even the small beginning in one or two specific industries. Specialized centers for dealing with each user industry's requirements will be increasingly in evidence, reflecting the desire of computer manufacturers to concentrate their expertise at one or more locations for each

user industry. Operating from these specialized centers, they will be able to offer the user all the assistance needed with installations of the changed equipment expected in the 1970's. However, these specialized efforts organized along industry lines are likely to increase the marketing costs as a fraction of the rental (or sales) dollar.

4. Greater Uniformity in Ways of Doing Business. This will include firm list prices, emphasis on customer upgrading, elimination of overtime rentals (and plans for lower and higher basic numbers of hours of monthly usage), and many other operating policies now prevalent in the industry. Large commercial users will try to obtain the advantages accorded the Federal Government at this time. Other levels of government (state and local) which have been slow to catch up with computerization will also attempt to deal like BIG BROTHER, hoping they can operate in the style set by Washington.

5. New Services. Several other types of services at present not available separately from DP equipment rental (or purchase) contracts will be offered by independent companies. A few of these services are beginning to be offered by small firms. A lengthy list can be made of these specialized services if one begins to minutely examine the activities of the large computer manufacturing companies. We believe there will be many opportunities for entrepreneurs among the ranks of all large DP oriented and related companies, since many services can be best provided by small organizations. Several activities, such as programming and leasing, will attain a firm underpinning as the shakedown proceeds in the existing structure composed of new and unseasoned companies.

6. Larger Used Equipment (and Computer) Market. This is something many have expected prematurely in recent years. The erroneous expectations were that the used DP equipment (and computer) market would blossom with the installation of third generation machines by IBM (starting in 1965). Thus the used DP equipment market will come into being at long last while a new sector of the industry, the second (and later) user services is being developed. Some type of systematic definition of what is available from computer manufacturers and other independents can be expected. This in turn, will assist and sustain the DP used equipment market, including computers of previous (mostly third) generation vintage.

7. IBM Equipment at Discounts. Substantial amounts of almost all types of IBM DP equipment (including computers) will be available at large discounts from current IBM prices. This equipment will be available from both leasing companies and present owners of purchased equipment. By 1971-72, these rentals could be as low as 40% of current prices. Eventually, most of these price changes will seriously impact equipment available from all the computer manufacturers, including IBM. From information currently at hand, it appears that these developments will slow down the rate of growth of all companies in the industry, particularly large main frame manufacturers. However, by creating a broader market for data processing products generally, if additional marketing efforts are made, these changes may be moderated.

8. Involvement of Financial Intermediaries. Sooner or later the financial intermediaries (like banks and insurance companies) will become involved

in the computer leasing industry. Some of the companies will become principals in the leasing industry; others will become integral parts of current industry participants. We believe the computer leasing industry is here to stay.

9. Multiprocessing. An increasing number of computer users will expect multiprocessing (especially in real time systems) and time sharing capabilities in their systems.

10. Peripherals. The computer peripheral equipment sector companies will seriously impact the mainframe system manufacturers at some date in the near future. Some of the peripheral equipment companies may emerge as full-fledged computer manufacturing companies. The price-performance relationship of input-output devices will become an increasingly important subject for the user and all manufacturers connected with the computer field.

11. Higher Performance. The user will demand greater performance and reliability (including uptime) from the equipment. He will become more familiar with systems and software techniques at present used by only a few of the so called advanced and large scale computer users. The role of consultants will filter down to users of small and intermediate size systems. There will be greater awareness and use of multiple suppliers of equipment, software and other services.

12. More Understanding. Top management of DP user companies will become more familiar and intimately connected with the goings-on in the computer and data processing field. This will be an outgrowth of the relative maturity of the computer industry. Many top managers will be drawn from those who came through the DP ranks in a company. With this top management involvement, users will upgrade equipment only after proof of availability of superior (and operating) software and substantially increased equipment performance for the rental (or purchase) dollar.

13. Divisions. Separate organizations (divisions or subsidiaries) will be formed within companies in the data processing industry (including IBM). As the different sectors of the industry (like leasing, software, supplies, and accessories) grow to a certain size, these separate organizations will become necessary in order to assure appropriate attention to these specific business activities. It appears that most of these new setups will include pricing separate from the equipment. One of the new sectors likely to emerge at an early date is maintenance (as IBM does through its Field Engineering Division now, but may do through a subsidiary company).

Questions:

1. What impact will IBM's new generation of equipment have on leasing Companies?

II

APPLICATIONS

REQUIREMENTS FOR THE DEVELOPMENT OF COMPUTER BASED URBAN INFORMATION SYSTEMS

STEVEN B. LIPNER

INTRODUCTION

Since early in this decade urban planners and systems analysts have advocated the development of computer-based urban information systems. Such systems would store detailed data about the environment in which planning agencies and governments operate. They would be organized to lend integration to data from diverse sources, to provide quick preparation of reports and to simplify and automate numerous clerical functions. Many attempts have been made to develop urban information systems with the characteristics mentioned above. Most have been unsuccessful[1] for a combination of technical and organizational reasons. This paper considers some technical requirements for planning information systems which deal with data associated with urban locations. The requirements are developed on the basis of experience in providing a prototype urban information system to the Boston Model Cities program. The next section describes briefly the experience of providing an information system to the Boston Model Cities program. Succeeding sections draw on this experience to develop general technical requirements for urban information systems. A technique for aggregating data by geographic area is presented and its implications for system file structure and utilization are explored.

INFORMATION SYSTEM FOR THE BOSTON MODEL CITIES ADMINISTRATION

During the spring of 1968, M.I.T. staff members held a number of meetings with members of the staff of the Boston Model Cities Administration to determine how M.I.T. might assist Boston's Model Cities program. One of the major desires of the Model Cities staff members was to see if an urban information system could be used to aid their planning and program evaluation activities. The Model Cities Administration was undertaking a survey which would determine the land use, building condition, and building size associated with each parcel in the Model Neighborhood Area. It was agreed that this data would make an acceptable basis for a prototype urban information system. Model Neighborhood residents employed by the Model Cities Administration were trained in keypunching and prepared approximately 8000 cards, one for each parcel in the area. (For comparison, the city of Boston contains about 100,000 parcels.)

The survey data was input to the ADMINS[2,3] system operating on the time-shared 7094[4] at the MIT Computation Center. ADMINS is an interactive program capable of performing data selection and cross-tabulation. It was designed for use in the analysis of social science surveys, and is best suited to operating on small files of coded or integer-valued data items. It is weakest in the areas of data modification, large file handling, and real or alphanumeric data manipulation.

Initial preparation of the data for ADMINS analysis was judged too complicated and machine-oriented a task to be performed by persons with little computer training. Accordingly the data was prepared for analysis by MIT personnel experienced in programming and in the use of ADMINS. The data preparation was simplified by the ability of ADMINS to accept data in arbitrary codes and formats and by the interactive mode in which it is used. Errors in the data were reported by ADMINS programs and corrected by using the time-sharing system's general purpose editing capabilities to modify the input files.

The analysis of the Model Cities survey data was performed by three groups of people: MIT staff members with substantial computer experience, professional urban planners with little or no prior computer experience, and Model Neighborhood residents with neither computer experience nor extensive formal education. All three groups easily mastered the mechanics of producing desired cross-tabulations, although a natural "fear" of the computer terminal had to be overcome by those new to it.

The response of the planners to the prototype urban information system was both interesting and significant. Although they had been instructed in the use of ADMINS at the terminal, and given freedom to produce reports as needed, the planners preferred to contact MIT or Model Neighborhood personnel, describe verbally the required tables, and have the resulting hard copy delivered to them. Whether this phenomenon was caused by the lack of proximity of the planners to the terminal, by the relatively tedious ADMINS language, or by a basic reluctance of planners to use the computer directly remains undetermined. (Placement of a terminal at the Model Cities office has been planned for some months but has been delayed by various administrative and operational problems.) When the planners have more direct access to a terminal and are provided with a system which, unlike ADMINS, is designed to serve as a true urban information system, it should be possible to determine if experienced planners without computer experience can successfully be trained and encouraged to use a computer as a planning tool. The implications of such a determination are discussed in the next section.

The analytic results were produced for the planners using ADMINS were useful, and all agreed that they were pleased with the results of the analysis. The limited computer experience, however, whetted the planners' appetites for more diverse capabilities. These capabilities included:

1. The ability to aggregate data by arbitrary geographic areas such as school districts, without being required to list explicitly every block contained in each area.
2. The ability to produce maps and graphs as well as tables.

3. The ability to merge data gathered by operating agencies and survey research organizations with stored data.
4. More general capabilities for numeric and alphabetic data processing than those provided by ADMINS.

The experiment in computer-aided Model Cities planning has been successful in two senses. First, it provided valuable insights into the capabilities required of an urban planning information system. Second, it introduced a group of planners to computer-aided analysis. In the future these planners should provide valuable data on the mode of man-machine communication appropriate for an urban planning information system.

REQUIREMENTS FOR URBAN INFORMATION SYSTEMS

The experimental provision of computer support to planners described in the previous section provided several insights into the capabilities required of an urban information system and the specific features required to implement them. Perhaps the most important capability indicated is that of combining and using in a single information system data from a variety of sources. Special surveys are an expensive and short-lived source of planning data when compared with operational data which must be maintained, often in machine-readable form, by agencies other than the planning department. Operational data from a given agency, in order to be useful to the planner, must be combined with planning survey data and often with data from other public or private operational agencies. Since different agencies often use different identifiers for each parcel, and since the street address is the only common and (presumably) unique parcel identifier, the conclusion is reached that a useful planning information system must deal with parcels identified by street address. Address matching programs[5] have been developed which standardize the formats of street addresses keypunched in free format. They must be included in an urban information system, along with file structures appropriate for the identification of parcels by street address. The need to merge data from differing sources implies the possibility of varying amounts of data describing a single parcel. Such possibilities must be handled by a flexible but efficient data file structure.

A second major requirement of an urban information system is the ability to aggregate parcel data by arbitrary geographic area. This ability is especially important in view of the numerous overlapping administrative and planning districts into which urban areas are divided. Programs have been developed[6,7] which aggregate data into districts by first assigning coordinates to each parcel, and then testing each parcel to see if its coordinates lie within a district. Such programs work but seem suited mainly to sequential storage systems using fast computers. The reasons for this observation and an alternate technique based on street addresses will be presented in the next section.

The importance of graphical display of data to planners was emphasized during the initial work with model cities planners. Any really useful urban information system must produce graphical as well as tabular output, preferably with minimal user description of coordinates, scales, etc. Existing programs and systems[8] are capable of producing a wide variety of graphic outputs. The major problems in applying these to urban information systems are, first, assuring that the outputs they produce are those required by planners and second, integrating the graphic components with data management components to minimize the complexity and cost of producing the outputs.

The area of man-machine communication is one which may be critical to the success of urban planning information system design. The experiment described above produced results which can only be described as inconclusive. However experience in the use of computers by engineers[9] would seem to indicate that the use of computers by persons who are not computer-oriented is greatly aided by the availability of interactive problem-oriented languages. In order to produce definitive results in the area of communication between computer and planner it will be necessary to provide both better terminal access and a problem-oriented language superior in both power and usability to that of ADMINS. The growing presence of planners who have had computer training should provide further assistance in improving man-machine communications.

In re-examining the requirements developed in this section, we find that all except those of geographic aggregation of data, address matching and graphical output would be common to any powerful information system: file structures which allow items to be described by varying numbers of attributes, file structures for rapid data retrieval, and powerful problem-oriented retrieval languages are all provided by many modern information systems.[10,11] Of the required features which appear unique to urban information systems the most significant seems to be that of geographic aggregation of data. Address matching is essentially a preprocessor function and graphic output an important output processor, while the geographic aggregation method will have a significant effect on the cost of many retrieval requests and some influence on internal file organization. For this reason, the next section is devoted to a brief description of an alternative to existing schemes for geographic aggregation of data.

A TECHNIQUE FOR GEOGRAPHIC AGGREGATION OF PARCEL DATA

The problem of geographic aggregation of parcel data in urban information systems has typically been handled by "point-in-polygon" programs.[6,7] Such programs require that each parcel which is included in the information system be identified by its x-y coordinates. An area for which data is to be aggregated is described as a polygon by specifying the coordinates of its vertices. Each stored parcel is tested by counting the intersections of a ray of arbitrary direction originating at its identifying point with the sides of the polygon. If the count is even, the point (and hence the parcel) is outside the polygon. If the count is odd, the point is inside (Figure 1).

Although the point-in-polygon test is a workable technique for geographic aggregation of data, it poses two problems. First, and less significant is the problem of assigning coordinates to every parcel. This problem is easily solved by representing every street as a sequence of line segments and using the numerical value of each parcel's address first to select the segment containing the parcel and then to define the parcel's coordinates by interpolation between the segment's end points. The second and more serious problem presented by the point-in-polygon technique involves processing time. Since the point-in-polygon technique is a test on one parcel, every parcel recorded by a system must be tested to determine which parcels should be aggregated into a given area. Thus, the technique is ill-suited to systems employing direct-access storage devices which could allow selective access to desired parcel data. Furthermore, the calculations required to determine whether or not each parcel lies in a given area involve one line intersection for each side of the area. On some small computers this calculation may be relatively time-consuming. Thus even if the parcel data base were recorded on tape, the time required to select those parcels in an area could be governed by processing time rather than by the time required to move and read the tape.

Techniques have been suggested[12,13] which, by dividing an urban area into subareas, would reduce the sequential file searching required by the point-in-polygon algorithm. These techniques would require checking of the retrieval area for overlap with preestablished subareas before individual parcels in the subareas were examined. If the check showed no overlap, no further examination of the subarea would be required. Otherwise every parcel in this subarea would be checked. The disadvantages of this method are principally associated with the size of subareas. A large number of small subareas requires a large number of overlap tests, while if a small number of larger subareas are used, there will be a large number of parcels requiring point-in-polygon testing included in each selected subarea.

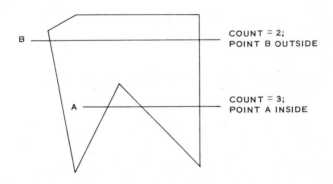

Figure 1—Point-in-polygon test

An alternative to the point-in-polygon technique for the geographic aggregation of parcel data was suggested first by Farnsworth[14] and later proposed independently and in more detail by Parson.[15] The algorithm involves using a map of the street network of the urban area within which new geographic areas are defined. Given a list of the names of the streets surrounding the area of interest, the algorithm produces a list of those parcels within the area. The paragraphs below present an illustration of the algorithm, followed by comments on the map file structure required to implement it.

In considering the map of Figure 2, let us assume we wish to isolate the area bounded by streets A, H, D and E. We first scan the street A until we locate the set of street segments (portions of a street between two intersections) on it between E and H. We then scan street H, marking the segments between A and D, street D for the segments between H and E, and street E for the segments between D and A. Since the list of bounding streets was given in a clockwise direction, we know that blocks inside of the desired area are to its right. If we have recorded the numbers of the blocks to the right and left of each segment, seen facing in the direction of increasing addresses, we may now isolate those blocks inside the bounding streets. To do this we record blocks to the right of segments whose increasing address direction coincides with the direction of the area boundary (street A and E) and blocks to the left of segments whose addresses run opposite to the boundary (streets D and H). Applying this procedure we obtain the list of contained blocks in Figure 3.

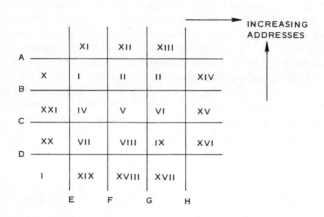

Figure 2—Map for geographical retrieval

As we make the list of contained blocks, we may also make a list of non-contained blocks (Figure 4). These are blocks opposite the contained ones which lie just outside (to the left) of the area boundary. Now we may make a list of blocks adjacent to those blocks listed in Figure 3, excluding blocks already listed as contained or non-contained. This list contains only one block, block V. Enumerating the blocks adjacent to block V we find that all have already been

I, II, III, VI, IX, VIII, VII, IV

Figure 3—First list of contained blocks

XI, XII, XIII, XIV, XV, XVI

XVII, XVIII, XIX, XX, XXI, X

Figure 4—List of non-contained blocks

listed as contained. Thus all blocks within the area of interest have been isolated. From the list of blocks in the area, we may develop a list of the address ranges along contained streets or of the parcel numbers of parcels contained in the area.

The algorithm and problem described are reliable only when used with a street network in which no two streets intersect more than once. Techniques have been developed by the author which generalize the algorithm to handle cases in which two streets may intersect more than once, by eliminating resolvable ambiguities or by reporting the presence of irresolvable ones. The generalization requires changing the initial analysis of the list of streets bounding the area from a one-pass to a multiple-pass operation. The first pass isolates all possible sequences of segments which could surround the desired area. The second and succeeding passes eliminate incorrect paths by searching for discontinuities in the transitions from one street to the next. The process is continued until one correct path remains or until no further incorrect ones can be detected.

Two files are used to allow a computer program to implement the algorithm described above. The first contains data about street segments for every street in the map, while the second contains lists of the blocks adjacent to every block in the map. The first file is used to isolate the sets of blocks just inside and outside an area described by its bounding streets. The segments along a street are ordered by increasing address range, and each segment is described by left and right block numbers, beginning and ending node numbers, and intersecting streets. Additional data on street address ranges and node coordinates for each street are typically included to broaden the utility of the segment file. The block file must include the numbers of the blocks surrounding each block, and should contain data to allow conversion from the numbers of the blocks in the desired area to the data themselves—either as street names and address ranges, as parcel numbers, or as disk identifiers of data records. Both files described above may be produced as by-products of the DIME editing technique[16] described by Cooke and Maxfield.

The algorithm outlined above for using a street network to facilitate geographic aggregation of parcel data has both advantages and disadvantages when compared to the point-in-polygon technique. Its principal advantage is that it is essentially a direct-access technique. The time required to isolate the identifiers of those parcels in an area is proportional to the number and length of the streets surrounding the area and to the number and complexity (number of adjacent blocks) of blocks in the area. Small areas may be isolated very quickly. If some sort of direct-access storage is used for parcel data, the parcels in the area are the only ones retrieved. If sequential storage is used, the algorithm can at least produce a list of parcel identifiers (for example address ranges) which will allow much speedier checking of individual parcels than would be the case with the point-in-polygon routine. The principal disadvantage of the street network technique is its limited flexibility. While the point-in-polygon technique may be used to select parcels in any area, the network technique is clearly applicable only to areas made up of whole blocks. This problem is potentially most serious in analyzing areas such as new highway corridors which do not follow block boundaries. It seems possible that performing such analysis by using the point-in-polygon technique on a set of parcels selected by the network technique might be more economical than applying it to all parcels in a city. However, this hypothesis must be verified.

FILE STRUCTURE

The basic implication of the geographic aggregation technique proposed above is that a direct-access file system is very desirable. The principal requirement of this structure is that it be capable of being tied to the block data of the street map file. One flexible way of establishing this tie is to use street address as the major identifier of each parcel and to store street names (or identification numbers) and address ranges in the block file of the street map. The street names and address ranges defining all block faces (one side of a segment) in an area could be merged together and sorted into an order corresponding to that of the parcel data file. Then retrieval from the parcel file could be directed by the sorted output of the aggregation algorithm. Retrieval of data about those parcels in a given area could proceed at a speed governed only by the efficiency of the parcel file's indexing scheme. Variable amounts of data for a single parcel could be stored either in variable-length data records or in multiple files each using street address as primary identifier. Two major advantages of using street address as the primary parcel identifier are, first that all inquiries about parcels by street address would be facilitated and, second, that additions or deletions of occupied addresses within a block face necessitate no alterations to the network data describing that block face.

If a sequential file structure is to be used for parcel data, for reasons of restricted data access, economy, or data volume, the comments about using street address as primary identifier still apply. Although sequential processing becomes imperative, the simplicity of processing allowed by using street address ranges as output from the geographic aggregation algorithm will still minimize the actual processing time required to select parcel data. This minimization may be important when processing data on a small machine or in a partition of a large one.

A PLANNED EXPERIMENTAL SYSTEM

The techniques used above are to be put into practice in an experimental information system for use by the Boston Model Cities Administration and MIT Urban Systems Laboratory. The system will include a street network file and street network geographic aggregation algorithm. The street network file will be tied to a parcel data file by street addresses. Multiple parcel data files will be used to handle multiple data sets (initially housing survey and demographic survey files) on direct-access storage. Control and problem-oriented language facilities will be provided by the ICES system.[17] The system should be implemented by June, 1969 and will be operated as a planning aid for the Model Cities Administration by Model Cities and MIT staff members In addition to providing basic statistical and cross-tabulation facilities, it is hoped that the system will allow the addition of analytic and modelling capabilities by planning researchers.

ACKNOWLEDGMENT

The work reported here was aided and influenced by many people over the last year. Especially worthy of mention are Professor Charles Miller, Professor

Robert Logcher, Mr. William Parsons, Mr. Ronald Walter, Mr. Donald Cooke, and Miss Betsy Schumacker of M.I.T., Mr. Edward Teitcher and Mrs. Colette Goodman of the Boston Redevelopment Authority, and Mr. Michael Warren, Mr. Richard Harris, Mr. Samuel Thompson, and Mr. John Myers of the Boston Model Cities Administration. The work reported herein was conducted at and sponsored in part by the Urban Systems Laboratory of the Massachusetts Institute of Technology.

BIBLIOGRAPHY

1   O E DIAL
    Urban information systems: A bibliographic essay
    Urban Systems Laboratory MIT 1968
2   S McINTOSH   D GRIFFEL
    The ADMINS primer
    Center for International Studies MIT
3   S McINTOSH   D GRIFFEL
    The language of ADMINS
    Cetner for International Studies MIT
4   P A CRISMAN
    The compatible time-sharing system: A programmer's guide
    MIT Press
5   H H COCHRAN
    Address matching by computer
    Proc Sixth URISA Conference 1968
6   R B DIAL
    Street address conversion program
    Urban Data Center University of Washington
7   S NORBECK   B RYSTEDT
    Computer cartography point-in-polygon programs
    BIT 7 1967
8   D F COOKE
    Systems, geocoding and mapping
    Proc Sixth URISA Conference 1968
9   C L MILLER
    Man-machine communications in civil engineering
    Department of Civil Engineering MIT
10 R E BLEIER
    Treating hierarchical data structures in the SDC time-shared data management systems (TDMS)
    Proc A C M National Conference 1967
11 E W FRANKS
    A data management system for time-shared file processing using a cross-index file and self-defining entries
    Proc S J C C 1966
12 K J DUEKER
    Spatial data systems
    Northwestern University

13 S B LIPNER
File structures for urban information systems
Internal Working Document MIT 1968

14 G L FARNSWORTH
Contiguity analysis using census data
Proc Fifth Annual URISA Conference 1967

15 W A PARSONS
Unpublished class project report
MIT Subject 1 152 1968

16 D F COOKE W H MAXFIELD
The development of a geographic base file and its uses for mapping
Proc Fifth Annual URISA Conference 1967

17 D ROOS
ICES system: General description
Department of Civil Engineering MIT

Questions:

1. What are the major technical requirements for an urban information system?

2. Discuss the possible uses of an urban information processing system such as the one mentioned in the article.

CALIFORNIA DMV GOES ON-LINE

BY R. E. MONTIJO, JR.

In 1965, registrations for more than 10 million drivers and 11 million vehicles were on file in the California Department of Motor Vehicles (DMV).

Surveys showed that by 1975 the state could expect three million new drivers and six million additional vehicles.

Meanwhile, every day, over 200,000 queries and data entries were being funneled through the department.

To cope with this situation, California decided to build a computer-communications network capable of supporting a thoroughly automated real-time system—moving the Department of Motor Vehicles from manual and key punch operations to video data entry display techniques and a massive automated data bank in just five years.

On October 20, 1966, the production phase of the Automated Management Information System (AMIS) got underway in Sacramento with the demonstration of conversion of driver license records. When AMIS is completed in 1970, hundreds of remote terminals and other devices will be tied into the department's state-wide electronic network.

The history, objectives, techniques and accomplishments of California's unique data processing system—one of the most extensive and ambitious programs ever undertaken—are the subject of this article.

THE NEED FOR AMIS

Growth, more than anything, led to AMIS—growth in workload, growth in the cost of non-automated recordkeeping, growth in the time required to do this work.

California DMV's workload involves driver licensing, vehicle registration, and other related activities.

A driver record and a legal file are maintained for each licensed driver. These contain a complete history of moving violations, accidents, and court convictions. Driver record abstracts are always available to the courts. Similar data are provided to drivers and insurance companies for a nominal fee. Administration of California's financial responsibility law and driver improvement program also requires maintenance of data elements within the driver files and analysis on a continuing basis.

Reprinted with permission from DATAMATION, (May), published and copyrighted (1967) by F. D. Thompson Publications, Inc., 35 Mason St., Greenwich, Conn. 06830.

Also, records must be maintained for each motor vehicle. These records are organized by vehicle identification number (engine number). New vehicle registration, transfers, and annual re-registration, including issuance of plates or stickers and collection of fees, represent an equally major portion of DMV's workload. Each year, on the day after Christmas, over 10 million registration forms are mailed to Californians. For the following three months, the processing of these forms—including fee accounting and updating of the entire file—is a major project.

The importance of accurate, up-to-the-minute records within DMV is underscored by a continuous flood of inquiries from law enforcement agencies, the public, the courts, and insurance companies. These inquiries must be handled in parallel with the department's regular duties.

Today, all of these pressure points are application areas for AMIS.

Surveys by the Department of Motor Vehicles, incorporated in its report to the Legislature, indicated it would be hard pressed to keep pace with information processing using manual methods. For example:

From July, 1965, through July, 1975, California's population is expected to climb 32%—from 18.8 million to 24.8 million. In terms of vehicle registrations, this means a 50% increase—from 11 million to 16.6 million. During the decade, driver licenses will jump 48%—from 9.6 to 14.2 million.

When these figures are related to DMV's projected workload, the number of driver licenses issued annually will increase 71.5%—from 2.8 million to 4.8 million. And annual court convictions entered in DMV records will zoom 100%—from 3.6 million to 7.2 million.

Even more dramatic will be the surge of requests for information in DMV files. Inquires will climb from 15 million to 39.2 million for a net annual increase of 160.8%.

Even with AMIS in operation, DMV's total work force will expand over the decade by 2,575 positions from 5,265 positions in 1965. But this workforce expansion expected is 590 less than without AMIS. Other important economic benefits include: recovery of all conversion costs; ownership of $13.6 million of electronic data processing equipment; net cumulative savings of $1.7 million; and recurring annual savings of $5.3 million for the fiscal year 1974-75 and thereafter. While costs and savings include personnel, equipment, land, buildings, and capital outlay, no dollar value has been placed on highly improved public service and other intangible but valuable benefits—such as the number of lives saved and reduced property damage through better service to the law enforcement community.

AMIS—ORGANIZATION AND AIMS

Organizing AMIS began in late 1964 when DMV outlined broad departmental goals and selected COMRESS, Inc., as consultant to develop a real-time system. A model was constructed, simulated and costed, using various manufacturers' equipment. Goals of the system were:

1. Economical operation paced to rapid population growth.
2. Fast, one-stop, over-the-counter service.
3. Timely information for DMV, related state and local agencies, and private business.

4. Instantly available information for management decisions.

Simulations run on the model by two DMV task force teams indicated the system's feasibility. Thereafter, invitations to bid were sent to some 15 U.S. edp vendors. A letter of intent was issued to RCA on August 16, 1965, for first phase equipment. Less than a year later the AMIS Spectra 70's were on the air.

Systems requirements included:

1. A total management information system designed to be fully operational by 1970, with phased implementation starting in 1965.

2. A system for real-time processing of input data and inquiries received on-line from remote locations, inter-mixed with locally entered batch-type input data—and for the directing of real-time output to remote locations simultaneously with local, high-volume, batch-type output.

3. A system capable of evolving from a manual or partially automated system with a minimum of problems.

4. An automated data bank—located in Sacramento—with storage capacity for over 15 billion characters.

5. An on-line system linking DMV field offices, law enforcement agencies, and courts with as many as 1,400 remote terminals.

6. A system capable of handling 16,000 transactions per peak hour and over 225,000 transactions per day.

7. Alternate path equipment connectivity and reserve fall-back capacity for high level reliability.

8. Programming modularity, segmentation and standardization for an orderly conversion and system buildup without re-programming, consonant with the most effective use of a multiprogrammed, multiprocessing operating system.

TRAINING AT DMV

Imposing a third-generation "total" electronic system on any organization creates problems. Suddenly gone are the baskets and casual pace of a paper system. Gone also are the familiar and protective time buffers of inter-office and inter-city mail. Electronic speeds can be disturbing. People-acceptance is clearly basic to success in such ventures and DMV's AMIS was not different.

A plan of attack was devised to overcome real and imagined technical problems and the barriers arising from people's reluctance to change, while at the same time satisfying the AMIS schedule. Headway was made through seminars directed to management and supervisory personnel. The department, in turn, conducted seminars for office workers on the new system.

Training assumed critical importance. Normally, users grow in edp sophistication gradually, as they add more sophisticated hardware to their systems. But at DMV, on-line conversion to random access processing had to begin a year later—and in the completely manual drivers' license operation. There wasn't time for a phased build-up in equipment or training.

The first step was concentrated classroom training for 60 DMV programmers and supervisors. Equally important was the cross-training given to RCA's on-site systems team in driver license and vehicle registration procedures and in the requirements of the Motor Vehicle Code.

A major objective was to acquaint the three working groups (driver license, vehicle registration and RCA systems representatives) with a working knowledge of the processing requirements of each division, as well as the characteristics of the hardware, software and programming languages.

To achieve this, two levels of month-long six-hour day classroom training began in September, 1965. One class for 20 DMV programmers involved general systems, Spectra 70 assembly language, and COBOL. A special course for 20 DMV edp supervisors and RCA systems men centered on systems programming design and specification. Several other classes were scheduled, too. Altogether, RCA conducted about 500 man-weeks of on-site training for programmers, supervisor/analysts, and management in general systems, programming languages, operating systems, and operations.

THE PROGRAMMING SYSTEM

An automation program of AMIS' scope requires vast sums of money and manpower. Applications programming costs are a large percentage of the total system costs. Any inefficiencies due to false starts, delays caused by poor scheduling or reprogramming downstream can easily absorb potential savings.

These factors became major considerations in all program planning decisions. Ultimately, they dictated the approach used in the design, specification, and execution of the first phase of implementation—to do a two-year job in nine months. The approach was based upon the completion of detailed system design specifications prior to programming, and a high degree of concurrency in all aspects of the effort.

RCA proposed the design and specification of a programming system super-structure. It set a four-month time limit for specifying the framework, with programming beginning late in 1966. This effort was analogous to:

1. Building the superstructure (or "overhead" programs) over a six to twelve-month period.

2. Then filling in the superstructure with the applications logic programs in a carefully planned order over a 5-year period.

This approach was called the AMIS programming system segmentation model.

This model includes the concept of an automatic file control to store and retrieve records from the largest random access file in the world within a half-second. It responds primarily to "get" and "put" commands, and is oblivious to all else in the system.

File control operates upon transactions entered from the input output domain, which includes local and remote keyboard-printers and other conventional peripherals. These I/O devices talk to the communications channel and to the peripheral channel I/O packages, which are sub-elements of the model's I/O control section.

The transaction processing section is where most of the action is. General control for the model resides within the real-time transaction and task control element. Calculating program elements are in the transaction logic processing area. The transaction logic programs are the primary application building blocks which will be produced, added, and modified as the superstructure is given substance.

The model introduced several nuances that required re-definition of older concepts. Terms such as *thread* programs, *run* programs, *overhead* programs, and *transaction logic* programs are part of the programming system.

The video-to-tape thread represented the first conversion application. This thread begins at one of 88 video terminals and moves through communications control, real-time control, transaction logic, and peripheral I/O elements before the input message is recorded on magnetic tape. After a tape-to-printer run, each input transaction batch is proof-read and verified in hard-copy form prior to the next operation. The input document images are then sorted, merged, and the mass storage file record image is created on magnetic tape for loading into direct access storage.

The tape-to-mass-file thread enters through peripheral I/O and travels through real-time control and transaction logic before entering the file control section. Here, an index is created and the new mass storage record is deposited in the mass store.

An inquiry thread travels through communications, real-time, transaction logic, and file control, then back through the transaction logic and communications, and finally to the requestor's output device.

Approximately 100 similar threads and 1,000 transaction logic program segments will be included in the completed DMV system.

The thread programming organization concept has some interesting characteristics. The three threads just described reveal more programming elements in common than differences. The only differences exist in the Transaction logic and in the I/O formats. All the other program elements are common to most transactions. These common elements were named *overhead programs*, because they are common to most DL (driver license) and VR (vehicle registration) transaction processing—and are to be programmed once.

Once DMV's superstructure of overhead programs is completed, transaction logic program elements may be added over the life of the open-ended system without redoing the data handling and housekeeping portions that often represent up to 50% of typical batch-type programs.

What is the relationship of overhead structure to the operating system? Thread and overhead programs are run in the user environment of the Spectra 70 operating systems. The real-time control package—a multi-processor in itself—controls and schedules overlapping of up to six transaction logic programs, including the scheduling of overlapped access to various mass storage units and maintenance of system restart and recovery points.

The Spectra 70 primary operating system-extended (POS-E), which has been in use since last July, will be replaced by the multi-programmed tape-disc operating system (TDOS) this summer. POS-E will remain in use in the Spectra 70/45E communications processor. TDOS will be run in the Spectra 70/55G processor.

CHOOSING A LANGUAGE

Selection of a programming language, naturally, was an important step. An initial objective was to use COBOL for all programs. However, COBOL's limitations in communications and random access programming, together with the innovation of the overhead programming concept, caused a re-evaluation.

Studies indicated that using COBOL to operate on a highly variable, packed record would significantly raise program core storage requirements. Even more important was COBOL's inability to handle efficiently the 5,000-byte-maximum and 200-byte-average mass storage records. Use of COBOL rather than assembly language would have meant raising the mass storage file capacity requirements four to seven times. Multiplying the latter factor by the 15 billion byte storage requirement showed the price to be prohibitive.

The AMIS' overhead programs are core-resident when the transaction processors are operating in real-time. They need be written only once. High flexibility and efficiency in bit manipulation also were desirable for programs directly interfacing communications and mass storage. Hence, assembly language was selected. All overhead programs and those which manipulate the highly compressed mass storage record directly have been written in assembly language.

Since the overhead program structure brings all transaction data, programs and records in exploded form into any of six standard overlay areas in core, COBOL and FORTRAN may be used for transaction logic programs at the customer's option. COBOL will be used on many batch runs due to its efficiency in magnetic tape record handling. FORTRAN becomes attractive for statistical and quasi-scientific models to which the automated file will be exposed in quasi-scientific support of planning by DMV and other state agencies. The Spectra 70 report program generator is also being used in certain I/O operations.

INPUT VIA VIDEO DISPLAY

DMV's original bid specifications did not include equipment for converting the huge driver record files to machine-readable form. Immediately after the selection of RCA as the supplier for AMIS, DMV conducted a new study to determine processes and equipment for the initial conversion.

Use of EAM keypunch-verifiers, as originally envisioned, would have required approximately 190 keypunchers or verifiers and 350 keypunch-verifier operators, working in two shifts for a period of two years.

This technique would have produced the 50-million-paper-document driver record file, which averages some four to five documents per driver, in punched card form for a card-to-tape input process. The sorting, merging, and master record building that is necessary prior to the mass storage file load process would follow.

DMV's study of input conversion methods and costs was conducted independently by its own personnel. Direct keyboard-to-magnetic-tape and on-line keyboard-video-device techniques offered by several edp manufacturers also were evaluated. All cost factors were considered. This evaluation showed a clear advantage for the video-keyboard technique by performing the input document conversion in the same time with 50% less operators, less document control costs, 100% less floor space, and no EAM card costs to offset a slightly higher equipment cost. RCA was also selected as the direct-entry sub-system supplier.

The use of video terminals as DMV's primary input device is an exciting innovation. The Division of Drivers Licenses has 88 Video Data Interrogators installed in a room adjacent to the central processor in Sacramento. Each of the 11 Video Controllers stores up to 16 different formats on a magnetic disc. The pre-stored formats may be the same or different within each controller, depending on the operation. Stored formats are instantly callable by each video operator by pressing a button on her keyboard.

The availability of 16 different formats to each operator makes a large dent in the problem of controlling the various documents that constitute a driver record. There's no need to fan out the component documents to various operators and input devices with single format capability. Each driver record is handled as an input batch by one operator without further subdivision. Each input transaction message is composed on the video screen for easy sight verification and correction of any key board errors prior to transmission to the communications processor.

When the input transaction data message is received, the video-to-tape program performs edit and validation checks prior to writing it out to magnetic tape. If any data errors are detected by program, the input message is returned to the operator's screen with a notation of the type of error found. The operator then makes a suitable correction and re-enters the message. If the input message is accepted by the processor, the operator receives a program-initiated acknowledgement message after the message has been written to magnetic tape and the read-after-write checks are satisfied. Only then is the operator allowed to proceed to the next input message. Each input message so generated is tagged with the system transaction code number, driver record number, the data, and the operator code. These input document messages are then sorted and merged for proof-listing and subsequent creation of the master record image for the mass file loading process.

The video terminals, with their respective controllers may be locally or remotely located, using private or common carrier communication channels or data sets.

The latter technique will be used by the Division of Vehicle Registration in the replacement of the current Los Angeles-based punch card tub-files which are used to service vehicle registration inquiries for Southern California. When these remote Video Data Terminals are installed by the division in 1968, all inquiries originating in the Los Angeles area will be directed to the mass storage data banks in Sacramento for immediate response and display on a cathode ray tube face or in hard copy form.

Response times from the moment of inquiring operator's message release until the response appears on the CRT screen run from one to five seconds, with a weighted average response time of approximately two seconds. If hard copy print-out is required, additional print time will vary as a function of the type of printer used and the length of the response message.

AMIS PROGRAM PROGRESS AND STATUS

The driver license equipment complex, which includes Spectra 70/45E and 70/45G processors, was delivered on schedule with software last July. Also included were the first 32 video units and two Model 70/568 mass storage units. Each mass storage unit stores 536 million bytes of data on magnetic cards 4" high by 16½" long. Eight removable magazines, each containing 256 cards, store approximately 70 million bytes of data. Average access to any card is 475 milleseconds and the read-write data transfer rate is 70KB/second.

Last October, all 88 video data units and a third mass storage unit were delivered and became operational. The 70/45G processor was replaced by a

70/55G in February. Next month, six additional mass storage units will be installed in the driver license complex.

In July, Vehicle Registration will receive its 70/45E and 70/55G processors, along with peripherals and a large group of video data units. Later, a 70/35 processor and peripheral equipment will be delivered as temporary equipment to process the 10 million vehicle registration forms mailed out at year's end.

From August through October, 1966, the production communications programs were used to train the newly hired staff of supervisors and operators on the video data units for the start of driver record file conversion.

Also, transaction logic programs were tested preparatory to the start of conversion in October, 1966. At that time, input from 54 million paper documents began, followed by mass storage file loading for 12 million driver records.

Today, vehicle registration programming and testing are well underway in preparation for the delivery of processors this summer.

PROJECT MANAGEMENT AND CONTROL

The entire AMIS program was placed on a rigid and complete project control system in late 1965. The project control system is comprised of a PERT diagram, a weekly PERT computer run which produces the weekly project status report, manually prepared weekly exception report, and careful surveillance of the critical path.

The PERT program includes all elements which relate directly or indirectly to the AMIS schedule, such as all program threads and program segments for the overhead and transaction programs, equipment and general purpose software, site preparation, operator hiring and training, and manual procedure design which is related to the revised flow of documents to and from the automated system.

The project status report lists all activities and events with minimum, maximum, and expected dates and slack time computations. Such schedule dates are provided for the following milestones for each overhead and transaction logic program segment in AMIS:

1. Analysis and programming started.
2. Specifications completed and approved.
3. Detailed flow chart and coding completed.
4. Program testing completed.
5. System testing completed.
6. Documentation completed.

The weekly exception report lists all scheduled activities which are either ahead or behind schedule and require corrective measures by the appropriate supervisors and edp management. These reports are reviewed regularly at DMV's edp steering committee meetings.

The project control system has been an invaluable aid in pinpointing potential problems for immediate management attention. As a direct result of the concurrent approach to the program implementation and the close control provided by the project control system, the total drivers' license complex of equipment that was delivered in July went on single-shift operation starting July

18, 1966. One week later, both machine sub-systems within the driver license complex went to a 17-hour-per-day, two-shift schedule and have operated at least five, and sometimes six, days per week.

During the 30-day acceptance period following the July delivery, DMV received 94% productive time for the composite system. System availability to the customer during the same period was 96%. Since then, both the percent productive time and percent system availability have risen into the 96 to 98% range, respectively.

IN CONCLUSION

When we look at one of these "total" systems, we should be concerned with the *whole* system by which work is done within the customer environment. Within this context the whole system is composed of the six "M's", man, machines, money, methods, materials, and management. The computer is only one element.

Success depends equally upon the computer and peripheral equipment selected, and the assimilation of the machine sub-system by its immediate users such as programmers and equipment operators, and those users who are once-or-twice removed, such as clerks and management.

In designing any large edp system, we concentrate on maximizing throughput and minimizing costs. Throughput is often only measured in transactions or operations per unit of time—whereas within the context of the whole system, it is a measure of the productivity of the composite system that is comprised of the six M's.

Perhaps the most important characteristic of third-generation implementation is that it portends the end of hardware- or software-limited systems. The power of the hardware and the software which is available today is well beyond most of us to apply and use most effectively. Actually, we have entered a new era in edp . . . an era characterized by its almost total dependency on an inadequate supply of experienced and competent systems analysts, systems programmers, and systems engineers, together with sophisticated edp-oriented management . . . an era whose end is not in sight within this human generation.

Questions:

1. Discuss the term "management information system."

2. What is PERT (Program Evaluation and Review Technique)?

3. What factors shoud be considered in choosing a programming language?

THERE'S ALWAYS ROOM FOR IMPROVEMENT

Businessmen have become quite familiar with charts tracing growth. The steady upward curve has become part of the business scene, considered remarkable only if it doesn't rise sharply enough. In fact, the businessman's goal might well be a line curving upward so rapidly that it becomes perpendicular.

This daydream promises to become a reality at the New York Fire Department, where it takes on more of the properties of a nightmare. The line is on a chart that traces the growth in number of alarms turned in every year by residents of the nation's largest city. In 1945, there were approximately 65,000. By 1967, the total had jumped to 173,000. At that accelerating rate of growth, it is anticipated the "curve" will be virtually straight up by 1970.

The highly trained professionals responsible for Fire Department operations are fully aware of the implications of this trend. Efficiency in every phase of department functions is not enough; it must be maintained with such consistency that it can almost be taken for granted even as further improvements are sought, refined and implemented.

The history of the New York Fire Department reflects the changing needs of a metropolis that evolved from a small Dutch settlement in the New World. The present organization had its formal beginnings in 1865, but its antecedents go back to 1648 and the administration of Peter Stuyvesant, when the first fire ordinance was established. In 1657 the famous bucket brigades were organized. Equipment consisted of leather buckets attached to wooden poles. In an emergency, fire-fighting was everyone's responsibility.

Later, this became the volunteer companies' job. Equipment and methods progressed through a variety of hand- and horse-drawn vehicles to the modern tower ladders and superpumpers. The last "run of the horses" took place nearly 50 years ago, on December 20, 1922. No one knows when the superpumper will make its last run, but the firemen are the first to insist that "there is always room for improvement—and come it will."

The emphasis on continuing efficiency has inevitably led to a need for more information, in great depth, produced and disseminated rapidly. The department began using IBM punched-card machines in 1951. At that time, the applications were essentially of a bookkeeping nature: controlling permits issued for the manufacture, use and storage of combustible and hazardous materials, collecting the fees that help cover the cost of yearly inspections and

Reprinted with permission from the November 1968 issue of DATA PROCESSOR, a publication of IBM.

accounting for pension checks. A first attempt was made at setting up a personnel file.

By 1961, processing of fire statistics had outgrown manual methods and become a major application. Data processing orientation turned toward producing data to assist management in decision-making and future planning, while accounting responsibilities continued to grow. During the next few years time was often borrowed on computers at various city departments. In June 1967, at the direction of Fire Commissioner Robert O. Lowery, a System/360 Model 20 was installed, making New York's the first fire department in the country to have a computer.

The system is programmed by career firemen who also double as operators. The Data Processing Unit of the Management Planning Bureau is headed by Battalion Chief Woodrow H. Holdsworth. A graduate engineer by training, a fireman by inclination and tradition—his father, grandfather, a brother and an uncle have all served in the Fire Department—Chief Holdsworth is in the 29th year of a career that has taken him through almost every facet of department operations.

Chief Holdsworth assumed his post in 1965, when the unit was still using punched-card machines. He attended courses on machine operation, and later took courses on basic computer concepts and Report Program Generator. When the decision was taken to install the Model 20, plans for finding and training programmers were ready.

PROGRAMMERS, A RARE COMMODITY

"There are several reasons why we preferred to train firemen as programmers," Chief Holdsworth states. "One of them is that programmers are in short supply. Beyond that, we can call on a manpower pool of 13,000 men who earn their jobs as a result of rigorous written and physical examinations plus a highly competitive civil service list. All are experienced in Fire Department problems. Our salaries are comparable to those of programmers in general."

The manpower pool was tapped by issuing a call through Fire Department channels. A total of 400 men responded. Of these, 207 took IBM programming aptitude tests conducted at the Fire Department training school. The top seven were chosen for training.

The training program was devised by the department. First, the men took and passed a programmed instruction basic computer course, followed by a Model 20 RPG programmed instruction course. Then, they attended the two-week RPG course at IBM's Education Center in New York City, where they gained hands-on experience.

To date, 90 programs have been written, 95 percent of them by firemen, the remainder being prepared with assistance from IBM's systems engineers. Lieut. Gerarde Albro, who is chief programmer and an 11-year department veteran, found the most difficult part in the transition from field work to programming was the switch to regular hours.

"It was hard, at first, getting up at the same time every day and reporting to an office," he says with a smile. "We're used to all hours every day of the week, and that lack of routine has its advantages. But the work is interesting; writing each program and seeing it run is always a new experience. RPG was easy to learn, and I expect to go on to learn Assembler language as well."

Working with Lieutenant Albro is Fireman 1st Grade Anthony Bruno, who also doubles as console operator. A civilian holdover from the punched-card machine installation is the chief console operator, Albert Alias, who easily made the transition to computer work.

Control of combustible fee permits, now grown to 300,000 (requiring a file of one-and-a-half to two million cards), is still a major application. The personnel records now include a skills and education inventory. Pension checks are still part of the workload. The unit also handles firehouse inventories of tools and equipment, donations to the New York Fire Department Museum, and accounting for donations to families of firemen killed in line of duty.

The most significant job involves fire statistics, broken down to include individual fire alarm boxes. They tell their own story:

- Of the 173,000 alarms in 1967, 48,600—almost a third—were false.
- 33,000 were for emergencies other than fire (the department responds to all calls).
- 91,200 were fires, an average of 285 per day. The great bulk were handled by one fire unit, 243 required a second alarm and are known as seconds, 83 were thirds, 15 were fourths, and five were conflagrations calling out five alarms.
- An average of 500 calls for help are received, and acted on, daily.

The calls come into the Bureau of Fire Communications' five centers from fire alarm boxes and by phone. Turnaround, the time between receipt at a center and notification of the specific fire unit that will respond, averages 30 to 40 seconds, and at that point men and apparatus start moving. Studies to reduce this time even further are part of an overall investigation aimed at introducing new efficiencies while improving the flow of information to management. Already on order are tape and disk units to expand the capabilities of the computer. For the future, department planners envision the need for an on-line system.

Right now Fire Department management gets a variety of valuable data. For example, reports show at which of the 15,000 boxes more than three false alarms were turned in during a given month. The reports also show the day of the week and the time of day or night they occurred. When a pattern is detected, such data can help police apprehend the guilty person.

"We also develop information for management that is used to recommend new legislation," says Chief Holdsworth. "Our facts may show that the large number of construction sites in the city, many with wood and other combustible materials left in the open, are an increasing source of fires. Management may therefore recommend to the City Council that a new law be passed requiring that watchmen be on duty at all times on these sites."

PROLOGUE TO THE FUTURE

Information available now is prologue to the future. "The men in the Fire Department constitute management's most valuable, and expensive, resource," Chief Holdsworth emphasizes. "There is a critical responsibility to utilize this resource at maximum efficiency within the framework of a reasonable workload. We hope to build a mathematical model which will indicate what future fire demands will be, and help determine how best to deploy our resources to meet them."

Plans also call for the computer to help develop data on water usage; to better control oxygen breathing equipment, to aid in departmental budgeting, to maintain cost and utilization records on each piece of apparatus and to maintain records of repairs to firehouses.

The importance of the department's Fire Prevention Program grows in direct proportion to the growth in demand for services. Plans for the future also call for putting this on the computer, to help evaluate the overall program and direct it to where it is needed most. In the final analysis, prevention may hold out the best hope for turning that straight line back into a curve.

Questions:

1. The New York Fire Department planners foresee an on-line computer system. Comment on what type of applications would require this mode of operation by a fire department.

2. Discuss the New York Fire Department practice of training firemen to be data processors.

BETTER PATIENT CARE -
THROUGH ELECTRONICS

By ROBERT M. SMITH

There are three major differences between the public outpatient clinics in even the best hospitals and the medical services available through a well-run doctor's office.

The inordinate waits that clinic patients must go through before seeing a doctor at all;

The cheerlessness, and the jammed conditions in which patients must wait to see a doctor.

The fact that most patients seldom see the same doctor twice if they must visit the clinic more than once. Just as patients are taken on a first-come, first-served basis, so the first available doctor gets the next patient waiting even though the patient may have seen an entirely different physician on his last visit. This of course aggravates the time delay since the new doctor must review the patient's entire medical record before treating him.

In an effort to cure all these maladies, The Children's Hospital Medical Center in Boston, which runs one of the country's busiest and best medical clinics, has taken two simple steps that are restoring to some degree the atmosphere of a private patient-doctor relationship for its clinic outpatients.

And if Boston Children's can do it, presumably any hospital can; an average of 40,000 patients make 150,000 visits a year to its 54 clinics.

It is accomplishing this plan, aimed at giving a more human dimension to clinic visits, through an unlikely but effective means, an electronic computer.

Boston Children's was the first hospital in the country to use a computer successfully for bed utilization control—determining on a real time basis how many beds are available in all parts of the hospital. (See "How to Automate a Hospital," M/S July-Aug., 66, p. 48.) At a time when many hospitals were announcing grandiose schemes for computers to take over much of the paperwork necessary in a hospital, Boston, through its own staff, advised by information systems specialists from Cresap, McCormick and Paget, international management consulting firm, put into effect a simple system based on a central on line computer linked to cathode ray display tubes at the Hospital's admitting offices and nursing stations. By a system roughly analogous to an airline's passenger reservation system, nurses could notify the computer immediately whenever a patient was discharged, or transferred. The computer's memory would be immediately updated. The admitting clerk, whenever a patient appeared, could immediately determine whether a bed was available by querying the computer and receiving a reply on her cathode ray screen.

Reprinted with permission from Management Services (June, 1968) a publication of the American Institute of Certified Public Accountants.

ADMISSION PROCESS SPEEDED

Patients were admitted faster; nurses, instead of laboriously preparing bed space changes manually once a day, could simply key in a few changes on a Teleregister unit at the nursing station.

It was a simple process and in its very simplicity lay its success. By not attempting to do everything at once, Boston got one very important application running smoothly and efficiently. But even then, the Boston planners and their consultants had a schedule for further computing applications designed to improve patient service.

The next successive step was scheduling service for outpatients in the Medical Center's 54 clinics. This was a more difficult problem than bed utilization because of the size of the patient load, and the scheduling of doctors. Hospital nursing and clerical personnel assigned to the clinics were no problem; their hours and availability were known factors. Private doctors who volunteered some hours of service were another problem, though; the hours they donated were their own choice, and occurred at odd times throughout the schedule. Too, demands upon residents made scheduling them difficult.

RESERVATION PLAN MODEL AGAIN

The approach to the new problem was a more elaborate version of that taken with bed utilization: adaptation of the basic airlines reservation system. The goal was to put each outpatient clinic on the same basis as a private doctor's patient, so he had a definite time for an appointment ideally and would always see the same doctor unless a specialist in some other field were needed.

The basic differences from bed utilization were the closer time factor—patients now had to be scheduled by fifteen-minute or half-hour time intervals within a given day—and the greater number of individuals, both doctors and patients involved.

The success and speed of development for the new program were immensely aided by the experience Children's had already gained from its bed utilization system and by a federal grant of $668,000 made to help the new development after the bed utilization scheme had been observed in operation by government administrators.

Children's Hospital still has the IBM 360 which was first used (and is still being used) for bed utilization records. But for the clinic scheduling system a larger-scale Honeywell Model 1200 computer has been installed.

The Teleregister units used at the admitting office and nursing stations in the bed utilization plan have been replaced in the clinic by Honeywell CRT (cathode ray tube) terminals with input keyboards. Actually, these are the same type of units as the Teleregister machines, although the keyboard has been changed slightly for the clinic scheduling application.

The way it works now is this: A patient comes to the clinic for the first time with his parent or parents. Say the child is not apparently seriously ill but displays a lassitude which seems unnatural. The parents want to find out what is wrong.

The clinic general admitting office would schedule such a patient to be seen in the General Medical Clinic. The admitting clerk would contact the computer to open a record on the patient and manually type in on the keyboard of her CRT unit the patient's name, sex, the appointment function, the date, and the clinic to which he is being assigned. The computer would record this information, assign the patient a number, and display all this information on the cathode ray tube display screen. It would also show the next free time slot on the General Medical Clinic schedule.

The appointment is made.

When the patient returns for his appointment—if there must be a time interval—he need no longer go through the main reception area on the first floor of the clinic building. He has an appointment now at the General Medical Clinic and, after paying his clinic fee, goes directly there. General Medical has its own reception area—as do each of the other 53 clinics. The reception clerk there has an appointment schedule for the day prepared in advance by the computer. Such and such a patient has an appointment at 10:30 A.M. with Dr. Jones. The patient arrives and is examined by Dr. Jones, who suspects a heart malfunction. The doctor wants the child to be examined by a cardiologist. He asks the patient's parent to stop at reception on the way out for another appointment. Then he contacts his own reception desk to say he wants his patient to be scheduled for examination in Cardiology. The clerk at the desk, while the patient is there, presses a "function" button of the console of her CRT unit for the next available free time at the Cardiology Clinic. The computer flashes back the next 40 dates that are available. The clerk selects the date most convenient for the patient's parent. The computer responds by displaying all free clinic times, from which a selection is made. The clerk then keys in the patient's medical record number—his main identification for the future —and the chosen time, and sends it back to the computer.

The second appointment is made.

PLAN USED IN ALL CLINICS

The same procedure is followed if the Cardiology Clinic wants further information and an appointment is necessary in another clinic.

Meanwhile a patient information file is accumulating in Medical Records, to which dictated reports, lab test results, etc., are sent from the clinics. Each time the patient is scheduled for an appointment in any of the clinics, the computer prints out the patient number, with the clinic for which he is scheduled, and the date of the appointment. All patients scheduled for each clinic are listed for two days in advance. The medical records library pulls all the records for each clinic number and ships them to the designated clinic by conveyor belt. If an X-ray print is requested, Radiology follows the same procedure.

Thus, if our hypothetical child patient should receive a clean bill of health from Cardiology and other clinics in which he was seen and be returned to his original doctor in the General Medical Clinic, that doctor, Dr. Jones, would have a complete medical history including his own findings and recommendations, and the findings of Cardiology and the other clinics, before he saw the patient again. And even after all the intervening clinics, if the patient were returned to General Medical finally, it would be Dr. Jones he would return to. For the doctor's name is part of his medical records now; the first doctor he sees is in effect his private doctor as long as he is being treated at that clinic at Children's Hospital.

The same system works for children who do have their own pediatrician but who are referred to the outpatient clinic for specialized diagnosis or treatment, except that in this instance, of course, the child can be seen directly in the appropriate clinic.

The scheduling system takes care of the main objectives of the hospital administration — establishing personal patient-physician relationship and eliminating the endless waits that are so characteristic of so many clinics. What about the drab, cheerless environment and the packed, uncomfortable wooden benches that are almost a clinic trademark in most hospitals?

Here Children's Hospital has been lucky. It has a brand new $12,000,000 building, the Fegan Memorial Outpatient Center, to house its clinics. The Fegan Building was designed with the children who were to be its clients in mind. The street floor houses the main reception area but each of the clinics on the other 10 floors of the building has its own reception areas as well, just as a private physician has a waiting room. Each reception area boasts comfortable cushioned chairs, bright colors, and even blackboards for children to scribble on while waiting for their appointment.

The child's only contact with the computer, which in a very real sense is guiding him through the Children's Hospital clinics, comes from the CRT unit used by the receptionist. The CRT set looks almost exactly like the television set familiar to him at home except that instead of cowboys and Indians, the set merely shows green type characters. And even the television-like set is made a little more interesting to the children by the resourcefulness of the receptionists. One has fashioned a paper flower which decorates her unit; another has gone her one better; her unit has flowers and a stuffed animal decorating it.

Personnel manning the reception desks are clerks, whereas in its previous bed utilization system the hospital had to depend heavily on nursing personnel to keep its records up to date. The clerks have proved easier to train on the CRT units than the nurses did, according to Jeanne Colt, R.N., Associate Director of Nursing for Systems, Children's Hospital Medical Center. Nurses do not like keeping records, when the job is simplified to the punching of information on a Teleregister, she believes, and they are apt to resent the necessity of recording information immediately if their nursing duties must be delayed. Clerks on the other hand are fully familiar with keyboard machines and can be trained on the CRT units in a comparatively short time.

CLERKS TRAINED IN MONTH

Children's Hospital trained its personnel at the reception desk in about a month's time for the new scheduling routine. Clerks were trained through a simulation program on the computer; they would type in dummy information; the computer would make its response on the basis of assumed information already programmed into it.

Miss Colt emphasizes there was no effort to make each clerk an expert in the entire system. They were taught the fundamentals of what they were to do and the theory beind the whole system. Then they were given a brief guide sheet to refer to for procedural steps if they forgot any of them and a more extensive manual describing the whole system in describing the whole system in detail, which they could refer to at any time.

With this seemingly simple approach to training its clerical workers, the outpatient clinic managed to start the sytem in its least busy clinics within a month or so after training started. To date, since training began in early February of this year, Boston has prepared about 75 clerical workers to handle the CRT units.

As for the computer itself, the Medical Center already had trained EDP personnel from its past experience with the System 360.

So far Children's has written 38 batch programs for such things as report and file maintenance, as well as several subprograms for the nine command functions established for the outpatient program: Admit, Update, Made an Appointment, Cancel an Appointment, Cancel a Clinic Session, Inquiry, Medical Record Request, Attendance, and Schedule Change. All programs have been written in the Easycoder assembly language.

TOTAL SYSTEM PLANNED

When Children's links its current computer to a second Honeywell 1200 to be installed later this year, it feels it will have the nucleus for a total information system integrating all of the hospital's medical, statistical, and financial data. The present computer will handle clinic scheduling and hospital bed control (Children's will retire its System 360 when the second Honeywell is installed); the new computer will process batch accounting, administrative, and statistical data.

Some of the reasons for the great hopes Children's Hospital places in its new computer system were phrased by the hospital director, Leonard W. Cronkhite, Jr., M.D., in a talk he gave when the new clinic scheduling system was publicly demonstrated in March of this year:

"We anticipate the clinic scheduling system will help have an effect upon reducing the total cost of care to patients by cutting down the number of clinic visits required per medical episode. Presently, many patients' parents are required to bring their children back to the clinic for repeated visits. Each time they do, they not only pay a clinic fee but also have baby sitter costs, transporation expenses, in some cases loss of pay and the like. In a large number of cases multiple visits are required because a child's condition demands he be seen in several different clinics—for example children seen in the General Medical Clinic may also require visits to Orthopedic.

"Until now, because of the tremendous volume of appointments we handle, it has not been easily possible to coordinate these appointments so both can be kept on a single visit to the hospital. Instead the child and parent have had to come to the hospital at least twice. We can now cut this visit per episode in half in most cases, with a resulting decrease in cost to the parent."

Obviously, the new system benefits patients and their parents, but what about the Medical Center itself? Will it run its costs up?

CASE LOAD SMOOTHED

Again Dr. Cronkhite provides the answer:

"More effective utilization of staff time is being accomplished through the use of the computer. Prior to going on line, the doctor's patient load per day varied from heavy to light. The scheduling system now gives the individual doctor a more balanced case load, provides him advance knowledge of who his patients will be on any given day and what their medical problems are, and, most important, allows him adequate blocks of time to handle the scheduled load. The same holds true with the ancillary personnel, such as the physical therapist, the X-ray technicians, and the like. There are two major spin-offs from this. We can set up a staffing pattern equal to the load instead of having to staff for maximum possible clinic attendance, which frequently is far in advance of the actual attendance. Secondly, we are convinced that we provide better patient care by eliminating the feeling of pressure a doctor gets when he knows there's a large number of patients still out in the waiting room to see him."

Questions:

1. The author states that presumably any hospital can have patient scheduling systems. Explain why you agree or disagree with the author.

2. How would you analyze a hospital's workload to determine the feasibility of a hospital scheduling system?

3. List some of the computer system characteristics required to support a system such as the one at the Childrens Hospital Medical Center.

THE IMPACT OF COMPUTERS ON EDUCATION

By ERWIN DANZIGER and SANDY HOBGOOD

In the olden days of the educational process, a student's usual complaint was that he was reduced to a solitary hole punched into a card. Nowadays he doesn't even have that to fall back on, as he is represented by an invisible trace of magnetism on a tape or disk file.

But even as his physical representation is reduced his intellectual progress is being guided more and more on the basis of his individual nature. As the physical size of his permanent file shrinks, the amount of information stored about him grows much larger. With this proliferation of individual attention there develops a potential for greater service to the student, his teacher, and the institution.

Innovation in educational data manipulation is moving ahead, and the potentialities of new hardware and programming techniques are generating new excitement on campus. Principals, chancellors, and provosts are realizing the advantage of computer managerial techniques and are demanding more and more sophisticated profiles and surveys on their students and curriculums. Historians and political scientists are realizing the labor-saving devices of abstraction and information retrieval. Teachers of education are noting with approval the experimentation being done in areas which use the computer itself as a teaching medium and clerical personnel are delighted with the time saved in class scheduling via computer methods.

We would like to discuss some of the things being done with computers in education today and what is promised for the near future.

ADMINISTRATIVE USES

A typical model of an educational information system was prepared by Bruce K. Alcorn and published in the spring 1966 issue of the *Journal of Educational Data Processing*. He divides all information in an educational institution into 5 classes: pupil, staff, program, facility, and finance. These five areas are necessarily interrelated. For example, as the male/female ratio at the University of North Carolina at Chapel Hill changes, alterations of facilities must be made.

The objective of any good information system is to demonstrate the overall tendencies of the organization, in addition to supplying appropriate

Reprinted from the April, 1968 issue of the Journal of Data Management and copyrighted by the Data Processing Management Association.

quantities of organized detailed information in which administrators can base decisions regarding growth and transition. The ideal information system is not with us yet. However, the need is obvious and the data is available. The time required for implementation is the only thing holding us back.

In order to achieve these ends, it has been demonstrated in industry that those responsible for the development of an information system should report to as high a level as possible in the management hierarchy. At the university, this presents special problems, but they are not insurmountable.

We at UNC have started the process of developing an information system for the university based on four principal divisions: student records, faculty and staff records, financial activities, and physical facilities. These divisions were selected from a thorough appraisal of the university's data-flow organization, and in particular, attention was paid to the logical division of information within the university. Much of our payroll work is now done on the computer, such as check writing, deductions reporting, labor distribution and preparation of various faculty listings. Our student records such as course registration, student fees, and grade reporting are now being converted to the computer. Classroom space utilization reports are made periodically, personnel records are being converted to magnetic tape, and eventually some more complicated applications, such as grant and fund accounting, will be automated.

We foresee the day when all these active administrative sub-systems will feed information into a large data base. This data base will provide the historical information needed to build and support a mathematical simulation model of the University. Such a simulation model should also be able to assist in long range forecasting of enrollments, budget requirements and facility needs.

Work along the above lines has been pioneered and demonstrated by Dr. R.W. Judy of the University of Toronto who has built a system called CAMPUS—an acronymn for Comprehensive Analytical Model for Planning in the University Sphere. A 1966 study made by the Oregon State System of Higher Education involving approximately 200 strictly publicly supported, four-year colleges and universities found that 73% of all four-year publicly supported colleges and universities were currently using computers for administrative work, and 99% (all but one) with an enrollment over 7,000 students were using computers. Eighty-five per cent of the computers (mainly the larger units) were leased; while approximately 15% (mainly smaller units) were purchased. Furthermore, the larger a university or college, the more likely to have a computer dedicated to administrative work.

Significant work is being done in some secondary schools in the use of computing techniques to develop comprehensive student information systems. For example, in Greensboro, N.C., a data base is being prepared which will support a student records system to be used by teachers, guidance personnel, attendance counselors, school health people, psychologists, and so on. All these student agencies will be grouped under a "Department of Pupil Services."

In Portland, Oregon, a computer is being used as a curriculum organizer—a sort of "remote textbook supermarket." A central computer is used to catalogue pertinent texts, pamphlets, files and other instructional materials for instant reference.

Another future computer application to test distribution involves the connection of a district's central data processing machine to feeder schools via teleprocessing lines. In preparing course material for the next day, the teacher selects and requests various handouts, poop-sheets, or quizzes from those stored in the computer's memory. The machine finds the required materials and generates messages to the remote unit where the actual pieces of paper are reporduced on some kind of image-producing machine. These are collated and placed in the teacher's boxes for morning pickup. Later, the teacher leaves completed quiz sheets in her box for remote grading and evaluation by the machine.

Other significant strides are involved in overall evaluation of the individual student and the curriculum. The computer can be programmed to evaluate each student response and, rather than produce a grade for each quiz the machine can produce a profile of student strengths and weaknesses which can run parallel through all courses. The curriculum itself can be reorganized and updated with respect to past analysis of effectiveness.

In Syracuse, N.Y., instant "evaluation" of the "learning reception" by large lecture classes is being tried. Every student has a keyset at his desk with which he may respond to multiple choice questions. The tallies of responses are reported instantly to the instructor so he knows immediately whether he made his point or not. At the end of the class the professor can check the answers of any of the students, giving him an immediate evaluation report.

Educators on many campuses are becoming more interested in information retrieval as a tool in research. Some are moving toward automation of library facilities which slice through some of the red tape and do away with some of the repretitive manual chores of traditional academic research. The library of tomorrow is seen as a center for information exchange where books will be kept on microfiche. (Microfiche are 4" X 6" cards that can hold up to 60 pages of printed matter and can be read in a simple viewer which does not require threading.) Frederick L. Goodman in the NEA (National Education Association) *Journal* predicts that libraries of tomorrow will be able to put people with like interests together, allow people to communicate directly with authors, and in general provide electronic cross-reference of all educational media (including the educators themselves). This would lead us toward sort of a gradeless classroom in which, for example, a businessman, a housewife, and a college sophomore could be put in touch with one another in a discussion of common interest of say, Indian folklore. Another development within our grasp is a "citation index" which is kind of an electronic *Reader's Guide* where, given a topic and other delimiting factors, the computer displays a complete bibliography for the subject, with computer-composed abstracts of certain articles.

Developed in connection with grade reporting, information systems can be used by counselors to chart a student's academic welfare. We can envision a real-time "behavior-appraisal" system to detect potential emotional or character disturbances based on continuous ratings from teachers, counselors, etc. At present, these ratings are made on report cards at the end of a grading period. However, the reports often come long after the damage has been done. Use of the computer can get identical reports for the same personnel in time to take corrective action. With the proper safeguards of personal data, guidance systems can become truly effective.

Another counseling service is college selection or job placement which can be handled on a national level by computer. GRAD–Graduate Resume Accumulation and Distribution–is a service whereby a job applicant fills out a form which includes job location preference, salary requirements, and the like.

Employers request the services of GRAD by mail or teletype. The applicant files are on disk, and the computer can produce a list of qualified applicants for employers instantly. A similar service, especially for public school teachers, was introduced in February 1967 by the NEA.

THE COMPUTER AS AN AID TO INSTRUCTION

The vanguard efforts in computer educational applications have been designed to create systems which are flexible enough to meet the needs of a complete range of students. Individual attention is considered by most experts as a necessary component; that is, the computer must be programmed to interact with any student regardless of his intelligence quotient.

The apparent leader of the research in this area is Dr. Patrick J. Suppes, who is the director of Stanford's Institute for Mathematical Studies in Social Sciences. With much technological support from a major computer manufacturer, he has established a two million dollar CAI facility at Brentwood Elementary School in East Palo Alto, California. There are 16 terminals, each of which includes a television-type screen, a tape response unit, a typewriter keyboard and a light pen.

The first lesson flashes a picture of a dog, a cat, a cow, and other animals on the screen as a mellow voice from the computer tells the child to "touch the dog with the light pen". If he does, the machine coos "That's right" and goes on to the next frame. If he doesn't, the machine allows him to try again and may insert a green arrow over the dog as a reinforcing agent.

And so it goes. If the student doesn't get the idea, he is sidetracked for remedial lessons, taught by the computer. If he is really in trouble, the machine will generate a message to the teacher for human intervention. The important object is to force the pupil to be involved in a learning effort especially tailored for his needs.

More recently, RCA has set up shop in Palo Alto with a new creation, RCA Instructional Systems, which is destined to "spearhead the development of computer-based techniques designed to overcome some of the nation's most pressing educational problems."

RCA is working closely with Dr. Suppes in this effort. General Sarnoff of RCA recently referred to the Palo Alto campus as the seedbed of educational reform in the United States.

A major experiment conducted some years ago at the University of Illinois called "PLATO" was designed as a time-sharing teaching system. Each student sat in front of a typewriter-like console and a television-type screen, upon which were displayed slides which could be selected at random by the machine's program. Of significance were the extra buttons on the typewriter by which the student could call for review session or concentrated help in a particular session by himself. For example, if the student understood a sequence he could press the "continue" button. If he wanted to go back over the material, he could press the "reverse" key. Each small sequence closed with a question. The student was allowed to try to answer as many times as he wanted. If he was really out in left field, he could press a button marked "help" for an intensive review session. If, while in the midst of a "help" sequence, the correct answer to the original question occurred to the student, he could press a button marked "aha" for a return to the original question slide.

PLATO was essentially a linear teaching sequence. The student had to take the initiative to get review sessions or help sequences. Dr. Suppes' techniques perform automatic branching as the student excels or falters. Thus the Suppes experiments are more suited to the younger student—he was, you will recall, experimenting with the first graders. The PLATO project was directed toward and is more applicable to a more sophisticated pupil. The experiments in CAI at Chapel Hill are proceeding more along the lines of PLATO.

Such experiments at UNC are in a less developed stage. Nevertheless some significant directions are being followed, particularly in respect to cost reduction and development for the IBM System/360. Much of the pioneer work at other universities was done on second generation equipment. Presently, researches at UNC are working with an IBM 1050 connected by telephone to the Triangle Universities Computation Center. This remote unit has a typewriter, a slide projector which is capable of showing up to 85 different slides at random access, and a random-access tape recorder. Source material is being gathered now for a course in PL/I and other subject matters will probably be added in the future. The actual make-up of the course is sort of a hybrid Suppes/PLATO in that students in difficulty are given extra review help automatically, or they may request further aid via "help" sequences.

Florida State University recently opened its new Computer Assisted Instruction Center and last fall, Stanford University began offering beginning Russian with CAI. Students attend language laboratory and do homework, but all lecture classes have been replaced by computer sessions. At the Irvine Campus of the University of California, CAI courses are used extensively by faculty members to "brush up" on statistical methods in the privacy of their office rather than in a class with freshmen.

In 1967, four schools in Philadelphia began planning CAI as part of their curriculum. The schools use a Philco-Ford central computing machine with 32 student consoles, 8 at each school. Plans call for instruction in biology and reading at the junior high level. A grant of 3.1 million dollars was provided as well as a 2000 Philco computer. The Philadelphia Board of Education together with Philco devised a language called INFORM through which curricula may be developed with more or less standard English. The system involves automatic evaluation of student answers with appropriate branching depending on past history.

Another more widely accepted language—or at least highly publicized—is called "Coursewriter". In theory this language allows the programmer to prepare a course in a modified version of the English language, but more significantly, to alter that program offline. A major drawback to some CAI programs is that unless the student answers with one of the exact answers provided, including exact spelling, punctuation, and form—the answer is considered wrong by the computer and the computer's answer to a wrong reply is unchangeable. With "Coursewriter," an instructor may anticipate various answers, and various forms of them, and provide differing responses (from the computer) for those replies. Nor does the instructor need to anticipate. The "Coursewriter" program may print a listing of all student answers from a previous session, and the programmer can update the course-(online) by providing responses to all the wrong answers listed.

There are great drawbacks to CAI, not the least of which is money. The facility at Brentwood cost $2 million while the same number of students enrolled in the same curriculum at the school across the street are allocated $180. The year before, when Dr. Suppes was experimenting at another nearby school, there were 30 children enrolled. Most of them learned two year's math in a year, but to keep them busy for only 5 minutes a day for 160 days of the year he employed programmers for 1,600 manhours to develop 96,000 exercises. His machine broke down an average of 100 minutes a day. The children's reaction when the machine fails is called "random behavior" by psychologists. Teachers, however, call it "hanging from the rafters."

Educators themselves are quite apprehensive about the cost which is estimated at around $3,000 per student hour for curriculum development. However, Florida State University claims to have prepared a year's course work at $81 per student hour. Actual machine utilization is much less expensive. Louis Bright, who is associate commissioner for research of the United States Office of Education, said use of the IBM 1500 educational system is capable of running at about $1.40 per student hour. The cost may drop to 35 cents per hour in the next few years, according to Bright. Dr. Suppes insists that individualized work in arithmetic and spelling could be brought to the schools at $40 to $50 per student per year. Beyond installation and curriculum development, he forecast systems available in the future at 30 cents per student per hour.

Some educators are rightfully jealous—though unjustifiably fearful—of industry's advance into the world of education. They have generally come to accept the fact that there is no danger in a machine's taking over clerical chores such as grade reporting and attendance keeping, but that a machine should actually impart knowledge is not welcome. A similar crisis took place in education some 300 years ago with the advent of the printed page. It is hoped that the differences between education and industry can be resolved at such time as technology in software has reached an operable stage. Dr. Suppes and others point out that the student could not conceivably be in front of the TV screen for more than one or two hours a day; and furthermore, the *raison d'etre* of CAI is individualized instruction, a goal common to computer researchers and education administrators alike.

Dr. Suppes identifies three levels of computer interaction which is a suitable frame of reference when discussing CAI. He calls them "systems" which is indeed what they are, since they involve a totally new approach to the learning experience. He categorizes them as the "individualized drill-and-practice" system, the "tutorial" system and the "dialogue" system.

The "drill-and-practice" system is best suited to courses like spelling and foreign languages, which require a good deal of drill work. Here the teacher is required to introduce the concepts—thus to do the actual teaching—and the computer is responsible for testing and evaluation. Hence the student's level of understanding is evaluated continuously and the school doesn't have to rely on achievement tests and the like for placement purposes. Rather the student is being constantly tested and channeled by the computer into the proper discipline level. He need not be placed on a block and remain there until the close of the year.

The second area of computer action, "tutorial" systems, aim at a geniune tutor-tutee interaction. These techniques are to help the student develop understanding or devleop skill in a particular subject by teaching him the basic ideas and then reinforcing them with exercises and review sessions. This type of instruction is best suited to subjects like addition and multiplication.

Lastly are "dialogue" systems which allow the computer and the child to talk with each other. The inherent problems associated with voice recognition have not, at this time, been solved to a point even where meaningful experimentation is possible. The machine would have to be capable of recognizing the babble of 30 or 40 first-grade children and to distinguish between each, which is hard enough for the school psychologist. Dialogue systems are in the future, however, and when operational we should be well on our way toward developing instructional systems which can sweep aside mechanical hindrances such as typewriter terminals and light pens.

A great theoretical run-around is engulfing computer-assisted educational research in that a sound theoretical base in the psychology of education has not been developed. The software development is forging ahead, but has not reached the full theoretical potential of the machines that are now available. Hence in education as in the rest of the industry, we observe a very real software lag behind the specialized third generation machines. However, the lag goes farther back than computer software, for it is not at all precisely clear, nor is it agreed among the experts which learning theory should be applied. In business at least we have existing systems, however primitive, which can be (to use a mouldy term) "computerized." And education has followed industry down the line as far as possible in automating clerical procedures of scheduling, attendance reporting, etc.

But the bridge is out when it comes to instruction. Granted there are many formalized teaching methods, but there is a scarcity of theory as to what makes geography find a lodging place in Johnny's brain. Not to say this is not being investigated, but the fact is that the theory is still behind the software which is behind the (theoretical limit of) the hardware. The "teaching techniquest" is still grasping at straws.

THE COMPUTER'S IMPACT ON PUBLISHING INDUSTRIES

Beginning as early as 1962 when Xerox acquired University Microfilms Inc., there have been dozens of major mergers of electronics firms wishing to break into the education market and publishers who perhaps wished to preserve and protect their very long-range prospects of making money. The year 1962 saw the marriage of RCA and Random House; the absorption of CBS of Creative Playthings, a manufacturer of children's educational toys; and Raytheon and the D.C. Heath Company. In 1964 IBM acquired Science Research Associates. In 1966, the 3M Company and *Newsweek* got together to publish current-events materials; and Sylvania is working with *Reader's Digest* on some educational problems.

Greater and greater stimulus to improve teaching techniques is coming from the federal government, which up to 1965 used appropriations from the Defense Department and the Office Economic Opportunity. But now money is available directly from the Office of Education and federal money is available specifically for textbooks, visual aids and other course material.

The industry, however, is still an embryonic one, and returns may be postponed by as much as 10 or 15 years. This perhaps accounts for the fact that only the larger companies have begun diversification in this manner. Larger firms are quite concerned, too, that a number of smaller firms may rush in at some premature point, without advantage of proper (much less thorough) research in the field, and bring discredit upon the whole movement through some dramatic failure.

Indeed, the educational community in some areas is wary of industrial inroads. Not many months ago teaching machines—mechanical non-computing machines—were hailed as a special educational revolution. Great claims were made to their effectiveness, since they were based in some manner on modern Skinnerian psychology and therefore couldn't fail. Regretably, the linear approach to instruction taken by these machines left much to be desired when used for human beings and the teaching machine received much scorn. These machines failed to capture the attention of pupils. They were "over-structured" for most people (i.e. the form of the answer is more important than the content), and they were wildly expensive. Many educators have come to regard teaching machines as elaborate and costly "page turners."

It is to this hostile environment that the research in non-linear individualized instruction is being directed. The rejection of teaching machines is not a rejection of machinery in toto, but it represents an attitude on the part of education administrators. Perhaps the academic community is especially prone to wax and wane in the dusty groves of tradition. Except in the sciences themselves, technology has made little impact upon effective teaching. So perhaps indeed the academic community must be educated to the scientific advances that have already been made. As *Fortune* magazine says, "the new business-government thrust is likely to transform both the organization and the content of education, and through it, the character and shape of American society itself."

TEACHING THE ART AND SCIENCE OF COMPUTING

The management consulting firm of Paine, Weber, and Jackson estimated that there would be 52,000 computers installed in the United States by the end of 1967, that there would be 70,000 by the end of 1968 and there may well be more than 100,000 computers installed by 1975. There are approximately 150,000-200,000 analysts and programmers today. On the assumption that for the average 1975 installation there will be systems manager and two analysts, and a programming manager and six programmers, we will need a total of 1 million analysts and programmers by 1975, or roughly five to six times as many as we have today. Where will they come from? Let's list some of the sources of newly trained programmers and systems analysts:

a) Computer manufacturers' training schools
b) Private programming schools
c) In-house industry training
d) Universities and colleges
e) Correspondence courses

f) Technical institutes

g) Computer software/consulting companies

There are advantages and disadvantages to each of these sources of trained programmers, but probably more important is the fact that even all these sources taken together will probably not fill our needs.

Fortunately this has been recognized by a few leading educators and such professional organizations as the Data Processing Mangement Association and the Systems and Procedures Association. Steps to help rectify this situation are beginning to appear. In our opinion, much of the final answer lies in the proper preparation and motivation of high school students for careers in the data processing industry, and the increased expansion of formal computer science and information science courses in technical institutes, colleges, and universities.

DPMA's "Future Data Processor" program has spawned hundreds of "computer clubs" in high schools throughout the nation and has been an important factor in bringing the computer "gospel" to this mass of potential programmers.

The Systems and Procedures Association has been active at the next higher level, where more than 170 colleges and universities now use the SPA "Business Systems" textbook to introduce programming and system techniques to many thousands of students. SPA is also developing a 55-lesson correspondence course for computer systems analysts.

We estimate that there are currently three dozen schools which have established formal computer science departments and are authorized to award degrees. This number will certainly double in the next several years. Colleges and universities teaching computer oriented courses range well into a thousand or more. (See DPMA's *Data Processing Courses at Colleges and Universities.*)

In 1963 Dartmouth set as a four-year goal the establishment of required elementary programming for most freshmen. They have trained about 80% of three freshmen classes since then. The aims of the Dartmouth project involve one particular area that is overlooked in many instances: changing the attitude of people away from viewing computers as ominous super-intelligent creatures that break down a lot and really, in the long run (after programming, debugging, and waiting on turn-around time) aren't very fast after all. Dartmouth also "puts the computer at the fingertips of the faculty" in a very real sense, so that projects which are applicable to the computer are done on the computer at considerable time saving to the user. About 40% of the faculty in all areas of the campus use the computer.

Dartmouth computer personnel attribute success in these two areas to two factors—use of the language BASIC and an easy-to-use time sharing system. BASIC was designed at Dartmouth and was worked out by Dartmouth undergraduate students. Granted it is not a powerful language nor is it formal in the sense of being syntactically perfect etc. But it is simple to learn, and reasonably sophisticated problems can be solved very quicly. For example, required problems of students in freshman mathematics include finding the root of a given quintic equation and simulating a 3-state Markov chain dealing with a fanciful weather system. Experience has shown that most student problems can be run (task time) in less than a second. A five-second terminate option is applied to most jobs (so that if it isn't finished in five seconds it gets bumped and the machine works on others until it gets enough free time to go back). The hardware used at Dartmouth was a GE 235 with a Datanet-30 for handling the communications with the teletypewriters. This has since been updated to a GE 625 with two Datanet-30's which will provide for up to 200 simultaneous users. The Dartmouth student is alloted ¾ of an hour per week on the teletype. The machine is also used as a CAI machine to teach the language BASIC.

The new Department of Computer Sciences at North Carolina State University awards the bachelors degree in Computer Science after 126 semester hours of study, 36 of which are concentrated in the major.

The major computer courses are as follows:

1st year: Algorithmic Languages, I (Primarily FORTRAN); Basic Computer Concepts.

2nd year: Algorithmic Languages, II (PL/I, and COBOL); Systems Analysis and Techniques; Introduction to Numerical Methods.

3rd year: Business Data Processing; Computer Organization Logic; Numerical Analysis I.

4th year: Numerical Analysis II; System Design and Computer Selection; Linear Programming; Computer Allocations.

There are 550 students enrolleed in the first course this year.

A student who already holds an undergraduate degree may obtain a masters or a doctors degree at the UNC's Department of Information Science. The prime objective of the department is to "train teachers and researchers at the Ph.D. level as a backbone for the new discipline." There are approximately 30 courses offered ranging from Fundamentals of Information Processing through Architecture of Computers. This fall there were 44 advanced degree candidates enrolled and the beginning programming course has approximately 300 students.

One of the most successful experiments in broad scale computer education in the United States has been the North Carolina Computer Oreintation Project (NCCOP). This project is designed to offer limited computing facility to all 80 institutions of higher learning in the state. Fourteen of these institutions are "on-line" with the Triangle Universities Computation Center today. These are:

Davidson College
A & T State University
Appalachian State University
Asheville-Biltmore College
Bennett College
Central Piedmont Community College
East Carolina University
Gaston College
Pfeiffer College
St. Andrews Presbyterian College
UNC at Charlotte
Wilmington College
High Point College
Meredith College

Nine others have applications to hook-in on file.

Each participating college is furnished a Model 33 Teletype terminal and a modest amount of communication and computer time purchased from Triangle Universities Computation Center (TUCC), a non-profit organization established by Duke University, North Carolina State University and the University of North Carolina at Chapel Hill. The center is located in the Research Triangle Park, and is equipped with an IBM System/360 Model 75 computer. Additional computer time and more elaborate terminals are available to the participating colleges provided they bear the additional cost. When the trial period ends, an institution may discontinue the service or continue it by assuming the terminal, communication, and computer time costs.

We in North Carolina are at least active in the game. It may be true that our educational computer efforts are not yet on a part with the California Institute of Technology in sophistication or MIT in quantity. On the other hand, we do feel that we are among the leaders in bringing educational computing facilities to many of the smaller institutions and certainly the shared TUCC facilities are unique in the nation.

The excitement generated by these new directions in computers is having far-reaching effects.

First and foremost, the efforts in CAI are causing a thorough re-evaluation of teaching methods and learning theory. In fact, many people in education are beginning to suspect that there has never been a method, in a formalized sense, in teaching. The essence of what makes Johnny learn (in its finest sense—the ability to theorize and abstract, not just remember) is being investigated as never before.

Secondly, this "computer magic" (as it were) is creating a new awareness of the importance of mathematics and its key relation to all other academic disciplines. The launching of the Soviet Sputnik 10 years ago kindled an interest in mathematics and loosened an avalanche (certainly not overwhelming but significant) of federal and other aid. But this was a negative stimulus in that we were put on the defensive and the emphasis on upgrading the mathematical curriculum was in order to "catch up". The computer revolution is more positive in nature. People are realizing the key position of mathematics, and educators are devising myriad new ways of bringing mathematics to "the people". Through the computer, people can see an immediate and valuable consequence of applied mathematics, and so its importance in the curriculum is enhanced.

A third sector caught up in the whirl of the computer age is industry. Historically worlds apart, the groves of academe and the jungles of Wall Street are moving inexorably closer as industry realizes an opportunity as well as a responsibility in American education, and as educators recognize the benefits of close cooperation with the business world.

Questions:

1. List and describe three levels of computer-student interraction.

2. What is the objective of any "good management information system?" How does the University of North Carolina system attempt to fulfill this objective?

3. Describe the major drawbacks to implementing CAI, and possible solutions to each.

MARIAN THE TECHNOLOGIST?

By RICHARD LANHAM

It could happen . . . by the lights of some prognosticators.

Libraries, like so many institutions these days, are the province of prophets. Some predict triumphs of technology: "procognitive systems" faster than a speeding electron, more powerful than an army of librarians, able to span vast document collections at the pulse of a light pen.

Usually they frame these visions as absolute essentials. (The Information Explosion is upon us!) Frequently they insist on a revised breed of librarian.

Here are the words of the director of libraries at a major university: "The bankers of the United States in 1935 or so had shown that they were inadequate for the needs of this country's financial growth and most of the old timers were kicked out, and a whole new breed of bankers had to be introduced in order to forward this economy of ours; and I very much suspect that a whole new breed of information officers will have to be introduced to forward this country's information problems [sic], if librarians don't rise to the occasion."

His counterpart at another university sees things somewhat differently: "Everybody is saying that soon we'll slowly smother to death under mountains of paper. It isn't here yet. As far as I can see, the libraries are working and people are finding the information they want to find . . . I don't think the chaos that has been described is even imminent, but I am perfectly willing to prepare for the future—prepare for the day when chaos would come if we didn't get going."

One (clearly scientific) research group reports still another possibility: "If current trends continue over the next ten years, the large majority of libraries will operate much as they do today." What will the future really be like?

TECHNOLOGY AND LIBRARIES

Obviously there are several ways to look at the prospects for libraries . . . and several ways to interpret the present. Each line of thought—from projecting technology's ultimate possible application to "everything will evolve satisfactorily in due time"—raises important questions.

Joseph Becker and Wallace C. Olsen, in the 1968 Annual Review of Information Science and Technology, observe: "Technology and public

Reprinted with permission from the November 1968 issue of SDC MAGAZINE, a publication of the System Development Corporation.

demand are rapidly pushing libraries into accepting new organizational responsibilities and performing functions that have often been left previously to other communications media." Just what are these new responsibilities and functions? How are the libraries responding to the push?

Certainly technology can provide powerful tools. Which ones are useful now? Which will be most appropriate and helpful later?

What additional skills will library personnel have to learn in order to cope with new demands and handle new tools for meeting them? How can those skills be taught most efficiently?

Last and possibly greatest, what first steps should be taken now to "prepare for the day when chaos would come if we didn't get going"?

SDC's Library and Documentation Systems Department staff, on behalf of the National Advisory Commission on Libraries, studied these issues in depth during 1967. The resulting report, entitled TECHNOLOGY AND LIBRARIES, is a comprehensive, balanced view of the present and likely future relationships between technology and libraries.

WHAT TECHNOLOGY?

The SDC study team points out that, "The technologies that are exerting force on libraries are vastly broader than the kind that can be used by libraries . . . the user of information services is increasingly a specialist, often in a field of knowledge that did not even exist twenty years ago.

"Such users need and are demanding more and better technical information support. They do not always find it in the conventional library, and this has given rise to a multitude of specialized information facilities . . . a technological force that the libraries must contend with." This in addition to a growing group of increasingly knowledgeable (therefore demanding) general users.

Even if general libraries decide not to concentrate heavily on the needs of highly specialized users, they will have to reckon with other developments, such as microform equipment and techniques, new kinds of audiovisual equipment and techniques, new publication techniques and new means for the rapid electrical transmission of materials.

"All of these," the team notes, "are certain to bring about major changes in the ways that information is generated, disseminated, processed, stored, transformed and retrieved."

How important is all this? In the view of Carlos A. Cuadra, head of the SDC group, "These things may or may not be of relevance to libraries. This depends on whether the libraries choose to become a major force in the new kinds of information systems and services that are growing up around us."

IF YES . . .

Libraries can expect help from computer systems; from a variety of related equipment and materials developments, including microform techniques, reprography, computer-assisted publication techniques, and materials handling and storage devices and procedures; and, to some extent, from "procedural" technologies for such tasks as document storage and retrieval, automated indexing and classification, automated abstracting and extracting, and automated question answering.

Several of these aids are still in the research and development stage, but more than a few are available now. Unfortunately, most of those extant are not tailored to the specific needs—or budgets—of libraries.

But this situation, like most, is likely to change. Computers—the equipment with the greatest potential impact on library operations—are a good example.

Computer equipment can be had in a number of configurations spanning a purchase range from $6,000 to $10,000,000. While available equipment cannot yet meet all of the processing needs of very large libraries, it is quite adequate for a wide range of individual library automation tasks.

Barriers in the way of more extensive library applications include cost, lack of adequate library-oriented computer programs, too little computer memory capacity, and limitations in the input and output equipment.

The pace of change in computer technology indicates that in the next five to ten years there should be at least a tenfold reduction in computer system costs for a given level of performance; while computer speed and storage capabilities will be multiplying. These changes will certainly accelerate the library use of computers both for internal processing tasks and for assistance on bibliographic tasks.

Increased emphasis on library applications should bring other helpful developments: better microform techniques and reading devices; conveyors and containers designed for libraries rather than industry; more appropriate data storage and retrieval systems, to name a few.

Fully automated indexing, classification, abstracting and extracting appear to be a long way off. But at least one flexible, fast computer-based bibliographic search and retrieval system, SDC's ORBIT, is available and working. (An early version of ORBIT is described in SDC MAGAZINE, September 1967.)

Cuadra makes another point: "There is yet another kind of technology that is rarely noticed: the technology of finding things out.

"It is rather universally conceded that library science is not a science in the experimental sense, but only recently has it become obvious that this is not an inevitable state of affairs. Thus we are now seeing the development of technology for studying user needs, a technology for designing library and information systems, a technology for evaluating their effectiveness, etc."

And another: "Incidentally, I am sure we can look forward to the likelihood that computer-assisted instruction will play an important role in training library personnel for work in computer-based systems as well as helping patrons learn to use such systems."

RIGHT NOW

A small number of U.S. libraries—about 3 percent as of 1967—have begun to use data processing equipment. All of the major library functions (acquisitions, cataloging, circulation control, serials management, reference work, etc.) are drawing attention; but the main emphasis is on functions related to technical processes and circulation control, rather than reference services.

Certain aspects of the acquisitions process lend themselves particularly well to data processing. Some groups of libraries have even been exploring the idea of cooperative or centralized processing for acquisitions tasks.

While the most popular cataloging application has been in the reproduction of catalog cards, book-form catalogs are returning to favor, with the help of the computer and computer-controlled typesetting procedures. In cataloging, as well as in acquisitions, the combination of interlibrary cooperation and new technology offers considerable potential for reducing costs and eliminating duplication of effort.

Data processing technology is also being used for tasks associated with circulation control and serials records control. Few libraries have automated their reference function or their information and document retrieval functions.

The Library of Congress MARC project is a potential first step toward a national network for distributing machine-readable catalog data. The work being done to determine what elements of information should be put into machine-readable records can provide a valuable framework on which individual libraries can build and through which they may eventually participate in regional or national networks.

Technologies other than data processing are also being put to use in libraries. Microforms especially are being used increasingly, but their true potential has yet to be fully exploited. Libraries are showing increasing interest in audiovisual media and are acquiring such holdings as slides, films and recordings as well as facilities for using them. Use of advanced techniques for such jobs as materials handling, communication and storage has thus far required adaptation of equipment and procedures developed primarily for non-library purposes.

PROGNOSIS

SDC's TECHNOLOGY AND LIBRARIES report points out that, "Today's library operates in three different roles. One role is as a circulating library, which permits material to be taken outside of the library and later returned; the second role is as a reference facility, which permits certain materials to be used only within the library. The third role is as a distributor of materials. This distributing function is presently of minor importance and is only evident from the copying machines now available at different libraries."

There are demands—and there will be more—for changes, both in the relative importance of these roles and in the ways they are fulfilled. There are tools—and there will be more—for meeting those demands.

The exact nature and extent of actual change will depend on the responsiveness of library professionals, the responsiveness of equipment developers, and—inevitably—the responsiveness of funding agencies.

SDC's report offers this prognosis: "A conditional view of library activities, which assumes major acceleration of effort over the next ten years, sees libraries becoming elements of one or more integrated networks. Through a connection with a network, libraries could provide their staff personnel with better tools, with relief from some processing chores better handled through the network, and with network-supported facilities for handling reference problems. The library's users could also be provided with much more in the way of materials and services, with outright distribution of certain kinds of materials replacing loans. The availability of nonbook materials could be increased in libraries of all kinds and sizes across the nation.

"There are a number of problems of transition from the present to the future that are not entirely technological in nature. Libraries, already facing serious staff shortages, may find it very difficult to obtain staff with the broad training and experience necessary in both the requirements of library operations and those of technology. Too, library users will need better training in exploiting available library services and facilities. Here, technology itself offers some promise of providing useful tools.

"Standards of operation, as well as standards necessary for the compatibility of bibliographic data, are still lacking in the library world. As new data files are created and old files are converted, this problem will become more serious. The several possible approaches to standardization need active consideration, if the many separate and independent library organizations are to achieve adequate cooperation and communication, using the new technologies."

WHAT TO DO

SDC's staff concluded that to rely solely on current mechanisms for library service improvement would probably result in a net loss of ground for most libraries. The demands are growing faster than improvements are evolving.

On the other hand, to plunge right into developing a nationwide, highly integrated library system—while it could produce some desirable accomplishments—would be rather impractical right now.

Accordingly, SDC recommended focusing on selected projects that have high potential impact on library operations. "This approach," the report states, "recognizes the operational independence of most of the nation's libraries while at the same time taking advantage of their willingness to participate in interdependencies that offer mutual benefits. The approach also has the advantage of not precluding the undertaking of other projects and programs."

Five specific projects were recommended:
    A prototype network of regional libraries
    An expanded, computer-based National Union Catalog
    A national bibliography
    A national referral and loan network
    A national library storage and microform depository system

Undertaken together, these projects could lead, in two to four years, to operational subsystems that could later be incorporated into a more fully integrated, nationwide system.

Concurrently, there should be a comprehensive program of technology-oriented library research, development, education and training. And a facility should be set up for testing and evaluating new forms of nonbook materials.

SDC's staff felt strongly that the momentum generated by the National Advisory Commission on Libraries should not be allowed to dissipate. They recommended a sequence of immediate steps:

1. Formally accepting the high-impact-project approach as the basic means for effecting library improvement

2. Reviewing and assigning priorities to the particular projects recommended in the report

3. Developing more detailed objectives and cost appraisals for the projects selected for implementation

4. Identifying all potential sources of support for these projects and obtaining the necessary funds

5. Placing responsibility for the program at a high administrative level in an existing or new federal agency or in a public/private body created for the purpose.

MEANWHILE

At SDC, important work is going on to bend technology to the needs of libraries. Some of it might be described as esoteric—advanced theoretical research in linguistics and other disciplines concerned with computer processing of language; and behavioral studies, under such titles as "Empirical Studies of Relevance Assessment," that deal with crucial problems of information use.

Some of it is aimed at problems of specialized, particularly technical, information centers. The specialized centers have no corner on the problems, however; and much of SDC's work in their behalf is transferable to general libraries.

A case in point is a current project, sponsored by the U.S. Office of Education with support from the U.S. Army Technical Library Improvement Studies project, to develop effective techniques and programs for on-the-job training of library personnel. The initial courses will be directed to the skills required in technical libraries.

A study to define the most needed kinds of training has been completed, and three course packages are being developed: one covering technology in libraries, one on reference tools and services, and one dealing with foreign and technical terminology. Several media will be used to permit library personnel—professional and nonprofessional—to assimilate the material through 30-minute lessons during the working day.

It is not hard to imagine that general-library personnel might benefit from some of the same lessons—or similar ones dealing with fundamental or new library skills.

Then there is significant SDC work dealing with basic requirements of general-purpose public and academic libraries. One example is LISTS (Library Information System Time-Sharing)—an independent research project sponsored and conducted by SDC. The goal of LISTS is to provide time-shared computer support for internal functions to libraries that have no computer of their own.

When the LISTS project began in 1967, SDC believed that it was technically feasible to build a computer-based system that would relieve busy library staffs of much of the routine clerical work involved in acquisitions, cataloging, circulation management and serials control. Three developments indicated it: the availability at SDC of the flexible, easy-to-use Time-Shared Data Management System (described in SDC MAGAZINE, June 1968); the advances being made by the Library of Congress and others in formatting large data bases for storage and distribution on magnetic tape; and the advent of computer equipment that could accommodate the large files that would be required.

The question was, would such a system be sufficiently economical and sufficiently more convenient than present methods to be of real value to small and medium-sized libraries that do not now have access to computer support?

To find the answer, SDC developed an initial version of the LISTS system, further simplifying the Time-Shared Data Management System approach so that little except prearranged information must be input by library staff users. Several libraries were then asked to participate in experiments with the system, with SDC offering to develop processes applicable to many functions of their internal operations.

Two public libraries, two junior college libraries, two university libraries and the SDC technical library joined the project—and all agreed to start with the acquisitions function. Experimental use of the system is scheduled to begin in December 1968.

Statistics will be kept to form a basis for evaluating and improving the system to make it more useful and more economical. As SDC and library staff members develop LISTS, they intend to document and publicize their experiences so that the knowledge gained can be appropriately shared by the library community.

IS IT INEVITABLE?

To quote Carlos Cuadra once more: "It is in no way necessary or inevitable that libraries shift the balance of their holdings and services to include microforms, digital information, videotapes, holograms and other trappings of advanced technology. It is not necessary that libraries shift their concept of operations from circulation toward outright distribution. It is not necessary that libraries invest in computers and other paraphernalia to provide users with a higher order of access to reference materials. It is not necessary that libraries become elements of networks for the rapid identification and provision of material to users, regardless of geographical location.

"However, these functions are going to take place; and if the library does not bring them about, some other type of agency will. That agency will then occupy the central role in the information business—the role that was once occupied by the library."

Certainly it is not necessary for libraries to abandon that central role. SDC believes that with appropriate awareness and use of technology libraries can become even more important than they are now.

Library professionals can prepare themselves for the future by first calibrating their knowledge of relevant technology and making sure that it is commensurate with the tasks they will undertake. A second desirable step for those not already involved would be to become associated with one or more of the cooperative or network arrangements that are working in innovative ways—even if the association amounts to little more than watching closely over the shoulder of a sister library.

Finally, concerned professionals should associate themselves with efforts to make nationwide planning for library improvement more effective.

"The need for library improvement is clear," SDC's report to the National Advisory Commission concludes, "and so is the potential contribution of advanced technology. Aggressive, concerted and timely action should be taken now to effect a nationwide improvement of our libraries."

Questions

1. How might standardization of data elements, codes, and terminology influence the impact of computers on libraries?

COMPUTERIZED COST SYSTEM
IN A SMALL PLANT

By JOHN P. MALLOY

FOREWORD

After Modern Machine Works, Inc. had suffered consistent losses for years, a new management team took over the helm in 1964. The group, headed by the author, instituted a long-range plan to restore the Wisconsin company to health. The key to the plan was a so-called manufacturing cost-performance system, a computerized procedure that has its locus in a control center located on the factory floor. The author describes in detail how the system works, and he relates how the company has regained its vitality.

Mr. Malloy was a consultant to Modern Machine Works, Inc. before he became its President and Board Chairman. He has been a Member of the Faculty of Marquette University since 1953, and is currently Professor of Business Administration there, on leave. Mr. Malloy began his career as an electrician and shop foreman in small companies and was Secretary of an International Brotherhood of Electrical Workers local before entering academic life. He has done consulting work for many companies, large and small.

In fiscal 1964 Modern Machine Works, Inc. lost $58,000 on sales of $1,220,000. By the end of that year its working capital had fallen to $94,000, its current assets/liability ratio was 1.6 to 1, and stockholders' equity was $116,000.

In fiscal 1967 the privately owned company earned $52,000 on sales of $1,955,000. At the end of the year working capital stood at $227,000, the current ratio was 2 to 1, and stockholders' equity had been built up to $254,000.

Those cold figures tell only part of the story of the turnaround achieved by this small manufacturer. The attitude of its employees, from management to lathe operators, has been transformed from one of defeatism to one of accomplishment and optimism. The company, formerly entirely dependent on its established business, is now seeking new customers and new markets.

Of course, this turnaround did not just happen. The contributing factors were many, but perhaps the vital one in the financial revival was the establishment of a computerized information system by which quality control was improved and costs were lowered.

This article describes how the program was launched and what its components were, and also touches on some useful by-products of the data bank which formed an integral part of the information system.

Modern Machine Works, located in suburban Milwaukee, makes precision metal shafts for manufacturers of internal combustion engines and pumps, and of air conditioning, refrigeration, air compressor, and farm equipment, who order in lot sizes varying from 50 to 5,000 pieces. The company purchases forgings, castings, and bar stock. It employs about 135 persons.

Founded in 1924, Modern Machine Works prospered for a long time on a reputation for quality and integrity. But after a boom period during World War II, it began to suffer from declining productivity, increasing costs, inadequate marketing, and a lack of valid, up-to-date financial information. Its marketing was particularly weak, since management depended on its acknowledged technical competence to bring in business. The company failed to realize that times had changed and that it had to meet the needs of the market, rather than expect the market to accept what the company had to offer.

All these factors combined to set the stage for a near catastrophe for the company in the early 1960's. The sales volume dropped, losses grew, equipment became obsolete, and management effort was inadequate to halt the plunge.

In the summer of 1964, when the company suffered its seventh year of losses in the past eight years, several capable and experienced managers and technicians were recruited by the company. This new group, together with the best of the old, began to plan the rebuilding of Modern Machine Works. The key team members were the president, the vice president in charge of manufacturing, the director of manufacturing engineering, the vice president in charge of sales, and the company's public accountant.

IMPROVEMENT PROGRAM

The executive group made an intensive survey of the company's operations. Based on its analysis, management formulated a detailed five-year financial plan. It also developed programs in marketing, manufacturing, engineering, and personnel relations.

It quickly became evident that an information system was necessary to provide better financial planning, marketing and sales information and control, production planning, production scheduling and control, and accounting information feedback. What we called the manufacturing cost-performance system was part of accounting information feedback—simply the use of information from the data bank to compare actual results in dollars and cents with what had been planned or budgeted.[1]

Parts of this newly planned information system were already functioning and were made use of. In effect, however, a totally new system was required for improved operational analysis and control.

The manufacturing cost-performance program was given the highest priority for development, installation, and computerization. The reasons for this were:

The development of the rest of the program depended in large measure on the data generated in manufacturing cost analysis.

Inadequate data on measured day-work and an error-prone timekeeping procedure made the existing cost analysis system quite unreliable. It was

---

1. For more detailed information on the entire system and its installation, see my article, "Computerizing the Manufacturing Cost System in a Small Production Shop," *Computers and Automation,* July 1967, p. 18.

particularly important to obtain a better reading of labor costs, since they made up a big part of the sales dollar and since changes in these costs affect profits so profoundly.

The company's competitive situation and the shortage of working capital (lending institutions declines to help because of the dismal profit picture) made necessary a substantial improvement in shop productivity. Faster shipments and higher inventory turnover were essential.

The unreliable cost system put a great deal of guesswork into product pricing.

Some work already had gone into developing the work measurement and cost analysis programs.

PROSPECTS FOR CHANGE

Before I discuss the installation of the manufacturing cost-performance system, it may be helpful to describe the framework within which the quality control function and its information system evolved. Both were facets of a manufacturing engineering program whose primary purpose was to boost the production function to a higher level of technical competence and efficiency.

In the five-year profit improvement plan already mentioned, the manufacturing engineering function was responsible for (1) establishing detailed process control, (2) installing direct and indirect labor standards, (3) vitalizing tool design and establishing tool control, (4) making significant production methods improvement, (5) modernizing facilities, and (6) realigning the inspection facilities and procedures.

As the plans developed by each key executive or manager evolved, priorities had to be established. In the manufacturing engineering program, achieving detailed process control was given the highest priority.

Interestingly, improvement of the inspection function was given substantially lower priority. The reasoning was that the customer was currently receiving a product of satisfactory quality, judging from the low level of customer complaints and returned goods. Technical first-aid could be supplied, we decided, to prevent any "blowout" of quality level during the interim period when engineering drawings were being cleaned up, process control was being established, direct work-measurement coverage completed, and the new standard cost system installed.

Meanwhile, the new information system was being planned, programmed, and made operational. Management anticipated that as these programs interlocked, a detailed picture of in-process quality deviations would emerge. We could then establish priorities to attack quality problems and to reduce in-process scrap and rework losses, both of which were inordinately high and thus a drain on profits.

As our plans developed, we became aware of a serious problem. Because prior intensive efforts aimed at saving the company had met with limited success, the old management team members and the shop crews did not believe that significant corporate change would occur. They had the attitude of losers.

This problem was not unique to Modern Machine Works, of course. A major difficulty that haunts the installation of new programs in any complex environment is the failure to change behavior at all levels. This is imperative if significant improvement is to he achieved. All too often, top management enthusiastically launches cost reduction programs, new systems, and procedures, which are stymied by the calloused attitude of lower level management and the work force. They usually do not frontally oppose such efforts—they simply ignore them. Eventually the programs falter and fail.

There was, however, a fortunate circumstance present at Modern Machine Works. The previous management had committed the company to the introduction of a new incentive system. The installation of an incentive program in the union-organized shop focused the interest of employees on management's plan to establish wage standards and reliable measurements. Considerable groundwork for the incentive plan already had been laid, so we decided to make it central to the reorganization of the production function. After installation of an intensive incentive system "selling" effort and a better human relations program, we were able to enlist the cooperation of the shop employees.

The strategy succeeded, as will be seen later when I discuss the results.

COST-PERFORMANCE PROGRAM

The installation of the manufacturing cost-performance system involved:

1. Establishment of estimated day-work standards where incentive standards were not yet available for direct labor.

2. A new timekeeping system.

3. A new chart of accountability. (For example, when data on scrap and rework costs were fed into the data bank, they were charged to certain accounts according to primary responsibility.)

4. Development of an appropriate input/output document format. (For example, new documents were drawn up on scrap-reporting, identifying the place, cause, and time. Data from these reports also went into the information system.)

5. Completion of the computer program. (Management tried to leave no stone unturned in making the information input complete. As I indicated, product quality was not a weak point in the company's operations—the level of returned goods amounting to less than 1% of sales—but data on returned goods were also fed into the system's memory.)

6. Orientation and training of all managerial and production employees.

Data collection: Any complex information system requires clean input data. To help achieve this, a control center was erected on the factory floor to house the dispatching-timekeeping function. Since the center is close to the production action, decisions influencing input data can be made almost at once.

As a first step, all time cards were removed from the hands of the workers and are now processed only by the timekeeper. The new time tickets are prepunched 80-column tab cards. They are supplied by the production planning department to the control center once or twice a week, when the computer generates the process routings and shop orders.

Certain fixed data are prepunched. Variable data are entered by the timekeeper with a standard key punch. The fixed data, giving information to the data bank for each step of the production process in each shop order, include:

- The part number.
- The operation number.
- The shop order number.
- The order quantity.
- The start day.
- The sales dollars produced.

A time clock with a key punch device records productive and setup time. The device is a job-cost recorder that punches start and stop times, to the nearest tenth or hundredth of an hour, into the standard 80-column tab card. To transfer an employee from one piece of work to another, for instance, the timekeeper selects his prepunched labor card from a job scheduling rack and punches the card for the newly assigned job, and automatically the employee is punched out on the job which he has just completed.

Subsequently, the timekeeper adds what variable data must be inserted to form a complete basic cost input record. This information identifies the operator, pieces produced, setup standard, production standard, load hours, and work station. The worker verifies its accuracy by signing the completed 80-column card. The combination of the computer key punch and the time clock is also used to record daily attendance.

I should note parenthetically that with this timekeeping system the need for subsequent key punching and verification of data for payrolls, financial reports, and so on, is eliminated. The data move directly from the control center to the processing computer.

My description of this and the numerous other data-processing applications in the company might lead one to think that large amounts of computer time are needed. But only four hours of rented time a week on an IBM 1401 are required. The budget for data processing is about $850 a month.

Charge-back system: Apart from its role in the work assignment process, the principal function of the control center is to allocate costs in the corporate chart of accounts.

Every worker in the unionized work force is assigned as either a direct or an indirect worker. In the control center all direct labor costs are ascribed to productive labor or setup labor, to an indirect account, or to one of four loss accounts: nonproductive, rework, nonstandard, or unearned guarantee. The authority to assign labor costs to these accounts is divided among several managers.

Each foreman has the authority to assign a worker under his direction to a variety of tasks as required by production scheduling. The foreman may not, however, determine to what account the worker's time will be charged. The determination of the worker's time as being either productive or setup is done according to the routing which the process engineer responsible for the part has planned.

When a foreman shifts a direct worker to an indirect task (for example, preventive maintenance) or to a nonproductive job (such as machine repair), the timekeeper assigns the work to the proper indirect or nonproductive account. To charge specific responsibility and/or cause, he uses the five-digit numbers available to him as part of the variable input on the time card. (I shall discuss these numbers shortly.) The three other loss accounts are handled this way:

1. An inspector assigns the appropriate account number for all *rework*. He also specifies the responsibility for the quality deviation incurred, such as vendor failure or improper machining by an operator. When additional operations are necessary, the inspector assigns the extra cost to the account number responsible.

2. If a *nonstandard* condition arises that results in a greater direct labor cost, that portion of the additional productive or setup time to be allocated as loss can be authorized only by the industrial engineer responsible for the work standard. Thus if excessive material hardness is discovered, the engineer verifies that extra work will be necessary and makes the charge.

3. The *unearned guarantee* condition reflects a loss incurred when a worker performs less than 100% of standard on either a productive or a setup operation. The pieces actually produced by an operator are compared with the engineered work standard.

There are several other variables besides worker time that form inputs in the charge-back system. During every shift an inspector assigns the responsibility for each one, using a five-digit account number. For instance, he assesses responsibility for excess costs related to scrap and salvage of parts. Another input is the analysis of costs arising from either reworking or scrapping returned goods with the reasons why it was necessary. Because of the sales and customer service implications, this input is the responsibility of the head of the quality assurance function.

The five-digit number on the time card serves as the numerical designation of responsibility for the cost of labor and materials (including the deviations from standard) for entry into the information system.

The first digit pertains to costs associated with quality deviations, which are assigned to one of five categories: operator failure, job failure, machine tool failure, tooling failure, or planning failure. The second digit specifies account responsibility by manager. With this control, budgets can be more accurately established, and cost and quality variances by manager and department can be periodically scrutinized.

The last three digits are used to pinpoint more narrowly the cause of a cost deviation. For example, when a charge-back is made reflecting a quality deviation caused by improper material, the excess cost is assigned to any one of five accounts: improper stock allowance, casting porosity, distortion, improper chemistry, or improper hardness.

Data output: Out of the wealth of information input, the computer generates what we call "quality reports" on a daily, weekly, monthly, quarterly, or annual basis. In addition, certain information is called out at the end of a shop order. If a problem is suspected, it can be selectively monitored on either a daily or a weekly basis. Reports which are or can be generated include those dealing with:

- Operator quality level.
- Work center quality level.
- Factory performance quality level.
- Part quality performance.
- Product quality by customer.
- Machine tool quality level.
- Supplier quality level.

- Material scrap by category.
- Material quality.
- Material quality by supplier.
- Quality by tool, jig, or fixture.
- Quality by engineering plan (such as process, standard, or tool design).
- Quality by inspection equipment.

With all of this information available, it is obvious that management might become inundated with paper. To avoid this, detailed information is generated only according to the exception principle—that is, management calls for a report summarizing a problem only when gross trend data, which are produced routinely on a weekly and monthly basis, begin to indicate a change in, say, quality level.

Apart from the continuous monitor which the data provide, the most practical use of the information is in pinpointing the responsibility for problems by function, machine, occurrence, and so on. In effect, management can disperse the fog that obscures its vision of production problems.

Such detailed facts also help line and staff people isolate and attack problems with greater assurance. For instance, daily shop performance reports not only are delivered to the executives' desks each morning but also are posted in each department. Thus a foreman knows how each worker performed on his shift (there are night and day shifts) the previous day. John Smith and his foreman both know that he produced X dollars against Y dollars of inventory and Z dollars of total labor cost, and that John had A amount of down time and B amount of setup time during his shift. The foreman can quickly spot deviations from the norm on productivity, rework, indirect costs, and other loss categories by operator, job, process, and machine.

Finally, managers and technicians use the data to project results of current operations and to forecast trends. After-the-fact analysis compares results promised with results actually achieved. In financial planning, for example, management uses computer output in attempting to isolate the key elements in profitability, variable cost factors, the monthly profit and loss statement and balance sheet, and the backlog.

PROGRAM RESULTS

The effects of the profit improvement program have been sweeping—reaching into every facet of Modern Machine Works' operation. A sense of confidence, optimism, and pride has taken the place of defeatism on the part of employees from top to bottom.

At the beginning of this article I outlined the healthy profit and balance sheet picture which the company now boasts compared with three years ago. Further substantial growth is anticipated in the current year. Other results of the profit improvement program include:

- A significant drop in the breakeven point, from $1.96 million in fiscal 1964 to $1.67 million in fiscal 1967. (We hope to achieve a breakeven point of $1.55 million this year.)
- An improvement in the delivery lead time, from 8.2 weeks to 6.3 weeks.

● A step-up in inventory turnover, from 6.4 times a year in 1964 to 8.2 times in 1967.

● A rise in productive capacity by the end of fiscal 1967 to 36% above the capacity three years earlier. (We are projecting a further 20% increase by the end of 1968, and we estimate that the company can produce $3 million in volume out of the plant's present 33,000 square-foot area.)

● A heightened sense of the importance of costs in relation to profits. (This is partly the result of the availability to all levels of the company of a wealth of operational information.)

● New interest in the company on the part of the financial community. (No longer are loans impossible to get. The company has obtained long-term loans for capital investment and an adequate line of credit.)

Though it is difficult to reduce to numbers, there has also been a significant improvement in quality. The reason, of course, is that prior to the installation of the information system the production data were incomplete and lacked reliability. The results are:

The detailed financial data, pinpointing excess costs of inadequate machines and quantifying operator and production planning performance, have better enabled management to take corrective action to improve quality.

In-process scrap and rework have been reduced at least 30%.

Suppliers are doing a better job because of closer scrutiny. Moreover, they are assuming certain costs resulting from their own deficiencies which Modern Machine Works formerly absorbed because of lack of reliable information.

New and more positive relationships have been established with customers' quality control departments. Their inspectors and managers recognize the improvements in production performance and information, and therefore have increased confidence in Modern Machine Works as a supplier.

Organizationally, the company has changed too, from a line-oriented operation to a line-and-staff-oriented one. More important is the philosophical reorganization, from a product orientation to a market orientation. The company knows which business it should go after and which its does not want. In the old days, a customer would come to the company with an engineering drawing that might be sound in design but costly or impractical to produce. Now the company attempts to discover the real needs of the customer, and it employs manufacturing engineers who can fabricate a metal configuration that is both functionally effective and practical from a cost point of view.

CONCLUDING NOTE

Although Modern Machine Works has benefited greatly from its computer-oriented information system, this system is but part of a larger effort to redirect the company's energies and resources. So one must be cautious in trying to point to a particular management action that caused certain results. I can state unequivocally, however, that the computer has proved a powerful, economically feasible tool at Modern Machine Works for analyzing costs and enabling management to upgrade quality.

Certainly this experience should demonstrate that, with proper planning and execution, the small manufacturer can make the computer and its related systems a productive tool in the years ahead.

———————

Questions:

1. What is the "exception principle" of reports?

2. Implementing a computer system requires much attention to detail. Discuss the advantages which accrue to a company due to this forced attention to detail.

ELECTRONIC DATA PROCESSING FOR THE CORRESPONDENT BANK

By JOHN B. TINGLEFF

They're natural partners—banking and electronic data processing. Reduced to simplest characteristics, banking depends on the manipulation of data, and the computer is the most effective data manipulator yet devised. Consequently, the question facing the correspondent bank is not *whether* to automate but *how* to automate most effectively.

The right decision for a bank, whether large or small, can be made only after the bank's objectives are defined and the various automation methods are evaluated. Once the method has been determined, one must assess the economics quoted by vendors.

Those of us who offer computer services to correspondent banks like to feel that our services were chosen by bankers who made an informed decision after evaluating the alternatives of acquiring their own equipment, joining other banks in a joint venture, or using an independent service bureau. This article will attempt to show some of the problems and advantages of the correspondent's use of a larger bank's computer center.

It may be of value to look first at the intangibles that the correspondent bank should investigate. By intangibles I mean those factors beyond initial costs or quantitative data. In time, these intangibles will have a direct effect on the correspondent's EDP program, and consequently on the bank's profit.

The following are among the most important points correspondent prospects should examine before choosing their servicing bank.

• *Look for profit-orientation.* The correspondent should determine how the larger bank is organized to perform its automated services. In the long run, it is profit that provides the incentive for superior EDP services. Is the EDP arm of the larger bank a sideline? Are correspondent services offered as "loss leaders," as lures to gain other business? Or is the EDP installation a profit-oriented division in its own right? (If not, I doubt very much if it is going to be the right bank for the correspondent.)

The application of electronic technology grows at a tremendous rate and at great cost, yet the correspondent must look beyond today's problems. The correspondent will be served best by a bank that intends to make a profit because profit will provide the incentive to offer the best possible services, both now and in the future.

• *Talk with other users.* It would be advisable for any correspondent to contact other users of the larger bank's services. Most banks in the EDP service

---

Reprinted with permission from the August, 1968 issue of The Magazine of Bank Administration, a publication of the Bank Administration Institute.

field are more than happy to provide a list of their present customers. A frank discussion with existing users will acquaint the correspondent prospect with the problems that the other user has faced, how the servicing bank worked with them and how well the relationship has stood the test of time. In this connection, we encourage a community of interest and interchange of ideas among Continental's users. Such cross-fertilization of ideas is in the best interest of all concerned as there is certainly no monopoly on creative thinking.

• *Check the experience level of the vendor's staff and the support available.* The correspondent should find out how much help he can expect from the servicing bank, especially during the conversion period.

While the qualifications of the salesman are important, of equal or greater importance is the experience of the customer service representatives. These men adapt the system to handle the detailed requirements of the correspondent, guide the correspondent through all the preparatory work prior to conversion, consult with the user in the selection of equipment and design of forms, and instruct user personnel in the new set of disciplines required in an electronic environment.

To convert a non-automated bank to EDP operations is a highly detailed task. Enormous amounts of detailed planning and work go into teaching the corredponsent's people the disciplines of a computer, familiarizing them with the reports they are going to receive and how to use them, teaching them how to provide the servicing bank with necessary data and much more.

At this point, vendor experience pays big dividends to the prospect; bank operations experience in patricular. The correspondent prospect should weigh this specific experience factor carefully.

• *Look for help in training.* Training aid becomes a highly valuable intangible "plus." Correspondents find this particularly the case as the bank enters on-line processing.

Larger banks can offer teller training to familiarize the correspondent's people with the new terminals. The first time the correspondent puts a teller on-line with a computer, he or she may be scared of the terminal. It's a perfectly natural reaction, and the servicing bank knows it.

Management training is equally important. The computer will provide management with timely, well organized reports that eliminate the assembling of much data and permits managers to manage more effectively. In many systems, bank management may shape certain reports into formats that are most meaningful for them. The value of these by-products may be lost unless management and clerical personnel are trained in the effective use of the new system.

Although training helps bring success to any business, it becomes particularly important in an automated environment. For the uninitiated, whether tellers or top executives, training helps overcome the mental hurdles that come with the computer-dominated world of EDP.

• *Investigate the larger bank's backup capabilities.* Look for the standby equipment of the servicing bank. This means equipment with a compatible configuration that can meet your deadlines if one computer shuts down. It's like having a spare tire; ready to resume operation with the least delay. Immediate availability of backup becomes increasingly important as we move into an on-line environment.

• *Transportation—at least for a while—can be a problem.* Transportation can place strict limits on services to correspondent banks. Movement of data can limit the choice of vendors to those in the correspondent's immediate area because the checks must be transported from the correspondent to the processing bank. The correspondent prospect should assess quite carefully the availability, reliability and cost of this transportation.

As more and more services go on-line, ground transportation will become less significant in the total automation program of the correspondent bank. Recent cost trends also indicate that the line charges associated with on-line applications will be reduced as will the cost of the interface devices.

In the meantime, we must innovate. Recent developments also indicate that timely ground transportation could become a less significant factor in the traditional DDP application. We are now intercepting 65% of all DDP items at the Federal Reserve Bank, and these items are first delivered to the correspondent after posting.

For several years, a large number of correspondent banks nationwide have been reducing their on-us items to paper tape and transmitting the data to the processing bank. Continental combines paper tape transmission of over-the-counter items with Fed Intercept, and the results have been very satisfactory to one correspondent located more than 150 miles from our computer center. In the future a correspondent will be able to receive information on the status of a checking account by either a teller terminal or an audio response unit. This electronic link would serve both parties by eliminating some of the bulky printouts now associated with DDP, as well as extending the time period for delivery of the remaining reports and the checks themselves.

It is to be expected that we will see more and more electronic data transmission between banks. The correspondent should bear this in mind as he looks for a servicing bank. Document transportation will fade as a problem. Therefore, the future planning of the servicing bank becomes just that much more important.

• *Beware of "Excess Time."* Parkinson's Law applies to the use of computers just as it does to most of man's other pursuits. Work—even electronic work—expands to fill available time. Most banks that have computers continually devise an endless stream of internal and external applications for conversion to electronic data processing. Consequently, I would advise the correspondent to beware of the "extra time" trap.

While both the processing and user bank can enter into an arrangement to use "extra time" on the larger bank's computer, this arrangement can become progressively less attractive to both parties as expanding requirements of the processing bank eat into the reservoir of unused time.

Before entering into any arrangement of this type, pause and calculate the total automation requirements of both banks and determine if, in fact, there will be "extra time" three to five years from now. If not, select a processing bank that adds the requirements of customer service applications to their own and schedules the arrival of additional computer capacity to provide for customer service processing as a part of their total electronic requirements.

These seven factors should be considered as the correspondent bank looks deeper into the problems it will face with EDP. Choose the servicing bank with care. Weigh the intangibles.

THE BANK'S EDP CENTER

From the operating man's viewpoint, let's examine the care and feeding of a bank's electronic data processing center. For those who have not had itimate acquaintance with EDP, I hope that my comments will be revealing.

Bank data processing is inherently a nighttime operation. Although a bank might capture some data during the day, it is after-hours that the bank must go into main sorting and posting operations so that it can have updated records ready for business next day. Until a bank goes into large-scale EDP, management may have no idea of the size and complexity of problems caused by stretching its supervisory staff across a multi-shift operation. Staffing for the odd hours presents a continual personnel squeeze.

During daytime hours at Continental Bank, our computer complex concentrates on internal operations including trust department and customer service applications. During the night, the center swings into service for our correspondent banks and updates our own account records.

Does the smaller correspondent bank want to assume this round-the-clock staffing and operating responsibility? Has it investigated the ballooning costs that go with three-shift operations? Or does it want to tie in with a system that is already in operation?

Certainly, for many banks—$35 million or larger, let's say—good equipment is available. Where these banks are most likely to run into difficulty is in the use of the equipment. And here is where the problems of the programming staff enter—problems of recruiting, hiring, training, motivating and keeping good people.

Banks compete aggressively for the best programming and support people they can obtain. And these people do not move to a new job just for more money. Like everyone else, the electronic staff wants to be well paid, but they also want a stimulating environment in which to work. They are basically a scientific-oriented group. Top electronics staff people are inclined to be explorers. And these are the individuals who will do the most creative and effective jobs on new computer applications. The smaller bank will find it difficult to compete for this type of person, not only in compensation but also in the scope of the job to be done.

Responsiveness is critical if any electronics program is to meet the user's requirements. None of the automation alternatives available today provide the correspondent any guarantee that his requirements will be fulfilled. A banker can find himself tied into an unyielding strait jacket if his work is being processed by either a service bureau or processing bank whose system does not meet the correspondent's requirements. Similarly, a participant in a joint venture can find his alternatives restricted if the other members don't like his approach or don't wish to offer customer services that appeal to him.

However, owning a computer is not necessarily the way to solve this problem. If the owner's programming staff is not sufficiently skilled and the owner is forced to depend upon outside software suppliers (either equipment manufacturers or outsiders), has he acquired the responsiveness he has every right to expect?

Responsiveness from a servicing bank depends on how well the services available fit the correspondent's needs. If the fit isn't exact, perhaps the supplier can modify his services to suit the correspondent. While conducting the search for a compatible supplier, the correspondent banker must match the future plans of the supplier with his own. If they agree, their mutual needs of the 1970s will be well accommodated.

Of course, I am not saying that a bank should not acquire its own equipment, use a service bureau or enter into a joint venture with other banks. But I am calling attention to factors—people factors, availability factors, service factors—that go beyond a cost-of-equipment-alone type of reasoning.

CORRESPONDENT ADVANTAGES

Speaking positively, what are the advantages for the correspondent bank that uses the services of a larger bank's EDP installation?

First, the servicing bank assumes operating responsibility for reliable and economical service. Prices must be competitive, and the economies of scale from using large systems can be passed back to the correspondent.

Second, it's the servicing bank's job to keep up with the latest developments in the EDP field. It's a competitive race to acquire and implement knowledge in an expanding discipline. For example, Continental Bank recently introduced on-line savings, both within our bank and to a growing number of correspondents.

Third, looking to the future, the servicing bank must consider the needs of its own business and those of the correspondents as well. The correspondents' business is not "add-on" business; their needs are considered from the very beginning. This brings me to a major point: The orientation or attitude of both partners.

Most banks in the past have been functionally-oriented instead of customer-oriented. To illustrate, it is possible that a bank customer's name may appear in many places—checking account, savings, mortgage, instalment loan, trust and more. Now, with the aid of the computer, we are beginning to bring all this information together, to consider what the bank can do for the customer—at a profit, of course—but organizing the bank's records toward this end, not merely to grind out the paperwork piecemeal.

The vocabulary of the banker has been expanded to include new terms—central information file, management information system, time sharing, etc. The concept is essentially the same, the focus being on the bank's services to the customer . . . or "how can we, as a financial service, offer more useful help to the customer while at the same time making a profit for ourselves?" As a result bankers are becoming less functionally-oriented and more customer-oriented.

Central information files, management information systems and time sharing have broad implications for correspondent processing. As the servicing bank develops these techniques and uses large scale common systems to fulfill both the requirements of the correspondents and themselves, the capability of the processing bank's management information system can be extended to the correspondents through time sharing. An early example is the on-line savings system, but other capabilities lie just ahead. As correspondents gain access to a common data base—the central file—through time sharing, each will be able to manipulate this information to suit its own needs. (Within the limitations, of course, that such use should not be anti-competitive or involve any breach of confidence. Effective safeguards against unauthorized access to or improper use of data information banks should be an integral part of all time sharing arrangements.)

Time sharing will have broad significance for correspondent banks, particularly for management reports. Today, the computer assimilates information into predetermined report formats and prints out the information. On-line service gives instant access to a portion of the file, and so makes the report print-out secondary. With time sharing, as we develop a central file, we can develop much broader information to suit individual needs.

Let us say, for example, that a customer is at an officer's desk and wishes to work out the mathematics of a leasing transaction—including residuals, investment tax credit, rates of interest and more. This could be entered into a terminal, and the computer used as a calculating instrument. Or perhaps a trust officer wants to know how many trust accounts have a certain stock and what the tax ramifications would be on each if the stock were to be sold. Computers plus a central data file make this type of report feasible.

As the larger bank develops these systems, the correspondents could have equal access to them. If the correspondents have selected an automation alternative which is not equally responsive to their long term needs, they will still be processing today's transactions in a functionally-oriented data processing environment. Competitively, such correspondents would be left far behind.

When considering automation alternatives, don't overlook customer services. Just as banks evaluate the automation alternatives available to them, so bank customers search for the answer to the automation dilemma. Many larger banks offer business services in conjunction with their correspondents. The correspondents' customers can avail themselves of the full range of the larger bank's customer services. Competitively, can any bank afford to take care of its own automation requirements and at the same time fail to consider the needs of its customers?

Payroll accounting is one example. The local bank, through its larger correspondent, can provide this extremely comprehensive service to its customers. Payrolls can be very complex with taxes to be figured (often for different states), changes in wage rates, piece work, shift differentials, employee benefits and more. Although the larger bank has the computer capacity to handle this puzzle, the correspondent has intimate knowledge of the local customer's problems. Working together, the two banks can perform a distinct service for the customer, and at a profit as well.

In this discussion, I have tried to show the pitfalls as well as the advantages when correspondent banks use the EDP services offered by a larger bank. Naturally, after some experience in this field, I have a bias toward this service. At the same time, I realize EDP is developing so rapidly that we will see great advances in the next 10 years. I feel that this growth—fueled by profit-oriented EDP service—is essential if we are to match the growing needs of our customers.

Questions:

1. List the important points a correspondent prospect should examine in choosing a bank to provide computer services.

2. Are the above mentioned points important to other users of computer services? Explain.

COMPUTER ON DEADLINE

Neither sun, nor surf, nor sand stays Miamians from their accustomed rounds of reading the morning *Herald*. Even the tourists in the nation's winter fun capital quickly pick up the habit.

This bright star in the firmament of Knight newspapers glows farther afield, too. Every day it reaches points as distant and disparate as the statehouse in Tallahassee and doorsteps in San Juan, Puerto Rico. And Air Editions are found in most other Latin American countries.

The *Miami Herald* Publishing Company has 1,300 employees, 2,800 independent carriers, and maintains 15 full-time bureaus to provide local news and pictures for special editions. Besides running 12 editions of its own publication (359,959 daily, 434,872 Sundays), the company prints its afternoon rival, the Miami *News* (110,118 daily) and four subsidiary community papers (104,500 weekly).

If a formula for such success could be constructed, certainly one of its chief ingredients would be the attitude of the *Herald* management toward change.

Several years ago management agreed that automation offered an antidote to the increasing costs of running a newspaper.

They built an imposing blue-white-orange plant on Biscayne Bay, rolled in 63 gleaming white Goss presses (and provided expansion room for 72 more), refurbished the stereotype and engraving departments with new equipment, and added a photocomposition department to step up advertising production.

And, in 1963, they brought in an IBM 1620 computer, one of the very first installed at a newspaper and one of the pioneer machines for much of the early development of what is now IBM's hyphenation and justification program. The same 1620 was also the vehicle for IBM's initial work in computerized photocomposition.

A flesh-and-blood symbol of the *Miami Herald* responsiveness to change is youthful Ken Schurr, Jr., formerly data processing manager, who was elevated recently to advanced systems development manager. At 31, Mr. Schurr directs one of the most advanced newspaper computer installations in the country.

In little more than three years, he and his staff have literally restructured the entire accounting procedure from a "paper and pencil" operation to a tight-knit system now built around a System/360 computer.

Reprinted with permission from the September 1967 issue of DATA PROCESSOR, a publication of IBM.

(The system, a Model 30, replaced an IBM 1460 last year.) This has meant, in the classified advertising area alone, a 50 per cent reduction in credit losses, an 80 per cent slash in manual measuring and marketing tasks, and attendant healthy savings in dollars and time.

THE HOT AND THE COLD

Meanwhile, on the production side, there are today two IBM 1620 computers controlling the automatic setting of "hot" type (for news and editorial copy) and "cold" type, or photocomposition (for advertising and display copy).

Interestingly, the typesetting side of the *Herald's* conversion to computers was less of a problem than the commercial changeover. "The computer," says Ken Schurr, "fit logically into the work flow of getting words into type."

On the business side, the classified advertising department was another matter. Into this pressure-cooker department—which processed thousands of ads daily but had no formalized procedures for doing things manually—came the computer. So a great deal of time was spent training everyone, impressing on each person the relationship of his particular job to the total job; and above all, impressing on each individual that if a procedure changed everyone else should know about it.

During the original education job, Ken Schurr remembers, he discussed with the sales manager what kinds of reports he felt he needed from classified statistics.

"At first," said Mr. Schurr, "all we could agree on was that the computer was like a bulldozer, it could either build us a mountain or dig us a hole we could fall into. The last thing we wanted to do was start producing and carting in a lot of meaningless reports. So, before we ever wrote a program, we took great pains to define what the sales manager needed in terms of what we had available."

Today, the sales manager knows and gets the kinds of reports he wants. To cite a few, he gets comparative lineage reports and order counts for every edition; he scans reports on competitive papers with comparative figures day-by-day, monthly and for the current and preceding years, and with percentage (plus or minus) calculations indicating exception areas; he studies salesman productivity reports showing the number of ads and linage sold for one-time, two-time, three-time, or more, insertions; and he reviews ledger accounts comparative reports, which give a detailed breakdown of each ledger customer for each salesman. Besides acting as a detailed "hard copy" ledger of each account for reference by the salesmen, this report projects the life of contracts, and points out, on an exception basis, those accounts that require immediate attention—showing, for example, that if a customer only maintains his present linage, he will fall short of the agreed-upon minimum amount of advertising he has contracted for.

The whole *Herald* classified procedure is now a well-oiled operation. For one thing there is real control over the application. On the bookshelf in Ken Schurr's office are a red-jacketed classified procedure manual and a green-jacketed retail advertising procedure manual written in-house by the data processing group and the *Herald's* training department.

"If an applicant comes in today for a job as ad taker in the classified phone room," Ken Schurr says, "she could read the chapter on how to take ads and sit down and go to work." In pre-EDP days, management statistics of any value for classified were sparse. The best that was done was a yardstick measurement of the paper every day, reporting whether linage was up or down. To ask where and why, was to ask a great deal of the system.

Today, the System/360 generates a variety of reports to help the daily handling of 10,000 classified and 500 retail display ads—from conception to billing. The computer is so proficient at getting the bills out, following up, and checking credit it has freed personnel to do a much more thorough job of researching the special problems and exceptions, where, in the old days, many of these things were left undone for lack of time.

On the fourth floor of the plant at No. 1 Herald Plaza, two 1620 computers run unattended in a locked room. There is no need for anyone in the room because a special device, called a "remote resetter," allows staff members to reset the console from remote locations.

"Once an hour," says Ken Schurr, "someone takes out a stack of cards, brings them to the System/360 room and 'plays' them on our 360 to check the credit on the classified lists. Incidentally, when we get our second 360 (next year), we'll be out of the business of using those cards, because the system will handle the entire production-accounting classified cycle in one pass."

Although one 1620 is basically dedicated to hot type and the other to cold type, in practice the two computers are interchangeable. In the heat of the daily publishing battle on the hot type front, both systems are pressed into service. During the peak period on the photocomp side, which occurs at night, both are often teamed to get the job done. If one of the computers goes down for a time, the "hots" and the "colds" may have their jurisdictional differences, but such occurrences are infrequent and, in Ken Schurr's view, have never created serious problems.

One reason downtime is not a serious problem at the *Herald* is because the 32-man data processing group has worked very closely with IBM Customer Engineers explaining the nature of their requirements. "They fully appreciate the fact," says Mr. Schurr, "that we can't send out 360,000 little slips of paper some morning saying 'Sorry, folks—there's no *Herald* today because the computer broke down!'" When the *Herald* makes an infrequent trouble call, it expects—and gets—a response within 10 minutes—either from a 24-hour answering service, or (as usually happens) in the person of a radio-dispatched Customer Engineer.

NICE CLEAN APPROACH

When the second System/360 Model 30 arrives to replace the twin 1620s, it will be an important way station along what Ken Schurr calls "the nice clean approach we are now following." From there the push will be made to refine the classified advertising operation to the point where ads are captured directly on-line to the computer via visual display terminals. As information is typed, it will appear on the screen, enabling the ad taker to see the ad text justified and hyphenated. This will allow the ad taker to quote actual linage and ad cost over the telephone. Meanwhile, the computer will check the customer's credit, and if a problem exists, the customer can be notified immediately. The display screen will also enable the ad taker to call forth for viewing any ads the customer may currently have running, killing or correcting them as the situation warrants.

Ken Schurr is an earnest advocate of high-speed photocomposition type as opposed to hot metal, and he thinks computer systems and supporting applications will lead the movement. "We're printing newspapers today," he says, "the way John Gutenberg printed his Bible. We engrave some characters into metal and squash some paper down on top of them. When you compare our industry with the airline industry, for example, over the last 20 years, you get a better idea of how little we've changed."

He also believes that running a newspaper is, in a real sense, like the old textbook operations research game. "You have men and machines, and you have to figure out the best way to use them to get the product out for the least cost. We play that game every day.

"The way it works now, when the paper is late, nobody really knows why unless it's obvious, and they don't know it's going to be late until it actually happens." Which brings up what Ken Schurr considers to be another logical EDP goal: production scheduling.

A budget of what tomorrow's paper is going to look like can be fed into the computer, and the system, using mathematical formulas, figures out what combination of men and machines it will take to do the job. And then, as things actually occur the next day, as stories start to come in, go through the computer to be typeset, go back out to be put into pages, as the pages get rolled, and the plates get locked up on the presses, all of this data can be captured as it occurs. The computer would be in the business of reporting to production management every 30 minutes, or even 15.

"And when a problem popped," Mr. Schurr concludes, "we would know exactly where it happened and what to do about it."

Questions:

1. At one time the classified ad section of the newspaper had very informal and unstructured operating procedures. Discuss the impact of the computer on this environment.

2. "Sorry, folks — there's no Herald today because the computer broke down!" is a quote which reveals the importance of the role of the computer in this newspaper organization. Discuss this point in reference to the newspaper industry and expand it to other types of operations?

WHERE EDP SPURS DIVERSITY

In 1918, two young men painted their names on the glass door of a small office near New York City's Bowery and announced that Fisher-Stevens was in the direct-mail business.

The firm began modestly enough. It had one account, a wartime charity, and no staff. In order to address envelopes containing the charitable appeals, Fisher-Stevens would recruit scriveners from the Bowery in the morning, equip them with pen and ink, trays of envelopes, and lists of addresses, and pay them off at night.

When the war ended, so did the charity account, but Fisher-Stevens, Inc. was just beginning. During the next 50 years the firm grew as the direct-mail advertising business grew (the entire industry now mails some 22 billion pieces a year). In the process, Fisher-Stevens made two kinds of moves. It moved physically as its needs demanded (first to a more fashionable uptown address, and then 13 years ago, to its present northern New Jersey home of Clifton). And, more significantly, it moved technologically—from hand-addressed envelopes to address plates and, five years ago, to computers.

But unlike the move to address-plate machines, which simply speeded the addressing process, the switch to computers has also opened whole new areas of collateral activity for Fisher-Stevens, including sales forecasting, promotion effectiveness testing and other operations research activities and even a computer-programming school. And with the growth in activity has come a growth in computing power: first one IBM 1401, then another, then an IBM 1410, and more recently a switch to two System/360 Model 30s and a System/360 Model 40. It is as though a rail splitter acquired a power saw and suddenly discovered the rich diversification of lumbering.

THE INITIAL NEED

The evolution began with the need to maintain the many lists of names that are the stock-in-trade of direct mail advertising houses. Fisher-Stevens specializes in lists for the pharmaceutical industry; its lists thus consist of names of physicians, dentists, drug stores, hospitals, and others in the medical world. After the pen-and-ink days, each name and address was embossed in a metal plate: Fisher-Stevens had perhaps a million names on file, and they were

Reprinted with permission from the June 1967 issue of DATA PROCESSOR, a publication of IBM.

represented by two million plates, because the plates were replicated and filed according to several profile features: one set according to name, another by state, another by county, a fourth by medical specialty, and the fifth by volume of prescriptions written.

The advantage of the multi-file arrangement was, of course, that an advertiser could specify mailing targets in terms of profile features and thus be sure of reaching, for example, New England pediatricians without wasted mailings to geriatric clinics in New Mexico.

Maintaining the currency of address plates for a million names was, on the other hand, a gargantuan task. As each of the persons represented on the plates moved from one place to another, changed affiliation, or died, five plates had to be changed. Since there were some 5,000 changes a week, 25,000 plates had to be tracked to their cabinets, traced to their drawers, pulled from their slots, repunched, replaced, refiled. And that discouraging task was further complicated because no cabinet ever held its full complement of assigned drawers: some might be at one end of the plant on one job, others elsewhere on others. In its pre-EDP days, Fisher-Stevens had 450 employees, almost as many of them engaged in the secondary task of maintaining the two million plates as performing the primary job of using them to address mail.

The sheer physical labor of maintaining and manipulating the address plates was all but eliminated in one swoop when, in 1962, the firm installed an IBM 1401 computer. The million-odd names on their mailing lists were magnetically recorded on tape in category master files, each name followed by profile data. The information a tape can hold is virtually unlimited; it is, in any event, far greater than that representable by the tabbing systems in address plates. Not only could name, address, specialty and prescription-writing activity be noted, but a long list of additional information: the physician's type of practice, whether he works in a hospital or teaches; not only his specialty but his secondary interests—he might, for example, be a pediatrician with secondary interests in dermatology, or a general practitioner with secondary interests in orthopedics. Information can also be maintained on the medical school attended, the year graduated, membership on various medical boards, and so on.

INFORMATION WITH INSIGHTS

All the information is professional, none is personal, and all gives some insight into the physician's characteristics as a user of ethical drugs. A medical school professor, for example, may not write many prescriptions but he influences those who do or will; a dermatologist, obviously, would be interested in some preparations but not others; a recent graduate might be more inclined to use some kinds of therapy than others.

With that finer-grained information, Fisher-Stevens could now supply additional services to its clients and could help them narrow their marketing targets. No longer need they expend the same promotional effort on a surgeon as on a general practitioner when the one might utterly disregard what might deeply interest the other. Manufacturers could tailor their promotional efforts almost to the individual physician. And having decided upon the interest profile of those it wants to reach, Fisher-Stevens simply programs its computer to search for those and none others. (As it happens, selecting from the master list was the most time-consuming job the 1401 had to do, and so it was programmed to select names for five different mailing jobs at once.)

And while one 1401 maintained the files and compiled the mailing lists, the other, taking the output from the first as its own input, printed the labels to be used for mailing. Working together, the 1401s facilitated the mailing of some 150-million pieces of mail a year, though Fisher-Stevens has an annual capacity (unexploited because of the seasonal nature of the business) of twice that number. But even working at that higher figure, the computers had sufficient unused power to support a rapidly diversifying range of activities.

SALES CALL REPORTING

The first of the new activities was sales call reporting, the notes that any good salesman makes about his customers, notes that enable him and his company to plan a more effective sales strategy. The detail man, as pharmaceutical salesmen are called, reports the physician's reaction to his company and its products, whether he left samples and how many, whether the physician is receptive to personal sales calls or might better be approached by mail; whether he dispenses his own prescriptions, and even how he reacts to competitors and their products and promotions.

In the system Fisher-Stevens now establishes for its clients, the detail men have no need to write out the information but merely to check appropriate boxes on printed forms. These are fed to an IBM 1418 Optical Reader, which scans up to 400 forms a minute and translates what it reads directly into machine language for the computers' magnetic tapes.

The tapes are then used to prepare individual records for the detail men, constituting for them a running diary of the physicians they have called upon and when another call was due, what the physician's attitudes and needs were, and even his nurse's or receptionist's name. The taped information also yields summary records for sales managers, keeping them apprised of the progress of their sales force.

But a new wrinkle of inestimable value also emerges from the detailed and current records a computer system has made possible. So rich is the information attached to each name on a mailing list that marketing programs can be built around them. Some physicians, for example, may not want detail men calling; they are reached by mail. The mailing piece might include a reply card with which the physician can request samples of a preparation; he might want a dozen samples sent him every two weeks. Fisher-Stevens programs its system accordingly. With the sixth such mailing (the computer keeping track of how many mailings have gone out), he might receive another reply card to check off other products of interest, or to report his opinion about the one he'd been getting. If he returns the card, he goes on another list for further mailings; if he doesn't, he goes on still another for a different kind of mailing. Such a branched program might be invoked for several of a company's products. This will constitute a dense network of communications tailored to the changing attitudes of tens of thousands of doctors with varying specialties in all kinds of environments.

And the manufacturer can see what is happening to any of his products in any sales territory—not merely sales figures, but the facts behind the figures. He can see why a particular physician is not using his product and so act accordingly through the coordinated efforts of his advertising, marketing and sales departments. As a result, those departmental efforts of Fisher-Stevens' clients are coordinated as never before possible. And the time between the introduction of a product and its wide-spread use has shrunk appreciably.

The experience and programming knowhow of Fisher-Stevens acquired in its call-report service is applicable to other areas of data processing. The company is now engaged in development and processing activities for a wide range of EDP applications. Subscription fulfillment, for example, is an area of operations fraught with no fewer variables than those of pharmaceutical marketing.

To most subscribers, the relations they have with a magazine are simple: they fill out a subscription order blank, check a box saying "Bill me" or "Payment enclosed" and forget the whole transaction, except for the one day a month or week when the magazine arrives.

To the publisher, however, the relationship is far more complex: he has, for one thing, thousands or millions of subscribers. They subscribed at different times for different periods at different rates; they paid or didn't pay; they have to be billed or told their subscriptions are expiring. Then they have to be reminded, and either billed for renewing or, if they didn't renew, coaxed and, if necessary, coaxed again. The logical branching of alternatives closely resembles the branching of pharmaceutical marketing programs, and similar techniques and computer programs are applicable. And, quite logically, Fisher-Stevens is now involved in magazine fulfillment.

Fisher-Stevens has diversified into yet a further area, that of operations research. This was stimulated because of the enriched records maintained on clients' sales, an ever-increasing technical staff, and the recognition of the vital need for information by top management in the future. A prime project in this area is sales forecasting. The information on, for example, a physician's attitude toward a product constitutes a variable that must be considered in predicting the likely sales of that product. Whatever his attitude is, it can be correlated with other factors in his background—his kind of practice, his prescription-writing activity, and so on—and those factors constitute further variables for prognostication. Already possessed of an extensive store of such information, all of which is current, Fisher-Stevens has developed mathematical models which are manipulating all of these variables and other pertinent data and forecasting the sales of new products—those without a history from which to extrapolate.

Having diversified into operations research, Fisher-Stevens is developing other OR techniques for marketing management. Notable among these is a program that would enable it to monitor the effects of various promotional techniques upon the number of prescriptions physicians write for a specific product.

LOWEST BIDDER WINS

Another operations research program in development is a decision model for competitive bidding. The model would show its user what his profit would be at various prices and which price would give him the best chance of winning the contract while still realizing an adequate profit.

All its diversified activities sprang from and are supported by the 1401s Fisher-Stevens installed in its Clifton plant in 1962. As computing capacity grew, applications developed, and more computing capacity was needed. At the end of 1965, the firm switched to a System/360 Model 40; in mid-1966, it added two Model 30s with an optical scanner, and it now has another Model 40 on order.

Fisher-Stevens likes to think of its computer capability as the newest link in a historical chain—one that began 50 years ago with an unlikely band of envelope addressers behind a glass door near the Bowery.

_____

Questions:

1. Fisher-Stevens has a vast amount of information at their disposal as a result of implementing a computer-based information system. Discuss some of the technical aspects of file organization that allows for the useful manipulation of the data in the system.

2. The Fisher-Stevens system allows for a certain amount of integration among their systems. Discuss some of the factors which have to be addressed when integration is considered.

3. How has automation changed the Fisher-Stevens organization? Might the same changes have occurred without the computer? Explain.

AIRLINE RESERVATION SYSTEMS

BY WILLIAM E. JENKINS

The development of today's sophisticated computerized reservations system is as significant to the airlines as the development of the jet engine. Reservations has finally caught up with the jet age. In the formative years of the airline industry, the reservations process was about as sophisticated as the Ford Tri-motor; however, it was a minor triumph for an airplane to depart fully loaded. As the airplane gained popularity and passenger volumes increased, advance reservations became normal practice for the vast majority of the air traveling public.

Eastern Air Lines' new third-generation computer system, required to handle today's reservations volumes, is one of the largest commercial computer installations in the world. The traveling public has adopted the telephone as the simplest and quickest means, versus a personal visit to an airline office, to make reservations. These telephone calles, in the case of Eastern, average 125,000 daily. The telephone, therefore, has become the major revenue pipeline to the airline.

It is the reservations unit's responsibility to serve the needs of these customers efficiently and effectively. Thus it is extremely important that the reservations unit have the necessary tools to respond promptly and to complete a reservation in minimum time. Reservations calls vary from 90 seconds for an information call to 717 seconds for a round trip booking, with an average of 237 seconds per call on a normal day.

Since Eastern schedules 125,000 seats per day over 27,000 flight segments between 98 airports, access to status records and control of inventory requires high speed edp capabilities with massive storage devices. This requirement is multiplied since customers wish to reserve seats well ahead of time—up to a year in advance—and the records must be maintained for that period.

The control and management of the airlines' seat inventory, as well as selling the product, makes the reservations fucntion a key part of an airline operation. The success of reservations depends largely on the capability and reliability of our computer systems. Fortunately, we have achieved both, which is partially attributable to the experience gained over the past 20 years as the airlines took advantage of technological developments.

A look at the progress airlines have made in reservations systems will best illustrate how edp has enabled the airlines to keep abreast of phenomenal traffic increases year after year.

The industry has progressed through many phases of reservations and seat inventory control techniques. One of the first of these was to allocate control of seats by city. Exchange of seats between cities was frequently required and handled through the airlines' radio network.

Continuing growth soon made it necessary to seek new communications methods for transmission of reservations data. Private line Teletype (PLT) became the new medium in communications and was quickly adopted as the basic reservations communication device. With improved communications facilities, space allotments by city soon became outmoded. Special control offices were then established to maintain inventory records and to confirm requested seats according to demand from the various cities. This system reduced the average time to process a reservation from approximately 24 hours to eight hours.

The next improvement was a "sell and report" procedure. Under this system, availability of flights was maintained in each office, permitting any city to immediately confirm a seat and report the sale via Teletype to central control for recording. When a flight was sold out, central control Teletyped this fact to all cities to update their availability records. The availability records in each office ranged from massive wall displays to simple clipboard charts—depending on the number of flights and personnel requiring access to the information.

Through this pre World War II period, traffic grew at a rapid rate. In 1935, 874,116 passengers were carried and by 1940, just five years later, the total had increased 264% to 3,185,278 passengers. By 1945, volume had increased 115% to 6,852,401 and there was no sign of let-up in the postwar period. It was evident that manual reservations systems would soon be incapable of handling the volume of reservations requests. Airlines turned their attention to the newly emerging electronics industry as the source of a potential solution.

The first attempt at mechanization was an electromechanical device designed for American Airlines by Teleregister Corp. (now Bunker-Ramo) in 1946. A key component of this system was the agent set or I/O device solved a major problem by placing the status of each flight at the agent's disposal, thus replacing cumbersome, hard-to-read wall displays. By depressing certain keys. illumination of lamps indicated if a seat could be sold on a flight. The central processing facility was based upon a pinboard technique and availability was changed manually. This initial system, although it had no electronic switching, computation, or magnetic storage devices, can be credited with paving the way for application of electronic techniques to the reservations process.

ENTER THE DRUM

By the early 50's, significant advances had been made in electronic techniques, control and computational functions. In addition, the magnetic drum had become a reliable and effective storage device. Teleregister, with their previous reservations experience, was quick to apply this new technology in the design of the first seat inventory reservations control system. At the same time, a new I/O device was developed which enabled the reservations agent to adjust inventory on a flight by depressing certain transaction keys, e.g., SELL, CANCEL. This system, installed in 1952, finally eliminated the need to report sales and cancellations by Teletype.

This system, or later models subsequently developed by Teleregister, was used by American, Braniff, National, Northeast, Pan American, United and Western. In fact, several are still in use today.

Univac was next to enter the airline reservations field when they introduced the Model I File Computer encompassing new schedule display features in the I/O device in 1956. Using 35mm slides, mounted in a cartridge, the agent displayed and quoted schedules and, through magnetic coding on these display slides, sold and cancelled specific flights by depressing associated keys on the agent set. This system was installed at Capital (which later merged with United), Eastern and Northwest.

In all of these systems, it was still necessary for the reservations agent to manually complete the passenger's reservations record on either a card or a chart—depending on that airline's procedure. The new systems had eliminated the manual space control and solved the availability display proglems. In 1960, airline traffic volume had grown 203% over that of 1945. This volume undoubtedly could not have been handled efficiently and economically without the aid of these electronic devices. Up to this time, however, the exchange of reservations data between airlines, which was handled by both telephone and Teletype, had received little attention except in the area of Teletype message switching centers to expedite traffic between airlines.

Since some of the previously mentioned electronic systems were already processing on-line Teletype messages and plans were underway for a fully automated system, the industry began developing standard machinable Teletype message formats in 1959. One was adopted as the standard format for all U.S. airlines in 1963 and later on a world-wide basis. With common machinable language, uniform programming for the new, more sophisticated computer systems under development could be assured.

SABRE STARTS

The first of this new breed, now referred to as "second-generation" systems, was initiated by IBM. The initial system was installed by American. SABRE, as the system was called, encompassed all the former benefits of inventory and availability, plus the capability of recording the passenger's name record (PNR) and automatically generating any required Teletype messages to other airlines. The system was also designed to perform many other functions formerly handled manually from card records. To name only a few—meal counts, boarding manifests, ticketing time limits, and checks for duplicate reservations. Another feature of significant importance is reconciliation of passenger name records with inventory. Under the former systems, manual name records and machine inventory were extremely difficult to reconcile because of communications lag and records out of file.

Delta and Pan American, however, followed American's lead with the IBM Passenger Name Record concept. Today, most of the airlines are installing or have on order highly sophisticated "third generation" PNR systems introducing the cathode ray tube (crt) and alphanumeric keyboards as the agent set I/O device. The following while not including all airlines of the world, is representative of what the airlines are doing and the vendors they have selected:

Air Canada	Univac
Air France	Univac
Atlitalia	IBM
American	IBM
BEA	Univac
BOAC	IBM
Braniff	IBM
Continental	IBM
Delta	IBM
Eastern	IBM
Frontier	IBM
Lufthansa	Univac
National	IBM
Northeast	IBM
Pan American	IBM
Swissair	IBM
TWA	Burroughs
United	Univac
Western	IBM

The new IBM system, which the industry refers to as a "PNR System," introduced the first alphanumeric agent set installed at each reservations agent's position. The set consisted of a modified typewriter with a functional subset for insertion of prepared schedule display cards. These cards were coded to enable the agent to perform inventory transactions through depression of keys. The alphanumeric keyboard was used to insert all other elements (name, telephone number, etc.) of a passenger's reservation. The pioneering of American and IBM in the PNR system concept paved the way for today's airline reservations systems.

In the interim, increasing traffic volumes forced several carriers to upgrade their first-generation systems by introducing real-time inventory control and availability systems without the associated PNR concept. Examples here include Eastern and Northwest, with Univac 490's and United with Teleregister's Instamatic. Shortly following Eastern's installation in 1962, one of the first approaches to time-sharing was introduced when Eastern made its system available to Allegheny, Lake Central, Mohawk, Ozark, and North Central. All of these carriers except Mohawk are still a part of this system which since has been upgraded to Univac 494's.

THE CROSSOVER POINT

Reservations system requirements are primarily related to the volume of traffic that must be handled. An airline handling 10,000 passengers per month can still efficiently and economically maintain a manual system without the aid of a computer. However, an airline with a volume of a million or more passengers a month must take the fullest advantage of today's electronic technology. It appears likely that the smaller airlines, heretofore denied the advantages of computerization for economic reasons, will be able to take advantage of these new systems in the future through joint participation or sharing.

Regardless of the volumes a particular airline handles, the same basic requirements for information and passenger processing exists. To describe the system requirements, one must examine the primary needs of an agent to promptly respond to a customer's telephone inquiry. These inquiries may involve not only the agent's own airline, but any airline in the world. Primary tools are:

1. Readily accessible schedule and fare information.
2. Means for determining availability status of flights.
3. Means for reporting sales or cancellations for inventory adjustment.
4. Ability to quickly record and subsequently access passenger records of itinerary, contacts, ticketing information, special service requirements.
5. Current date operation flight information.
6. Other travel related information such as rental cards, hotels, documents, ground transportation, city inforamtion and baggage requirements.

In addition to these needs, many other complex functions occur in the reservations process. These supporting fuctions formerly represented manpower requirements nearly equaling the number of personnel servicing incoming telephone calls. Once a telephone sales agent has booked a customer's reservations, the computer system must be capable of performing these supporting functions which combine to make today's total computerized reservations system so extremely complex.

Fortunately, today's technology has enabled us to eliminate pencil and paper in the reservations process and those arduous and time-consuming supporting functions of sorting, filing, searching, counting, changing and communicating. Except for certain static forms of information which cannot be economically stored and retrieved, the new PNR systems efficiently and effectively accommodate the reservations requirements for a total system.

To describe the new PNR system in more detail, I will use as an example Eastern's IBM 360/65 system which was initialized when the first reservations office cut over last July. We are at the mid-point of conversion from the Univac 494 system.

Ten regional reservations centers—located in Atlanta, Ga.; Charlotte, N.C.; Chicago, Ill.; Houston, Tex.; Miami, Fla.; Montreal, Can.; Woodbridge, N.J. (New York area); San Juan, P.R.; Seattle, Wash.; and Tampa, Fla.—will be connected by a network of high speed data lines to the central processors in Miami when conversion is completed this summer. (Two foreign offices in Bermuda and Mexico City are connected by Teletype.) To handle the anticipated 1969 traffic volume of 40 million telephone calls, 1700 crt agent sets will be active in these 10 reservations centers. In the same period, we will handle more than 20 million passengers (excluding our no-reservations Air Shuttle). This will require the creation of an estimated 22 million PNR's (a party of two or more traveling together requires only one PNR), allowing for normal cancellations.

THE SYSTEM

The basic hardware components which make up the system are as follows:

Quantity   Unit
   3 IBM 360 Model 65 processors (524K core storage each)
   3 Large core storage (6 million plus characters each)
   3 2703 Transmission Control Units
  20 2314 disc file system (200 million plus characters each)
676 Movable disc packs (25 million plus characters each)
  24 Tape drives (9 track, 1600 bits per inch)

     Here's how the system fulfills the needs· of a reservations agent in responding to one of those 40 million telephone calls.

Schedule Information. Depressing a special key plus a simple input of date, city pair (from-to) and time, will obtain 10 current flight schedules, displaying flight number, city pair, departure and arrival, type of equipment, meal service and number of stops.

Availability. Depression of another key and the same input will display schedules of four available flights. The computer spans a 34-hour period in its search for seats available nearest the time requested.

     A seat may be sold on one of the displayed flights by entering only the line number, class of service and number of seats, followed by all mandatory elements required in the PNR. If the agent fails to enter an element, the computer politely reminds the agent what has been omitted. Mandatory items are:

Passenger name(s) which must correspond to seats sold
Telephone contact
Ticketing information
Who booked the reservation

     The up-to-date schedule and availability display is the most significant advancement over earlier PNR systems. Higher speed processor and crt capability allow storage and retrieval of this information. For example, extra sections may be added immediately after being set up for sale. Only flights scheduled to operate are displayed. No longer does an agent have to watch for fine print denoting exceptions such as "no operate Sunday," or "Saturday only." Pick up any airline schedule and you will see what I mean.

     Space does not permit covering all the functions performed by the system, so I will briefly describe several of the more important ones.

Retrieval of Passenger Records. An agent in any one of the 10 regional centers can instantly retrieve any passenger's record if the customer calls to cancel or change his itinerary, which occurs with some frequency. A complete history (PNR) is maintained until the passenger has flown the last segment of his itinerary. Each subsequent transaction involving a record in the system is time-stamped, "fingerprinted" with the agent's symbol, and notes who (passenger, secretary, etc.) made the change.

Automatic Message Handling. The system automatically generates messages to sell or request seats on other airlines. Eastern maintain availability on 24 other airlines, accommodating more than 90% of the requests we receive. Also, we supply many other airlines with Eastern's flight availability. Messages selling or requesting seats received from the other airlines are automatically processed and replies sent if necessary. Messages are automatically sent to other airlines advising of schedule changes. A reply of seat confirmation or advice from another airline of a schedule change is automatically processed and placed on special queues alerting the agent to notify the passenger. All such messages (an estimated 37 million in 1969) previously were handled manually.

Waitlist. As seats are canceled on flights previously sold out, the system will automatically search the waitlist file; if names are listed, it will select the earliest record, confirm the seat and place the record on a special queue for an agent to call the customer.

Schedule Change Processing. Airlines historically change schedules in the spring and fall concurrent with Daylight Saving Time changes, and at other times of the year to meet seasonal or market requirements or to phase in new aircraft deliveries. A very intricate process takes place when a new schedule is loaded into the computer. Flights are matched and, if a flight changes, the passengers are automatically booked on a flight most similar to their previous reservation. Each PNR record is adjusted and queued for agents to notify the passenger. This seemingly simple process is one of the most complex and difficult operations performed by the system.

Other newly automated internal processing functions of significant importance include cancelling PNR's with expired ticket time limits, duplicate booking checks, alphabetizing PNR's for boarding manifests, and placement of PNR's on queue at appointed time for tickets to be mailed or sent by Teletype.

Another feature of vital importance is flight information. Facts pertaining to non-routine operating conditions and revised arrival and/or departure information can be retrieved through a simple transaction or given automatically with a schedule or availability display.

RELIABILITY AND RESPONSE

In addition to performing these feats, the system must meet severe performance standards in response time and reliability in order for the reservations unit to service the 125,000 telephone calls received each day. Reliability takes on its real meaning when you consider a reservations agent in the process of making a reservation for a customer. Suddenly the System Available light goes out. The agent no longer has the ability to access flight schedules, seat availability or flight information. The customer is still on the line. This is just one agent, but when you consider there are 1,7000 agents in this same situation, you can visualize the effect of a complete system failure. Imagine, too, that it's not just one customer. In our system, the scene is being repeated at the rate of 262 times each minute. This problem is further compounded when you consider all the support functions and the other departments in the company, dependent upon information from the system. I believe you can quickly understand why we must have a totally redundant system—from incoming power, to processors and storage devices—which duplicate every record stored in the system.

Response time becomes critical, too, when you consider a normal round trip PNR may involve 10 or more separate entries, each requiring a response from the computer before the transaction can be continued. If our response time standard of eight-tenths of a second is not met, you will note pauses in the conversation with the customer. Besides embarrassment and inefficiency, the added seconds can be extremely costly. To add five seconds to work-time-per-call would require 31 additional personnel in our system to handle the same number of calls.

Variable length of PNR's, variable number of PNR's stored a year in advance and variable loads by hour of day, day of week and month of year give the computer sciences department a tough job of design, programming and operating to maintain these critical system performance standards.

Design of such a huge and complex reservations computer system involves the interaction of the professionals in both the reservations and edp functions. Neither can act independently if the system is to be successfully implemented and operated profitably. The user department—particularly in a function as intricate and wholly independent on the system as reservations—must have a strong voice in establishing design and operating criteria.

Reservations management, based upon operation knowledge and experience, must study, evaluate and analyze the specific needs of the function in order to present to the edp unit a concise, in-depth, comprehensive statement of definition of requirements. Through the application of technical knowledge, the edp specialist can identify and select the system which most nearly meets the needs of the user.

One of the grave problems that the development of the science of edp has generated is an ever-widening communications gap between the management of an operating unit and the technical specialist. As the state of the art in edp progressed and the subject became less intelligible to those outside the function, the responsibility for the identification and definition of requirements and the selection of hardware, programs and peripheral equipment fell more and more to the edp technician. He, while a specialist in his own field, did not possess the depth of knowledge and experience in an alien function to properly identify and define its particular requirements.

The mutual responsibilities of these units, therefore, cannot cease with planning, development or even implementation of the system. Constant communication of ideas and facts is vital. Requirements and capabilities must be reconciled. Refinements and new programs must be defined and developed. All of this can be done effectively only through continued meshing of the background, knowledge and experience of the operating unit and the edp unit.

Reservations management must accept their responsibility for identifying and providing detailed functional specifications in order to close the technological and communications gap between the user and supplier. The user, particularly in an airlines reservations environment, must have edp-oriented personnel on his staff to insure complete continuity and understanding of the task to be performed. The edp unit must recognize and accept the fact that reservations is the telephone selling and service unit of the airline faced with dynamic circumstances which will not permit subordination of their requiremtns to those of the edp unit.

Questions:

1. Trace the development of airline reservation systems.

2. Discuss some of the technical characteristics of past and present reservation systems.

3. Discuss the problem of computer system reliability in systems with the customer service requirements that exist in the airline industry.

THE INTEGRATED COMPUTER

The objective is simple: connect any person to almost anyone else in a matter of seconds. To meet this mark, however, requires a machine scattered all over the country, with billions of parts intermeshing in perfect harmony. This machine must grow to handle a volume of calling that increases at the rate of about ten per cent a year—to about six billion calls in 1968.

The new parts added must reflect the latest state of the art in electronics. And since elementary economics dictate that you can't scrap a multi-billion dollar investment every time you conjure up a better relay, all new electronic gear must work with the older portions of the system.

Besides keeping its own parts internally harmonious—and plugged, soldered and beamed together over decades—the big machine also is called upon for other feats of flexibility. It must, for example, be able to handle telephone calls, data messages and even visual signals without distinction. There are, in addition, thousands of independent telephone companies who depend on the Bell System network to link their customers with the rest of the country and the world.

The network also demonstrates great flexibility by the variety of ways it handles calls. Basically, it has the capacity to speed calls via the most efficient route. To re-route the traffic during peak-load or emergency conditions, the machine constantly searches its own innards. The labyrinth it looks through consists of 12 regional switching centers, each of which is divided into sectional and primary tool centers. The machine "knows," by the dial pulses and tones fed into it, what center it has to reach to put the call through. At each point, the system probes to find a direct pathway to the call's destination. Elapsed time for all this probing and decision making: less than 30 seconds.

All of the local and long distance centers in this huge circuit switching network, make it, in effect, one giant integrated computer. It contains all the elements of a computer: control, processing, and memory devices, as well as input and output units. But despite its flexibility, a malfunction in one area can have adverse effects in other parts of the system.

The machine gets human guidance when it needs it. A centralized control center in New York follows the national telephone traffic picture on large maps, complete with the color coding and flashing warnings familiar to moviegoers who have watched the U.S. repel mythical invasions.

By watching their own "Big Board," AT&T Long Lines Department strategists can order adjustments to overcome congestion and delays caused by

---

Reprinted from *Bell Telephone Magazine,* (May-June, 1968 issue), with permission.

peak loads at critical hours and occasional natural disasters that wipe out circuits or increase the load.

The time zones of the nation are used to get maximum use and flexibility out of the system. Suppose for example, calling volumes between Boston and Miami at 10 a.m. spurt beyond the circuit capacity of the network connecting the two cities. On the West Coast, it is only 7 a.m., when some transcontinental circuits are usually idle. Batches of calls can then be switched from Boston to Miami over these idle circuits via the regional switching center at San Bernardino, California—flashing across the country and back in a matter of seconds.

Amplifier technology developed by Bell Telephone Laboratories makes possible this touting of calls without lower transmission quality. In the under-30-second interval before completion, a given call can travel 5,000 miles or more, pass through hundreds of relays, trip countless switches, be amplified several thousand times, travel by cable, carrier, and microwave radio and still come out sounding like a call from down the block.

And all this happens so automatically that no one knows just what route a given call has taken. For, as long as the big machine is working properly—and it's programmed to tell when anything goes wrong—there's no need for anyone to know. Most billing, also done by a computer system activated by the network, also is automatic and is based, of course, on the distance between the calling parties—not the devious paths that the machine may take to connect them.

In the future, as more and more electronic gear replaces the electro-mechanical components, the basic principles of self-searching and bulk routing will become even more sophisticated. The time factor will also change. All-electronic equipment will put through calls about as fast as they can be dialed, punched or, perhaps someday, spoken. After all, why waste 30 seconds?

Questions:

1. Explain the use of the word "integrated" when referring to the telephone system.

2. Speculate on the impact of the tele-communications system on automatic data processing systems.

THE IMPACT OF
DIGITAL COMPUTERS UPON
STEEL WORKS OPERATIONS

BY W.E. MILLER

An order of magnitude change in man's ability to perform a task has usually resulted in a profound influence on his way of life. Such change is represented by today's commerical jet aircraft, which are roughly an order of magnitude faster and larger than the first commercial airplanes. Application of the digital computer to process control promises change by an order of magnitude more significant and beneficial than these jet aircraft, which have so greatly altered our personal and business ways of life.

While process control via local regulators such as automatic gage control on the hot strip mill have brought benefits in productivity and product quality, these sophisticated systems are not the final answer; they must be set and reset by human operators, who have the limiting human traits of varying attention, concentration and accuracy. Process computer systems not only overcome these human weaknesses, but are being used in some cases in adaptive modes.

GROWTH OF PROCESS COMPUTER APPLICATIONS

The first on-line real-time application of a digital computer to process control occurred in 1958 in the petro-chemical industry. Since then the growth has been exponential; there are now approximately 1600 process computer applications throughout the world. Digital computers for the control of industrial processes have, in a relatively short period of time, achieved a position of importance and acceptance unparalleled by any other industrial change in the last four decades. It is difficult to estimate future growth; in 1966 the Midwest Research Institute, Kansas City, Missouri, predicted a total of 3000 process computers in all industries by 1970, and a futher increase to 10,000 by 1975. There is little doubt that this is the era of the digital computer, for plant operations, for finance and engineering, for space exploration, for automatic landing of aircraft through all kinds of weather, and more besides.

THE STEEL INDUSTRY

The steel industry is already a significant user of digital computers for process control. The exact number is difficult to estimate, but is probably close to 300. Recent strong competitive demands have been imposed upon steel producers to improve continually their product quality, yield and productivity. These have resulted in a hope that adaptive and self-learning control techniques might be achievable via digital compuers. Steel plant process control via local regulators such as automatic gage control on the hot strip mill are reliabile multi-loop systems and have brought benefits in productivity and product quality.

ADAPTIVE TECHNIQUES IN THE HOT STRIP MILL

As an example, a recently patented system as used on a hot strip mill stores data on grades of steel to be rolled, mill and drive characteristics, effects of rolling variables and a mathematical model of the rolling process. The system calculates and selects the best settings of the mill controls prior to rolling of each specific bar.

Once the identity and final product specifications of the steel to be rolled are established, the system sets up the mill based upon data derived from the process model. It determines, for example, initial roll openings and roll speeds and then readjusts the mill as the bar proceeds from stand to stand to compensate for measured departures from anticipated rolling characteristics.

Throughout the entire rolling operation data is acquired from the process. This information is used for updating the process model to improve the quality of subsequent bars.

A significant aspect of this sytem is the adaptive capability. More efficent production and better quality steel products result from an adaptive system.

The high production rate and high contributed product value, especially of the hot strip mill, provides the economic return required, while the extensive prior work on automatic gage control has provided the process model and know-how required to develop the computer instruction programs for these and other rolling mill systems.

There are many types of reversing hot mills, possessing varying aptitudes for computer control. Most universal slabbing mills, structural mills, and blooming mills have been operated very satisfactorily by card program systems. Beginning in 1967 however a significant percentage of new mills were purchased with computer set-up. At the end of 1967 the percentage for the year was so high as to predict very few new card program systems.

Plate mills are, however, different; they are finishing mills with operating characteristics that tax the ability of human operators. Program control systems are of little merit since the incoming ingot characteristics are variable, and it is impossible to predict consistently the rolling schedules that will make the width required in the finished plate. Then, too, the finished plate is a final shipped product, having quality requirements for flatness, cross-sectional shape, and accuracy of gage and width. Thus, on-line computer systems for plate mills and other reversing finishing mills have significant value.

PROGRESS IN STEEL MAKING SYSTEMS

The amount of effort being expended on data logging and investigation of operation of Basic Oxygen Steel Making is rapidly adding to the knowledge and understanding of this process. It is very probable that many, if not all, of the installations presently fitted with digital computers for data logging, or for predictive calculations for the operators' guidance, will soon become direct closed-loop controllers with adaptive feedback.[1]

On-line computer control systems for large continuous processing lines are a natural response to the recent rise in coil-form orders for strip products. Such production created a need for continuous digital-type production data analyzers and accumulators. Upgrading these machines to computer systems has not been an unnecessarily expensive step, and has usually resulted in a system possessing much greater capabilities with economic advantage. Applications are found primarily on tinning, continuous annealing, and shear and cut-up lines.

IMPROVING PLANT YIELD

Potentially, the digital computer offers steel works the most significant improvement in profit and user market position of the decade. Steel works processes are characterized by large investment, large throughput value, and large raw material and in process inventories. Steel users demand and receive plate, strip and sheet products to their specifications based upon "best current practice" which may be twice as tight as "commercial tolerances".[2] As a result mill yield, i.e., the ratio of tons shipped to ingot tons poured has declined; a decline in the USA of 5½% between 1962 and 1964 prompted the question, "How Much Steel Makes a Ton ?"[3]

CRITERIA FOR JUSTIFICATION OF COMPUTER CONTROL

Rationally, any process is suitable economically for computer control if any of the following criteria apply. Several justification examples have been selected from the many that could be cited for the various steel works processes.

1.   THROUGHPUT VALUE
The product throughput value is high enough to justify the added cost of the computer system.—
With a hot strip mill throughput of $1,000,000 to $2,000,000 per day, the added investment is equal to one or two day's production.

2.   QUALITY EFFECTS UPON SUBSEQUENT PROCESSES
The quality of product produced has a decisive effect upon following process efficiency.—
Two or three coils rolled to the same nominal gage in the hot strip mill are welded together for further reduction in the tandem cold strip mill. Thickness variations at coil ends cause step changes in thickness at the welds, and while tolerated contribute to strip breakage, or cobbles in the cold strip mill, damaging rolls and causing mill delays. Computer control of the hot strip mill can cut this effect by more than two to one. Hot strip mill computer control also, reduces end-to-end hardness variations and strip-body-to-strip-body thickness variations, further facilitating cold mill operation.

3.   DETERMINATION OF END PRODUCT QUALITY
The process decisively determines the end product quality regardless of succeeding processes.–

Shape, size and thickness should be obtained on the plate mill. Losses in the plate production process are very significant. Whereas the slabbing operation may give an ingot-to-slab yield of 86 to 88 percent, the ingot-to-plate yield may average 70 to 75 percent with particular plates varying significantly from the average yield. Computer control offers crown control, gage control and width control to minimize shearing scrap losses.[4]

4.   PROCESS COMPLEXITY
The process is complex, having many variables requiring frequent, rapid, and accurate adjustment for most economic operation.–

On the hot strip mill, the incoming metallurgy, temperature, width and thickness can all be varying as the bar goes through the mill. Besides, there are internal disturbances, or noise, such as improper operator adjustments, thermal variations in the mill, and electric sub-systems even during the 90 seconds a bar is in the finishing stands. There are system element interactions or coupling; a change in strip tension changes rolling pressure and strip thickness, while at the same time width-profile and flatness can also be affected. There are changing biases, such as mechnical wear, thermal level changes, electrical drifts, and crew operation capabilities.

The effectiveness of the computer system is well proved in this process.

5.   UNSTABLE PROCESSES
The process is inherently unstable, subject to rapid drifts requiring continual manual attention.–

As slabs are heated inductively, the coil inductance changes non-linearly. Capacitors must be switched to compensate for the change. In effect, the power supply is tuned to the load and the power factor corrected.

Each slab heater consists of a number of coils. All the coils are used when heating large slabs, while fewer may be needed for smaller slabs.

After the slab has been heated, the computer regulates the desired temperature by switching the heater off and on intermittently. Thrysistor power switches are used for this purpose.

If there are six furnace lines, each consisting of three heaters, and the heaters are rated 15,000 KW, 10,000 KW, and 5,000 KE, then the process could not be controlled manually. Computer programs are required to cope with the control requirements due to non-linear varying inductance, termperature control, power demand equivalent to a city of 160,000 inhabitants, and the logistics of receiving, transferring, and delivering 680 tons of steel slabs per hour. The digital computer unquestionably implements the process in a manner that will bring important savings to steel producers and users.

KNOWLEDGE IS THE KEY TO RESULTS

Today, it would be hard to find a steel man who would argue against the computer for a hot strip mill. There are too many successful installations to dispute success.[5] Yet, we are still on the threshold in applying digital computers for directing and controlling processes. Today, there are process computer enthusiasts and process computer pessimists; there are believers and doubters. A key to resolving these significant and often quite emotional differences in opinion is improvement in presenting knowledge and information, evaluating *all* the alternatives including that of no action, and in reaching a decision based on total value.

A digital computer as a piece of hardware connected to a process drive system can be a stupid beast, valueless, and even a potential hazard to production. A digital computer properly structured into a total system and with a carefully organized program in its memory can be a delight to operators and customers and a pleasant profitable venture for management. Unfortunately, management is only slowly becoming aware of the problem of getting results.

SYSTEM STRUCTURING BECOMES MORE CRITICAL

Application of digital computers to control of processes has focused attention upon system structuring. Process drive and control systems as used in steel works have become increasingly larger in total horsepower, the functions provided, automatic sequencing, and the various process and product qualities that are automatically regulated.

SYSTEMS STRUCTURE MUST BE PRACTICAL

A system must be designed and structured for performance, reliability, and cost. The system must be practical to implement within the capabilities of real people that will exist during design and start-up. It is rare that any two suppliers will create exactly the same sub-systems, or exactly the same total system structure; it is improbable that detail hardware implementation will be the same. Thus, the user-purchaser will always have a difficult evaluation to perform; and the comparison is not apples with apples, or apples with oranges, but fruit salads with fruit salads.

The expensive intangible factor in bid evaluation is the software portion of system design and structuring. Equipments can be compared, but the comparison of software takes real depth in understanding, cold logic in evaluation, and a review of history will show either a previous exciting success, or a dismal failure in avoiding the temptation of the apparent bargain.[6]

Software is just as essential as hardware in the system structure. Understanding is critical to success. Every intended action and every intended relationship must be expressed in mathematics of concise English. All these expressions must then be arranged in correct sequence.

Performance, reliability, and cost will be optimized by a proper balance between hardware and software, and through a corresponding balance between analog and digital techniques. Neither is always better than the other.

Large, complex systems require a "top-down" engineering view.[7,8] Each sub-system must be specified and designed with total system value and performance in mind. Each sub-system must contribute to the value of the whole. The digital computer will contribute significant value when we use its remarkable capability to multiply the human operator's task capabilities per unit time.

SYSTEMS DESIGN

Today, practically all digital computers applied to steel works processes are structured into the total drive and control system. Several early computer installations were attempted on the basis of experimentation and regression analysis. However, experience proved that controlled experimentation on a large key production facility was a mere fond hope; the steel plant processes were too complex, with non-linear inter-relationships. The chance of "discovering" these relationships and the necessary systems structure was concluded to be practically nil. The only sure thing turned out to be expense.

Systems design involves creativity, innovation and analysis. Analysis of complex systems is best handled through a multilevel approach. This approach involves: (1) decomposition of the complex system into a set of sub-systems, each of which can be easily handled in terms of satisfying a local or subsystem objective; and (2) coordination of the solutions of subsystem problems via computer simulation, so that the objectives associated with the overall system are satisfied.

The approach is iterative in that one works from the total system to the many sub-systems and back and forth, until a model is developed that satisfies the real world of required performance, time, and value.

Comprehensive system development and design work prior to manufacture and installation assure a minimum implementation period consistent with the priorities of production and profit generation associated with high-through-put processes.

A comprehensive system design program will produce knowledge and data permitting development of sound and realistic planning for the system installation and start-up. Task times and costs become definable and finite and can be scheduled with critical path network techniques.

PERMANENT EFFECT UPON PROFITABILITY

The higher productive capacity of new rolling mills and the increased functional complexity of their drive systems have brought corresponding increases in the dollar value of the investment and increased investment risk to steel companies. The trend to dependence upon digital computer automation and increased factory preassembly of the electric control system makes the purchaser more dependent upon the performance of his electric drive system supplier and the system supplied. Thus, this purchasing decision not only has higher initial value, but of even more significance is the permanent long term effect upon the profitability of the total mill investment.

A new hot strip mill has a throughput value of $1,000,000 to $2,000,000 per day. A 0.5% difference in yield, 250 days per year over 10 years is equivalent to an additional $12,500,000 to $25,000,000 before taxes. Degrees of sophistication in computer systems may provide differences in process yield. The present value of estimated variations in system performance and process yield should be part of the investment decision. Risk analysis involving assignment of probabilities to various levels of performance for various systems can be used to convert intuitive analysis to value analysis.

INSTALLATION TIME IS COSTLY

The investment decision is further complicated by the tremendous complexity of the installation and start-up tasks. The investment does not produce value until saleable products are ready for shipment. The pressures for time compression are tremendous.

The net result is that more tasks must be carried out simultaneously. Extensive manpower and material resources are required with corresponding management planning and flexibility of resource assignment to meet critical path needs. Planning must evaluate the costs for time compression against the capital charges for the idle investment. Also total costs may be greater if production is commenced before installation is completed. Alternatives need to be evaluated on a cost-benefit basis.

If start-up of a hot strip mill is unnecessarily delayed, the capital earns no income. Interest charges alone at 5% amount to over $400,000 per month. Delays whether the result of inadequate planning or inability of suppliers are costly. On time start-up has value. Structured planning and analysis permit value based selection of the available start-up alternatives.

COST-BENEFIT ANALYSIS REDUCES UNCERTAINTY

Cost-benefit analysis really requires assignment of probabilities to achieving various levels of performance. Actual risk is how much we stand to lose if we fail, multiplied by the probability of failure. A final decision can be true value based, with confidence of minimum risk and lowest uncertainty. When such analyses are not made then risk is replaced by uncertainty. The decision must be made upon intuition. Intuition can turn out to be expensive when $25,000,000 or $125,000,000 is affected, and in reality applies a very low value function to accurate information.

The decision tree/probability approach to cost benefit analysis is work; but work that can be successfully used to prove the justification for, and would expand the use of digital computers for the control of processes.

RATIONALIZING AGAINST STRUCTURED ANALYSES

We have experienced almost a standard rationalization against the use of structured approaches for decision making and planning. This rationalization is about as follows:

a. People won't give you accurate information;
b. The available information is conflicting;
c. Yes, lots of information is obtainable;
d. Evaluation of the information is impossible;
e. Structured approaches are too much work;

f. Structured approaches tie you down;
g. Structured approaches, not followed, will later haunt you;
h. Experience and intuition are just as good (as logic);
i. OK, we will use it.

This final acceptance is usually accompanied by a sickening realization of being trapped by the inevitability of change, and of this new, unexpected, silent, logic-oriented master looking down from the office wall!

THE VALUE OF SOFTWARE

There is a dawning realization of the significant importance of software, the intangible factor that we recognize as logical, but brush aside because we can't explain it to the satisfaction of our peers. Yet, they, too, subconsciously sense its value for it is their stock and trade; their ability to logically sort the information, consider alternative courses of action, evaluate potential results and select or create the proper program to follow.

The system engineer must create a systems design or plan to suit the project or problem requirements. He is also involved in determining capability of proposed sub-systems and may work with other engineers to create new sub-systems required for the total system design.

The success of a computer controlled rolling mill installation is completely dependent upon the team of engineers and analysts who put many man years into creating, defining, flow charting and coding the design and also every possible course of action that might logically be encountered in operating a rolling mill. (See Table I.) These engineers and analysts must also be intimately familiar with the mathematics of the plastic flow of metal in the roll bite, roll bending, roll flatenning, mill stretch and more. Every routine must be logically organized, assigned a priority level and put together into the computer memory.

SECRET OF SUCCESS

The secret of success here as almost everywhere is creativity and an organized, structured approach based upon a broad and firm foundation of analytical and process knowledge. Significant, planned advance development is a pre-requisite to computer control of a complex multi-variable process. Expectations of success from controlled experimentation and regression analysis for model synthesis have led some to almost infinite time and expense and project abandonment because of production requirements.

To quote the trade journal *Iron Age*, "It would be hard to find a steel man who would argue against the computer for a hot strip mill. There are too many successful installations to dispute success."[5] The same people are applying similar approaches to the rolling of slabs, plates, cold strip, slab reheating, continuous casting, and steel making. Many of these process installations are being implemented now. All will be completed during the coming year. Many firms are well advanced into the era of the digital computer for process control.

OUTLOOK FOR THE FUTURE

The increased use of digital computers for process control and the effectiveness of digital computer control is limited only by our capacity to create new ideas, organize our thoughts and the process functions in a logical manner, anticipate process and operator malfunctions, and provide for them. If we miss only a few, and in advance, recognize and plan for our limitations, the odds are that we will have a successful installation. There are many in the world today. They will number in the thousands in ten years, and like other order of magnitude changes will have a profound effect upon our personal and business lives.

TABLE I

ENGINEERING DEVELOPMENT ACTIVITY
PLATE MILL PROCESS MODEL

(Does not include primary data input, tracking, logging, sequencing programs)

		ENGINEERING/ PROGRAMMING MAN WEEKS	
		ESTIMATED	ACTUAL
I	PLATE TEMPERATURE STUDY	10/8	12/2
II	ROLL FORCE PREDICTION	30/8	21/4
III	SHAPE CONTROL	30/12	35/5
IV	PRE-INSTALLATION TESTING	20/0	20/5
V	SCHEDULE GENERATION & FEEDBACK ANALYSIS	60/20	66/25
VI	COORDINATION & FACTORY TESTS	16/2	19/8
VII	ON SITE ACTIVITY	24/0	*
	TOTAL	190/50	*173/49

*Not completed at time of paper preparation

REFERENCES

[1]"Closed-Loop Control of Basic Oxygen Furnace Process", V.A. Leitzke, *Iron and Steel Engineer,* August, 1967.

[2]"Thickness Gaging: Where the customer's mike is always right," *33,* May, 1967, pp. 67-78.

[3]"How Much Steel Makes a Ton?", *Iron Age,* September 10, 1965.

[4]"Tehcnical and Economic Considerations in Plate MIll Process Control," D.J. Fapiano, *Iron and Steel Engineer,* October, 1966.

[5]"Process Computer—The Controversy Over Control", *Iron Age,* March 2, 1967, 8 pp.

[6]"Computer—Tool or Toy?" (editorial), *Automation,* March 2, 1967, pp. 3-5.

[7]IEEE Transactions on Systems Science and Cybernetics, *Vol. SSC-2, No. 1, August, 1966, 7 pp.*

[8]"Systems Engineering in an Industrial Environment", D.J. Fapaino and G.E. Terwilliger, *IEEE Transactions on Systems Science and Cybernetics,* Vol. SSC-3, No. 1, June, 1967, pp. 61-66.

Questions:

1. What would you consider in determining the feasibility of installing a process control computer system? Compare these considerations to those required for installing a management information system.

2. How should a system be designed and structured, according to the author? Comment.

A MODEL OF VISUAL ORGANIZATION FOR THE GAME OF GO

by ALBERT L. ZOBRIST

INTRODUCTION

No successful GO-playing program has appeared in the literature, although Remus[1] used GO as the subject of a machine learning study, and Thorp and Walden[2] have considered some of its mathematical aspects. Another author[3] considered GO to be somewhat mysterious, making it a challenge to those interested in automating it. Apparently the game was described as being mysterious to indicate that people were able to play it without knowing how they were able to play so well. More study of this complex game may reward us with new insight into human perceptual and problem solving abilities as well as foster the development of new techniques for artificial intelligence. This report describes a program which plays GO. The program uses an information processing model to produce perceptual features which are seen by human GO players, and is capable of several responses to the recognition of significant configurations of these perceptual features.

A BRIEF DESCRIPTION OF GO

The rules of GO are deceptively simple. The two players alternate in placing black and white stones on the intersections of a 19 x 19 grid. Stones of the same color which are connected by row or column adjacency form a *chain*. Diagonal adjacency is not sufficient to connect a chain. The empty intersections which are adjacent to a chain are its *breathing spaces*. When a chain has no breathing spaces, it is captured by the opponent, and the captured men are removed from the board. A player may place his stones anywhere on the board with two exceptions: (1) he may not form a chain with no breathing spaces unless he is capturing, and (2) he may not capture one stone which has just captured one of his stones on the previous turn. A player may choose to pass at any turn. The game is over when both of the players pass in sequence. A player's score is the sum of territories surrounded by his color plus the number of opponent's stones captured.

Some of the basic consequences of these rules are illustrated by the right side of Figure 1. White can always capture the top black chain, but cannot capture the bottom black chain, if black moves Figure 1 properly. If black

---

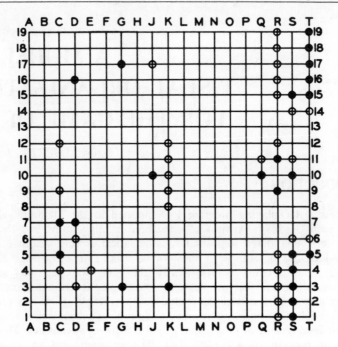

Figure 1 — An illustration of GO

moves at either T2 or T3 then white cannot occupy all of the breathing spaces of the black army without committing self-capture. This is because the black army would have two separate *eyes*. The ability to form two eyes is what determines whether an army is safe or not. White will score 16 points in the upper right, and black will score four points in the lower right corner. If white moves R10, then black may not respond R11, but must move elsewhere on the next turn. This prevents cyclic capture.

The rules scarcely describe how GO is actually played. Interested readers are advised to seek a demonstration from someone who plays GO, or to read one of the beginner's books.[4,5] The situations in the left hand corners of Figure 1 are representative of real play. Although the stones are not connected into long chains, they threaten to form chains which will surround territory along the corners and edges of the board. Efficient play requires that as much territory be sketched out with as few stones as possible. Throughout the rest of this paper such aggregates of stones which threaten to invade or surround territory will be called *armies*.

THE PROBLEM OF COMPLEXITY

GO is considered more difficult than chess by many people who know both games.[5] Numerical measures of the complexity of checkers, chess, and GO tend to support this belief. The number of paths down the move tree has been estimated at 10^{40} for checkers[6] and 10^{120} for chess.[7] A rough estimate for the number of paths down the move tree for GO is $361!$ or 10^{761}. By this reasoning, GO played on a 6 X 6 board would be comparable to checkers in complexity, and GO on a 9 X 9 board would be comparable to chess.

A slightly better estimate of the true complexity of these games may be obtained. For checkers, suppose that a choice of three reasonable moves occurs approximately 20 times per game. Then 3^{20} is a crude estimate of the number of checker games which might occur in ordinary play. Good chess players usually consider less than five move choices, hence 5^{50} estimates the number of reasonable chess games. A typical GO game lasts about 300 moves and a choice of 10 reasonable moves occurs at least 100 times, thus there are at least 10^{100} GO games which could occur in human play.

Such calculations, however crude they may be, are important to anyone interested in the automation of these games. The complexity of GO may hinder attempts to program it with the methods developed for chess and checkers.[6,7,8,9] The move tree for GO is exceedingly deep and bushy, hence any form of heuristic search can explore only a relatively small portion of the complete tree. An alternative approach might be to concentrate upon extremely powerful methods of evaluation of the board situation, thus enabling better play with a more restricted search. Another possibility might be to have the lookahead be directed by pruning methods which correspond to the development of strategies. Time will tell whether a successful GO playing program can be written using such methods.

THE VISUAL NATURE OF GO

The recognition and discrimination of meaningful perceptual stimuli presupposes the active formation of stable perceptual elements to be recognized and discriminated. A person lacking this process would combine all sorts of stimuli into meaningless groups.[10] The choice of a move in GO usually involves the recognition of configurations which are meaningful to the player. This raises the question as to whether certain basic perceptual processes are necessary for the comprehension of a GO board. The following examples might suggest that the answer is yes.

First, consider the spontaneous grouping of stones of the same color which occurs during visualization of a GO board. The stones are organized into distinct groups, clusters, or armies even though they may be sparsely scattered about or somewhat intermingled. Grouping is usually the result of proximity of stones of the same color or the predominance of stones of one color in an area, but can be affected by other characteristics of the total board situation. For example, stones which fall into a line are likely to be grouped. Kohler[11] and others have found grouping to be a basic perceptual phenomenon. Yet the recognition and discrimination of groups or armies is necessary for competent GO play.

Closely related in grouping is segmentation, which is also discussed in Kohler. The area subtended by the board is divided into black and white territories, each of which maintains its own integrity in the visual field. These segments are a measure of the territory which is controlled by either side, hence are an important factor in the assessment of a GO board.

Another example is the formation of "spheres of influence" about a stone or group of stones. Influence is not an inherent property of stones, but appears to be induced in them by our processes of perception. Yet they are a crude measure of the potential of a stone or army of stones for controlling territory on the board.

The spontaneous image formed by the visualization of a GO board appears to be a complicated assemblage of perceptual units and subunits. For example, the stones themselves have their own perceptual identity while at the same time they are parts of chains or groups of stones. The phenomena discussed above show that some of these perceptual processes may be very important to the ability of GO players to comprehend this complex game.

It is not within the scope of this report to discuss further the psychological nature of these perceptual mechanisms, or to speculate upon the physiological basis for them. Let us adopt the term *visual organization* to mean the formation of such stable perceptual elements as have just been discussed, and let the resulting "mental picture" be called the *internal representation*.

Given that a player "sees" a fairly stable and uniform internal representation, it follows that familiar and meaningful configurations may be recognized in terms of it. The result of visual organization is to classify a tremendous number of possible board situations into a much smaller number of recognizable or familiar board situations. Thus a player can respond to a board position he has never encountered, because it has been mapped into a familiar internal representation.

This report will describe a simulation model for visual organization. It will use transformations which create information corresponding to the perceptual features discussed above, storing them in a computer internal representation.

A HEURISTIC FOR VISUAL ORGANIZATION

We now examine the problem of modeling the basic visual organization of the GO board. A reasonable goal would be to determine the segmentation of the board, the domains of influence of the stones, and the armies of stones, storing that information in a computer internal representation. Before building the computer model, it is of interest to consider physical processes which give some measure of the influence of physical bodies.

There are many candidates in the physical sciences for the process we desire. For example, white stones could be electrons, and black stones could be protons. Contiguous areas of positive or negative potential could determine the segmentation of the board, and the value of the potential would measure the influence of the stones. Of course, the solution would be discretized to the points of the GO board, and the potential at an unoccupied point could determine how well protected that point is by black or by white.

For another candidate, let the GO board be made of blotter paper and simultaneously place a drop of oil under each black stone and a drop of water under each white stone. Contiguous areas of oil or water would determine the armies and the segmentation of the board. Since the oil and water would spread evenly, the concentration would not indicate the influence of the stones or even their location.

Other possibilities might involve electrical networks or heat conduction, etc. These physical models are considered because they are well defined and easily calculated, whereas the visual process we are attempting to model is ill defined. Let us consider in more detail the first two examples given above. In the center of Figure 1, the electric charge analogy would give the black stone at J10 some weight to the right of the wall of white stones, whereas oil from the black stone would never get past the wall of water spreading from the white stones. Perceptually speaking, the black stone has no influence to the right of the white stones. The oil and water analogy could not differentiate between the two situations in the right hand corners of Figure 1, whereas the electric charge analogy would show four strongly surrounded squares in the lower corner. Thus the oil and water analogy does not reflect our perception of this situation. The finite difference method used by the program was chosen with both of these models in mind, and has the good features of both.

It is assumed that a game is in progress and the board position is stored. The position is transferred to a 19 X 19 integer matrix by placing 50 for each black stone, −50 for each white stone, and 0 elsewhere. Then each point which is positive sends out a +1 to each of its four neighbors, and each negative point sends out a −1 to each of its neighbors. These numbers are accumulated as this procedure is repeated four times. Figure 2, which is taken from the game listed at the end of this report, illustrates the results of the visual organization heuristic. The negative integers are indicated by an underline.

Segmentation can be assessed by determining the contiguous areas of positive or negative integers. The dashed lines in Figure 2 indicate the resulting segments. The stones which lie in a segment may be considered to be a group or army. The integer values at a point give a measure of the degree of influence exerted by the stones nearby. The influence of stones of the same color may reinforce one another, whereas the fields from opposing stones seem to repel and cancel one another. Inspection of Figure 2 should convince us that at least a crude resemblance to perceptual processes has been obtained. The array of integers from the visual organization heuristic contains, at least implicitly, information corresponding to an internal representation. This heuristic, together with a routine which is capable of creating an explicit computer internal representation of the resulting information, will be part of a model of visual organization. The specific details of the entire GO-playing program will now be given.

THE PROGRAM

The program is written in ALGOL for the Burroughs B5500 computer. Interaction is provided by remote teletypes. Each move requires 5 to 8 seconds of central processor time or about 5 to 20 seconds of real time, depending upon the number of users being serviced by the system. The machine code occupies 6300 words of core memory and 5400 more words are required for storage arrays. The program has two distinct parts. Part I has a coordinated set of procedures, including the visual organization heuristic, which operate on the board position to produce a computer internal representation. Part II has a set of procedures which use the internal representation to calculate a move.

Part I realizes a model of visual organization for GO, producing an analogue of a human player's perception of the board. Part II is not an attempt at simulation, but a collection of heuristics which may or may not resemble cognitive processes.

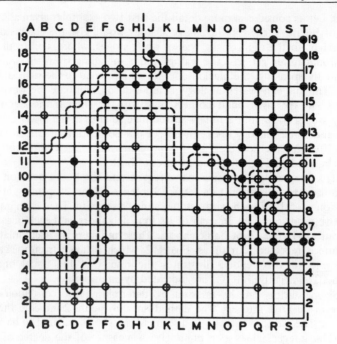

```
0   2   4   5   6   6   4   1   7   7   6   5   5   5   7  10  59  12  57
2   4   8  10  10  11  11   2  50  12  10  10   9   9  10  62  16  63  61
3   7  10  62  10  57  57  56  42  56  13  62  12  11  12  14  63  14  11
5   8  10   6   0   4  56  57  56  64  12  12  12  62  13  64  64  14  59
7  10   8   0   7  56   7   6   6   5   8   9   9  11  12  63  15  13  10
8  62   6   3   6   1  56   8  57   3   3   6   8   8  11  14  64  63  11
7   9   1   7  54  56  14  13  12   5   4  10   8  10  12  63  65  16  59
2   0   3  11   6  58  13  62  10   2   7  58   5  12  63  16  65  56   4
1   4  10  62   6   6  11  10   7   1   2   0  47  49  66  57  50  50  54
2   5   9  12   7   6  10   9   6   3   2   7  12  48  42  42  50  65  12
1   4   8  12  54  56  12  11   8   6   8  10  12  14  48  50  42  57  60
2   5   9  11   5  58  13  62  10   8  10  62  12  62   8  51  49  15  11
1   3   7  61   4   8  12  10   8   7   8  10  11  13  56  50  50  57  53
3   3   0   8   3  58  12  10   7   5   6   8  10  13  56  57  58  57  53
6  11  53  54   1   9  62  10   8   7   7   7  10  62   7   2  58   7   4
8  12   6   4   1  11  12  10  10  10   8   8   8  10  12   5   6  55   3
8  61   6  44   5  62  11   9  10  62  10   6   6   8  10  62  11  11   7
7  11  11  56  63  12   8   6   8  10   8   4   3   4   8  10   9   7   4
4   6   8   9   9   7   4   3   4   5   4   2   0   2   4   5   5   3   2
```

Figure 2 — Results of the visual organization heuristic

PART I

This part of the program consists of a set of computations which transform the board position into a computer internal representation. The internal representation contains an analog of important perceptual features of the board position. This information is stored in seven 19 X 19 integer arrays in an explicit fashion. That is, the integer values are a direct measure of the features they represent.

For example, consider the features of perceptual grouping and segmentation which have been determined by the visual organization heuristic. It would not be easy to reference this information in the array shown in Figure 2. Another process must create an array which gives a direct measure of the size of the segments and the groups of stones.

Figure 3 illustrates the results of the processes which calculate perceptual grouping and segmentation. These processes act upon the array of integers produced by the visual organization heuristic to produce an array of integers

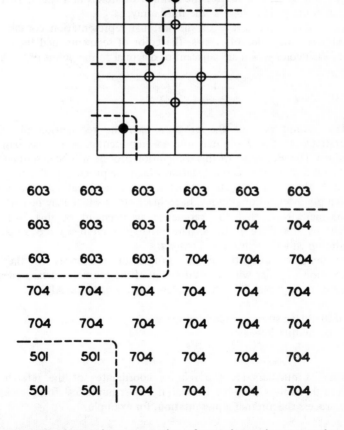

Figure 3 – Internal representation of grouping and segmentation

which are a part of the internal representation. One of these numbers (e.g., 603) may be interpreted as follows: the hundreds indicate the size of the segment which covers that point (600 is a medium-sized segment) and the ones indicate the number of stones which lie in that segment (there are 03 black stones hence 600 + 03 = 603). 500 indicates a small segment with less than 10 empty intersections, and 700 indicates a large segment with more than 25 empty intersections. If no segment covers an intersection, then 0 is stored in the corresponding cell of the array. The empty intersections in a segment are counted as they are a better measure of the safety of the army of stones in a segment. The information is compressed by having the size and the number of stones in the same array for purposes of efficiency only.

The array shown in Figure 3 is typical of the seven arrays which constitute the computer internal representation. Numerical values correspond in an explicit fashion to feature which we have considered to be formed by visual organization.

The second array gives a numerical measure of the influence of the black and white stones. It is an exact copy of the array of integers shown in Figure 2.

The third array measures the number of breathing spaces in a chain. This array is illustrated in Figure 4.

The fourth array measures the number of stones in a chain. This array is calculated in the same fashion as the third array.

The other three arrays of the internal representation contain integers which indicate the color of stones, the color of segments, and the number of stones of each color which are adjacent or diagonal to the points of the board.

PART II

The second part of the program uses the recognition of "familiar" configurations in the computer internal representation as the basis of its calculations. The mechanics of this recognition process will be described first.

Figure 5 illustrates a configuration which the program is able to recognize. At point A, there is a black stone which has only one breathing space left. Point B is an empty intersection. Point C has a black stone which may be part of a safe army of men. Note that the geometric arrangement of this 3-tuple is as important as the three features. The program contains a prototype of this configuration which we shall call a *template.*

A template consists of an n-tuple of references to the internal representation together with a specification of the geometric arrangement of the elements of the n-tuple. Thus the template for our situation ABC is:

(0,0)   black stone, 1 breathing space
(1,0)   empty intersection
(1,1)   safe black stone.

The pairs of numbers are the relative coordinates of the references. The references themselves must be translated into a numerical form which can be used to process the internal representation, for example:

safe black stone = 601 thru 900 in array 1 and 1 thru 1 in array 7.

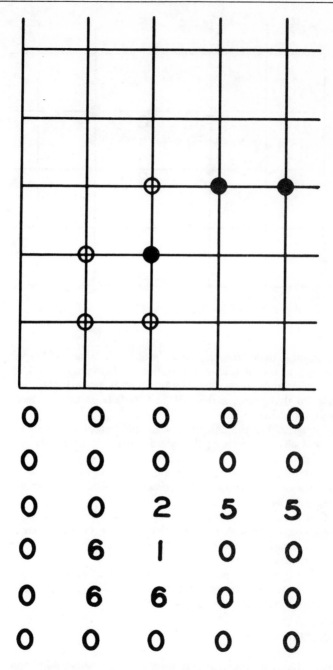

Figure 4 — Internal representation of breathing spaces

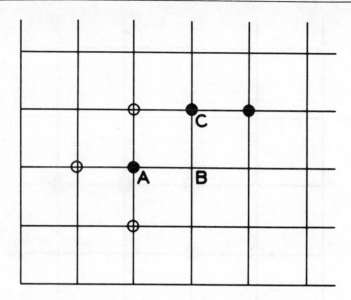

Figure 5 — Illustration of a significant configuration

That is, a point satisfies the reference "safe black stone" if the value of that point in array 1 of the internal representation lies between 601 and 900 inclusive and the value in array seven equals 1. A 1 in array seven tells us that we have a black stone on that point, and a 601 to 900 tells us that we have at least a medium-sized segment.

The program has the ability to scan such templates to all positions, all rotations, and all reflections of the board, thus recognizing the configuration ABC wherever it occurs. If the template is carefully specified, then configuration ABC can be quite a general occurrence. For example, Point A could be connected to a chain of stones with 1 breathing space left. Allowing this would give the template more generality.

The present program has 85 templates capable of recognizing a wide variety of configurations. A template that matches implies either a move or a heuristic lookahead procedure. In fact, there are two types of templates for these two purposes.

The first type of template specifies a weight of implication and a pair of relative coordinates for the move which is implied. For example, the template for configuration ABC described above would specify

(1,0) 500

which means that a weight of 500 is assigned to the point B in Figure 5. These weights are stored in a special 19 X 19 array reserved for this purpose. Several templates may imply the same move in which case the weights are summed in this array. The highest sum of weights indicated the best move. Bad moves and illegal moves usually have a negative weight.

One more example of this type of template will be given:

(0,0) white segment
(0,0) black segment
(0,0) weight 40.

This template implies a move with weight 40 at the interface between opposing segments. A weight of 40 is relatively small, hence it will merely give a tendency towards moving in these areas. This template is very general; it can match as many as 100 times in a single scan of the board. It gives a slight tendency to move between opposing armies which helps the program's play.

There are 65 templates which imply moves in the manner just described, the other 20 templates imply a heuristic lookahead. The difference between these two types of templates is that instead of a weight being placed in the weight array, an x is-placed in a 19 X 19 array as an indication of the template match. The x's are a mark to indicate that a move tree search should be performed in the local area about the x. All of the templates are applied before the search is begun. Figure 6 illustrates a configuration which would be matched by some of the 20 templates, and the location of the x's placed by those templates.

The array which contains the x's is used as a mask to determine the extent of the search and the depth is fixed at two moves for each side. The search is actually performed twice, once for white moving first, and once for black moving first. At the end of these searches, it is noted whether either side can force a capture by moving first. This information tells the program whether a move is necessary to cause or avoid a capture.

For example, if black can capture whether he moves first or not, then it is unnecessary for him to move. The decision to move is recorded by placing a weight of 4000 in the array already discussed in connection with the first type of template.

In many cases a depth of two moves is not sufficient to determine whether capture takes place or not. The most common instance of this is known as the "ladder attack" which is illustrated in Figure 7. These situations are characterized by the repeated occurrence of moves which force the opponent to reply or to be captured. In such cases, the search procedure continues to a depth of up to 100 moves to see whether capture finally takes place. No branching takes place during this extension of the look ahead.

When all of the templates have been applied and the heuristic search procedure is through, the program simply chooses the move which corresponds to the highest sum of weights in the array of weights. If the maximum weight is below 100 then the program passes.

This completes the description of the program except for a few minor details of operation. Three seconds are used for the creation of the internal representation and two seconds are used by the template matching procedure. The heuristic search takes from .1 to 4 seconds. A challenger has the option of moving first or second, and can also give the program a handicap of any number of stones on the board. The program is not able to haggle over the final score as GO players often do, hence a referee may be required to supervise the scoring.

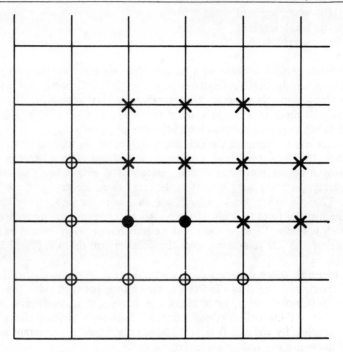

Figure 6 – Creation of a mask for lookahead

RESULTS

The program now has a record of two wins and two losses against human opponents. The opponents can best be described as intelligent adults who know how to play GO, have played from two to twenty games but have not studied the game. The program appears to have reached the bottom rung of the ladder of human GO players. Interested readers are urged to get a GO board and play through the game listed at the end of this report.

The first type of template, those which imply moves, are responsible for about 80 percent of the moves made by the program. These templates give the program fairly good positional play, especially in the first part of the game.

The remaining templates, together with the look-ahead search, are valuable for avoidance of traps which cause the loss of a stone or two. The opponent's play is also restricted since he must play more carefully. The loss of one stone can have a great effect upon the outcome of the game. The program is able to play without these templates, hence without the search, but opponents soon learn to take advantage of this weakness.

The program plays as if it can "see" such things as the influence of stones, the segmentation of the board, and the armies of black and white stones. This alone makes it a reasonable candidate as a model of visual organization for the game of GO. It would be of interest to test the model by performing standard psychological experiments. For example, a drawing of a GO board could be shown to a human subject with the instructions to segment the board with

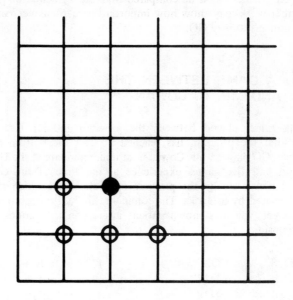

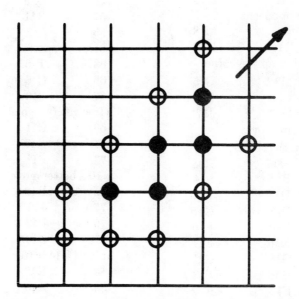

Figure 7 — Illustration of the "ladder attack"

dashed lines. The results could be compared with the segmentation given by the program. Further work may show how important perceptual mechanisms are to the ability of humans to play GO.

APPENDIX: A GAME BETWEEN THE PROGRAM AND MR. G. COWAN

The following game, played between the program and Mr. George Cowan, demonstrates that the program has reached at least the bottom rung of the ladder of human GO players. Mr. Cowan is an undergraduate at the University of Wisconsin, and had five games experience at the time of the contest. The even-numbered moves are by the program (white). Moves which resulted in a capture are indicated by asterisks. The comments are by Professor Paul Purdom, a good GO player, who has shown patient interest in the various GO-playing efforts at Wisconsin.

1.	D 3	Q3		47.	R 6	S 9
3.	E 9	D17		49.	T 8	T 9
5.	Q16	H12		51.	S10	T 7*
too early for such a move				53.	T10	R10
7.	F15	R15		55.	Q 9	S11
too close to opponent				57.	R11	T11*
9.	O16	M 8		59.	S12	O 8
11.	R14	H 8		61.	S 6	P 7
shouldn't give up the corner				63.	T 6	P 9
13.	M12	C 5		65.	Q 6	Q10
15.	D 5	F12		67.	P10	S10
17.	D 7	J17		a free gift from black		
still important moves				69.	O11	Q12
remaining in the corner				71.	R13	O10
19.	M17	R 8		73.	P11	N11
21.	R 5	S 4		N10 a better move		
23.	D11	K 3		75.	R12	H17
25.	Q11	G 5		77.	J16	D 2
27.	Q15	F 6		79.	P12	B 3
29.	K16	F17		81.	Q13*	B14
31.	G16	G17		at last! C14 better		
33.	H16	F 3		83.	K17	S17
35.	E13	E 2		85.	R16	S15
still ignoring upper left side				seems to ignore sacrifices		
37.	Q 7	F 8		87.	S14	S16
wasted move				89.	R17	R18
39.	J18	S 7		91.	Q18	F 9
41.	Q 8	O 5		93.	S18	S19
43.	R 9	P 6		95.	R19*	T17
45.	S 8	R 7		97.	T19*	T14

both players wasting moves

99.	T13	F13
101.	T16	T15*
103.	T18	G14
105.	T16*	J14
107.	J10	J11
109.	J12	K12

K11 better

| 111. | N10 | J13* |

wasted

113.	O 9*	P 8
115.	N 9	L14
117.	M14	L13

M13 better

119.	K15	K 9
121.	L15	M10
123.	M11	L11
125.	N12*	N13
127.	Q 5	M13
129.	M15	O13
131.	N 7	N 6

should connect N8 and cut stone

133.	O 7	P 5
135.	P14	Q 4
137.	L10	M 9
139.	L 9	K10
141.	L 8	L 7
143.	K 8	J 8
145.	L12	K 7*
147.	K14	E 5
149.	K13	H10

wasted

151.	N14	P13
153.	F16	E16
155.	E15	D15
157.	C16	C15
159.	E18	E 7
161.	E17	D18

163.	D16*	C17
165.	B17	C18
167.	B18	F18
169.	E19	H18
171.	K18	G19
173.	J19	F19

the program would be much better if it could recognize eye possibilities

175.	E16	B19
177.	B16	H15
179.	E12	F11
181.	E14	B 7
183.	B 8	C 8
185.	B 9	R 4
187.	C 9	S 5
189.	A 7	T 5*
191.	B 6	D 6
193.	D 4	D 8
195.	C 7*	C 6
197.	B 7	E 8
199.	D 9	C 4
201.	E10	B 5
203.	E11	E 4
205.	F10	G10
207.	G15	G 9
209.	J15	H14
211.	F14	G12
213.	L 4	L 5
215.	L 3	K 4
217.	K 2	M 3
219.	M 2	N 3
221.	M 4	N 4
223.	L 2	N 2
225.	K 5	J 5
227.	M 1	K 6*
229.	J 1	H 2
231.	J 2	J 3

It was agreed to stop the game at this point. The resulting score was: Mr. Cowan . . . 59, program . . . 66, a seven point victory for the program. Approximately 15 minutes of computer time was used, and the entire contest took less than two hours of real time.

ACKNOWLEDGMENTS

This research was conducted with the support of NIH grant MH 12266 and NSF grant GP 7069.

BIBLIOGRAPHY

1 H REMUS
   Simulation of a learning machine for playing GO
   Proc IFIP Congress 1962
2 E THORPE W WALDEN
   A partial analysis of GO
   The Computer Journal Vol 7 No 3 1964
3 I GOOD
   The mystery of GO
   New Scientist January 21 1965 427
4 O KORSCHELT
   The theory and practice of GO
   Tuttle Rutland Vt 1966
5 E LASKER
   GO and GO-MOKO, the oriental board games
   Dover New York 1960
6 A SAMUEL
   Some studies of machine learning using the game of checkers
   IBM Journal of Research and Development Vol 3 No 3 1959
7 A NEWELL
   The chess machine
   Proc Western J C C 1955
8 C SHANNON
   Programming a digital computer for playing chess
   Philosophy Magazine March 1950
9 R GREENBLATT D EASTLAKE III S CROCKER
   The Greenblatt chess program
   Proc F J C C 1967
10 P GREENE
   Networks which realize a model for information representation
   Transactions of the University of Illinois Symposium on Self-Organization
   1961
11 W KOHLER
   Gestalt psychology
   Liveright New York 1947

Questions:

1. Define "Heuristic" (contrast to algorithm).

2. In the "visual organization" model, is the computer program capable of making better decisions than the person who wrote the program? Discuss.

3. Illustrate a practical example for this type of an application.

COMPUTERS AND
THE LAW OF PRIVACY

By RICHARD I. MILLER

It has by now become commonplace to observe that Americans leave a trail of records behind from the moment their birth is happily recorded on their parent's income tax return until the day the Social Security death benefit is paid. In addition to such non-governmental files as those maintained by banks, credit services, insurance investigations and the like, county, state and federal agencies have our school records, property holdings, licenses—for dogs, businesses and marriage—military records, income, public claims and court records. They are on file cards, microfilm, punched tape and magnetic storage media. They are scattered through hundreds of records centers in the commerical, governmental, educational and military systems. In an age in which life races ahead of art and science outstrips fiction, little imagination is required to postulate a society in which the record centers speak to one another in a common language. And intuitively the individual feels trapped in the web of his own history.

The reason that the relationship of the computer to the right of privacy is so profoundly disturbing is that it is quite dissimilar to the relationship of any other device or technique to the right of privacy. Unlike the vest-pocket TV cameras, snooperscopes, and sophisticated surveillance devices, the computer does not "invade." It does not look. It does not take blood or analyze body fluids. It cannot even be used as a device to improperly gather evidence. Rather, it stores information that is given to it, correlates it with other information in its memory, and retrieves it at the request of the operator. And because the prospect of a machine which knows all and never forgets fills many with dread, that is quite enough to compel a re-examination of the entire concept of "privacy."

Let us first look at the operations of the computer with respect to that concept. Secondly, let us briefly examine the concept of privacy as it is evolving in American case and statutory law and, finally, propose a few recommendations about how the law may help us to live with the Biggest Brother of all.

INFORMATION FOR SALE

The acquisition and sale of data is a lively business: credit, insurance and personnel investigations are burgeoning. Organizations such as Retail Credit

Reprinted with permission from DATAMATION, ® (September), published and copyrighted (1968) by F. D. Thompson Publications, Inc. 35 Mason St., Greenwich, Conn. 06830.

Company and Associated Credit Bureaus are unhampered by state or federal regulations. The clerk of court will send a certified copy of any court record for a nominal fee. Large retail credit investigating companies assure clients that any search can be strengthened by drawing upon reports made in previous investigations. Lawyers' services exist to acquire public documents of all kinds. But it is still true that compiling a complete dossier on any individual who is not in military service is a time-consuming, expensive proposition. Therefore, there has been some consolation in the knowledge that a semblance of privacy is preserved by the inefficiency of methods of data retrieval.

Until now the unauthorized use of data or the redistribution of data was held at tolerable levels, such as the rental and sale of subscription lists. That is changing with the advent of giant computers which increse the investment in, and the value of, personal data. A typical credit file contains a person's address, family status, place of employment, approximate salary, credit income, charge accounts, payment income and even, in the case of insurance company files, medical and hospital records and "moral hazards"—extramarital affairs, homosexuality, heavy drinking or other social observations which could affect the risk. It is no longer a question of "whether" total documentation on the lives of every individual in the country will be quickly and inexpensively available, but "when," "by whom" and "under what circumstances."

It is equally apparent that although public attention has been fixed on a "National Data Center" concept introduced by the Statistical Standards Office of the Bureau of the Budget, the federal government is not the only party interested in personnel data storage and retrieval. Even if, as it now appears, the BOB concept has been aborted by the House Committee on Government Operations and the Senate Judiciary Committee, the rate of personal data distribution is rapidly accelerating in the private sector of society. All too often, a higher standard of conduct is expected from government than from the governed. If privacy can be violated by indiscriminate access to a personnel data center, whose records are not subject to verification, it is as truly violated by a creditor or a litigant as by a public servant. It is not enough to draft regulations curbing the excesses of government alone. Rather, the legal concept of privacy must be woven into a chain of mail which will protect the individual from onslaughts from any quarter.

Computer experts draw a line between (1) statistical information systems and (2) intelligence systems. In theory, the former produces information that only identifies characteristics relating to a group of individuals or "populations," whereas the latter generates data about individuals as individuals. A statistical question might be "What proportion of the residents of Roxbury earn an income of less than $3.000?" An intelligence question would be: "What is the income of John Doe?"

There are those who argue that a statistical information system can be designed and administered in such a way that it cannot be used as an intelligence system. They point to the Bureau of the Census, which is legally forbidden to disclose confidential statistical data, as an example. Other experts challenge the distinction and argue that as the speed of computers goes up and the cost comes down, it becomes more efficient to store raw data in a statistical system which can then be probed for intelligence purposes. There must always be at least a coded identity for any longitudinal study. Thus, the earnings of a Roxbury resident in 1968 must be linked to the earnings of the same resident in 1967 to abstract information about earning trends for a subpopulation.

To a layman it would appear that if the analyst is satisfied that he has derived all possible statistical information from the raw data, then the contention of separate systems is supported. But there is always a new way to cut the deck. A good analyst is constantly probing his data for novel and useful correlations. The fact that it is easier to do so with the larger machines suggests that the complete separation of statistical and intelligence systems is, at best, a receding goal.

Prior to a famous article in the Harvard Law Review by Warren and Brandeis in 1890, there simply was no legal right to "privacy" in American law. The notion of a concept of privacy was *implied*—as, for example, in the search and seizure provision of the Constitution, in the common law of privileged communications, in the law of trade secret, and of defamation—but the invasion of privacy as a distinct, actionable wrong was not recognized by the courts. It is still not a right which can be simply delineated. In fact, it has been analyzed as four distinct, rather unrelated legal actions:

1. Intrusion of physical solitude.
2. Publication of private matters violating ordinary decencies.
3. Creating a false public image, as by forging a letter attributing to a person views that he does not hold.
4. Appropriating some element of a personality for commercial use without permission.

In each of these forms, the "right" of privacy emerges as a right to be let alone, to be free of prying, peeping and snooping. This is also characteristic of legal subjects in which the individual's claim to a private personality is couched in doctrine other than "privacy." Thus, in search and seizure cases, the Supreme Court recently condemned all sorts of sophisticated electronic, optical and acoustical devices which are used to improperly intercept private communications. It stated in *Katz vs. United States* that " ... The Fourth Amendment cannot be translated into a general constitutional 'right to privacy' ... " but the protection of a person's *general* right to privacy—his right to be let alone by other people—is, like the protection of his property and of his very life, left largely to the law of the individual States.

Legal problems raised by the computer are different. They involve the accuracy or improper use of information voluntarily communicated rather than the improper taking of protected information. As the Court observed in the case above, "What a person knowingly exposes to the public, even in his own home or office, is not a subject of Fourth Amendment protection." Thus, the local laws of privileged communications and defamation are a bit more pertinent to the issue at hand.

In the former case, the law may not compel a party to divulge a protected communication, as between husband and wife or lawyer and client. Although one spouse may not legally restrain another from disclosing a communication, at least the applicable principle is that voluntary communications may be protected because of the relationship between the communicants, rather than because of the way the information comes into the hands of a third party. Defamatory statements are defined as tending to expose a person to hatred, ridicule or contempt in the minds of any considerable and respectable class in the community.

Most of the cases involve a balance of the right to privacy against the freedom of the press. Happily the law does not require a physical intrusion of any sort. But these cases typically involve statements *about* the plaintiff rather than statements *by* the plaintiff. Thus, the courts will enjoin the publication of an unauthorized biography of a private person, but will not even award damages for the publication of a private telephone conversation by one of the parties to it. Yet, this is as far as the common law has developed with respect to the kind of "privacy" which is violated by the computer. If one would look to the evolving case law for protection, it offers scarcely more than a fig leaf.

TWO RELATED PROBLEMS

Statutory law is developing in two directions at once: we are, at one and the same time, concerned with the growing power of the government to accumulate inforamtion and keep it from the people, and disturbed lest it disclose information extracted by force of law or voluntarily offered for particular purposes only. So there are "freedom of information" laws to ensure the availability of information and "privacy" laws to inhibit its availability.

To advance the right to know, congress passed a "freedom of information" law to give every citizen a right to learn what goes on in official Washington. The act theoretically opens the books to all but:

1. Defense classifed documents.
2. Federal Bureau of Investigation files.
3. Income tax returns.
4. Patent applications.
5. Executive branch memoranda.
6. Trade secrets and industry financial data.

It is most unlikely that all agencies will readily comply with the law; in fact, it is a virtual certainty that certain records will not be disclosed without litigation. These would include Veterans' Administration records, agency tests of commercial products, Food and Drug Administration new drug applications and Civil Air Board complaint letters, among others. On the other hand, the Department of Agriculture, in an unusually cooperative spirit, announced that it will now let anyone see a thick dossier of the names of all farmers who received more than $5,000 in government payments during the preceding year. Of particular relevance was the agency's explanation that the disclosure of these records (which theoretically have always been in the public domain) " . . . is not the result of the new law but of the Department's new computer, which for the first time permits a national compilation of farm subsidy data previously available only at the county level."

The other side of the coin is illustrated by the privacy statutes which are springing up to extend the case law noted above. The New York privacy statute, for example, prevents " . . . the appropriation and use in advertising or promotion of the sale of goods (by the use) of another's name, portrait or picture without his consent." Although the interests protected are primarily economic in nature, the trend is towards infusing social and moral considerations in the administration of justice.

BALANCING RIGHTS AND PROTECTION

The most important statutory developments affecting "privacy" in the broad, rather than the technical, sense are, of course, those pertaining to the propriety of securing evidence through wiretapping, compulsory physiological examinations, polygraph use by public agencies and the like. In these instances, the right of the individual to privacy is weighted against the right of a society to protect itself against crime. These issues do not involve the disclosure of voluntary communications by the recipient and hence are not directly related to our subject. It is important to note, however, that the areas of greatest statutory activity are not related to the computer's particular assault on our claim to a private personality.

Experience in the product liability field, particularly the design of automobiles, has taught that the law can only effectively regulate technology by controlling its form as well as its use. It is not enough to test, license and control the driver. The law must affect the design of the vehicle itself. The notion of product regulation to protect public interests other than health and safety, such as air and water pollution, is expanding. Let us, therefore, recommend a few technical safeguards which can be built around the use of computers for storing and distributing personal data:

1. Minimal cryptographic protection for transmission lines which carry personal data has been devised and should be utilized so that eavesdropping may be a bit more complicated and expensive than tapping a telephone line is today.

2. Personal data should never be filed in a "clear" state, so that a simple access to storage will, in a sense, open every safety deposit box in the vault at once.

3. Auditing of computer programs that store personal data, to be certain that no programmer has deliberately or inadvertently short-circuited access routes, should become as standard as the audit of bank records.

4. Recording devices should be built into computers to verify and record the source of requests for personal information interrogration.

These suggestions will undoubtedly raise the cost of computers, as seat belts and padded dashboards raise the cost of automobiles, but if one accepts the proposition that computers are destined to play as significant a role in our society as automobiles, the time to build in the additional cost is now.

In order to extend the legal definition of privacy, it is not necessary to wait for the first defamation cases to arise out of the dissemination of false information in a data center, or the malicious use of true information. Professor Charles Reich of Yale Law School has observed that the authors of the Constitution protected privacy in every way in which it was understood in those times: they protected speech, religion and incriminating knowledge. They protected people against unwarranted search and seizure and forbade the quartering of soldiers in homes. Even the right to bear arms can be considered as an extension of privacy, as then known. Extending their concerns to today's world, should we not consider at least these few modest propositions?

EXTENDING LEGAL RIGHTS

First: Any government agency or private individual or firm which gathers personal data from several sources for the purpose of distributing that data to third parties should be required to:

a. Give notice to individuals that such data is being collected about them.

b. Afford access by such individuals to the data for the purpose of verification.

Second: Public authorities should not be authorized to purchase or use edp equipment for the purpose of storing and distributing personal data to third parties unless a satisfactory plan is filed with the highest administrative office in the agency, or a board reporting to him, disclosing the agency's program for protecting the privacy of individuals. It is expected that standards would be gradually created and adopted appropriate to agency operations and equipment.

Third: Public agencies and firms, and their agents and employees, engaged in the business of gathering and distributing personal data, should be liable to injured parties for the dissemination of false data or the knowing transmission of true data for defamatory purposes. The injured party should have a right to enjoin the transmission of such data.

If the observation of totalitarian societies, hospital or prison life, has taught us anything, it should be that an individual's life ought not be an open book—unless he chooses to make it so. Society has a right to demand that the pages be exposed from time to time, but anyone who wants to compile the book by collating the pages and publish the contents without the permission of the author must accept responsibility for its accuracy and proper application. Nathaniel Hawthorne and the Concord transcendentalists observed in the nineteenth century that it was a most serious crime to probe the secret heart. If we fail to protect ourselves against the reach of our own technology, there may well be no secret hearts to probe.

Questions:

1. Discuss the possible ramifications of a National Data Center. Would it aid the federal government? Would it affect the privacy rights of citizens?

2. Compare statistical information systems with intelligence systems.

3. Could the National Data Center concept be implemented without utilizing computers? Explain.

A NEW CONCEPT IN TIME SHARING: DEDICATED SYSTEMS SHARE ONE COMPUTER

By GERALD J. SMOLEN

In a unique type of sharing, four dedicated real-time, on-line systems share one computer concurrently, and three similar systems share another, at our company's new data processing center in New Jersey. Although hardly "time sharing" in the usual sense of the term, this technique provides the same basic advantage: each user enjoys the benefits of a real-time EDP system for a fraction of what it would cost, for hardware, software, and operations, to establish a comparable in-house capability.

The seven separate shared, but dedicated, systems include a hotel/motel reservation system, a rental car reservation system, a military troop movement control system, an airline reservation system, a container control and freight administration system, and two steamship line reservation systems. Additional systems could be added to either of the two computers, the only limitation being the maximum response time which any one of the separate systems could tolerate. This type of sharing of dedicated information systems would be appropriate to virtually any system requiring immediate reference to up-to-the-minute information.

An unusual aspect of these two computer-sharing systems is that, although the hardware is owned by one of the subscribers in each case, the computers are located at a neutral site and operated, under contract, by Aries Corporation. This assures protection of proprietary information. It also has the advantage that system design, programming, and operation are performed by experienced Aries personnel, relieving the subscriber of the necessity of employing a large EDP staff merely to make such a system operational.

SYSTEM REQUIREMENTS

All seven systems presently sharing the two computers have the following requirements in common:
1. Large mass data storage.
2. Real-time operation.
3. Conversational communications mode.
4. Random intermittent processing.

The real-time, on-line hotel/motel reservation system is an excellent example. Many remote stations must be able to communicate at any time with a central computer having access to a large file of current information.

Yet actual processing requirements are completely random. They depend only upon the receipt of individual requests for reservations. Thus, actual processing time is only a fraction of that available, but it must be available when requested.

COMPUTER OPERATION

Each dedicated system shares a mass storage device while operating concurrently with the other systems within the central processing unit. Processing time is not distributed between users on a time basis, but is used as needed by each system.

Every system communicates with the computer through dedicated lines, and only one entry is necessary to begin processing. The line through which the message is received identifies the subscriber and determines and confines the programs and storage area to be used. This is in contrast to conventional time-sharing techniques in which an introductory conversation is required to identify the user and the proper program.

Also, programs are dedicated and specific to each system, rather than general, as is the case with more conventional time sharing. This design eliminates introductory dialogue, affords complete protection of each system's programs and data, frees message texts and formats of inhibitions imposed by usual time-shared programs, and permits unlimited flexibility in the selection of remote equipment. The two systems illustrate (but do not limit) the diversity of remote equipment which can be employed.

Only control programs are permanently core resident. All application programs are stored on the drum. Message processing is initiated on a first-come, first-served basis, but subsequent processing is intermixed.

This technique takes advantage of the fact that the core executes program instructions in microseconds, whereas peripheral operations take milliseconds. For instance, if two messages arrive simultaneously, one is partly processed and then referred to the appropriate peripheral — to the drum for execution of an application program, let us say. The core is now free to switch from the control program for the first message and accept the second message. When that message is referred to the appropriate peripheral device, the core again switches programs, either to receive a third message for partial processing, or perhaps to receive the data requested from the drum in response to message number one. Thus, a portion of each program is executed in the core, then a portion of another, and so on. Processing of messages in this interleaved fashion increases core efficiency by eliminating the long waits for information to return from the slower peripherals as in sequential processing.

Although all programs appear to be executed simultaneously, the computer is constantly switching from one unique dedicated system to the other. Each message is handled in its turn, but the computer is able to take advantage of those fractions of a second during which each message does not actually require processing in the core memory.

SYSTEMS DESCRIPTION

As previously stated, two computers are presently operating with shared, dedicated systems. The older system, which has been in operation since early 1967, combines three separate reservations systems and a military troop control movement system using a Univac 491 central processing unit with a 32K, 30 bit-word memory. Peripheral equipment at the computer center includes one (1) Univac Fastrand II drum with 128 million character storage capacity and an average access time of 90 milliseconds, four (4) Univac VIC tape drives, and one (1) Univac 1004 printer, punch, and card reader. This equipment is fully duplicated to insure 24-hour operation 7 days a week, 365 days a year.

RESERVATIONS SYSTEMS

The three reservation systems presently employ 1,800 remote Rixon Agents Sets located throughout the United States, including Hawaii and Canada. They communicate with the computer through 58 low-speed (10 characters per second) and 4 high-speed (2,000 bits per second) communications lines.

The hotel/motel system provides an interconnecting real-time reservation service for chains which either do not have the message volume to justify, or which want to avoid the capital outlay required by a proprietary system. The system also enables subscribers to offer a much wider choice of accommodations than a single-chain proprietary system, and thus better customer service.

The rental car reservation system provides real-time reservation service for a national car rental company. It can make reservations by type of car desired for up to a year in advance.

The airline reservation system is not yet in service. When it is, it will use identical remote equipment and the same communications lines as the other two reservations systems. The purpose of this system is to connect travel agents throughout the country with the automated reservations system of a national airline. Travel agents will no longer have to telephone for reservations, but will be able to reserve space on over 80 percent of the scheduled domestic airline flights in the same manner as presently done by computer through airline offices.

The two reservations services presently in service handle an average of 33,500 messages per day with an average response time of 2 seconds.

TROOP MOVEMENT CONTROL

The military troop movement control system is designed to determine the most efficient and economical method for moving troops within the continental United States. The computer is connected to a single remote control center containing the following equipment: 9 Bunker Ramo CRTs, 1 high-speed Univac DCT 2,000 printer, 1 Bunker Ramo paper tape reader, 1 Bunker Ramo paper tape punch, and 1 Bunker Ramo R/O printer. This system handles 4,000 messages per day.

SECOND SYSTEM

The second shared computer handles three separate dedicated systems. It is a Univac 418 central processing unit having a 32k, 18 bit-word memory. Peripheral equipment, storage, tape drives, printers, etc., is identical to that of the first system. Communication with remote sites is by means of 7 low-speed and 5 high-speed lines.

The first system on line with this computer is designed primarily to control the movement of shipping containers from the time they arrive in the United States until they embark again for a foreign port. Eventually, upwards of 15,000 of these "seagoing boxes" will be tracked through the system. Remote stations include sixteen (16) ASR 33 TWX sites and five (5) ASR private line sites. This system is presently handling about 1,800 messages per day, and information about the location and status of any container is obtained in 7 seconds.

In addition to container control, the system is also used for freight administration and documentation. For this purpose it is connected to a remote Univac 9300 satellite computer, a high-speed printer, punch, and card reader.

Each of the two steamship line reservation systems connects the central computer to one remote location where inquiries for reservations are received by telephone. Reservations clerks communicate with the computer through Uniscope 300 CRTs and can reserve space within seconds. Just prior to sailings the computer will prepare reservations lists and tickets.

The steamship line reservation systems are an excellent example of the practicality and economics of this type of computer sharing. Although the lines are competitive, system design absolutely protects the integrity of proprietary information. However, because the programs are identical, the two lines were able to split software costs.

EVALUATION

The combining of several discrete real-time on-line information systems in one computer has obvious advantages to a great many businesses for which a proprietary data processing system would be too costly. Although all but two of the systems presently operating are reservations systems, it should be apparent that a variety of management information systems could be accommodated in this manner. Some possibilities might be multi-list real estate systems, inventory control, information retrieval for comparative purposes, resource allocation, and many others. The only criteria of suitability is the need for large mass storage and real-time operation in a conversational mode.

This type of "time-sharing" is also ideal for demonstration or experimental real-time systems or for the early phases of systems which will eventually be large enough to justify their own central processing unit. Rather than start out with a smaller computer and then be forced to rewrite all of the programs in order to move up to a larger, more sophisticated device, the programs of the shared system can be applied directly without significant modification.

The approach also has the advantage of utilizing the talents of experienced system design and programming personnel, capable of getting such a system operational in minimum time and with a minimum of "bugs". It is interesting to note that several of the subscribers to these systems were able to go "on-the-air" with a real-time system without any programmers on their own payroll. Similar systems can put real-time EDP within the reach of many organizations which do not enjoy its benefits at the present time.

Questions:

1. Discuss the advantages and disadvantages of having an independent agent manage a computer system that is shared by more than one company.

2. Compare the system described to more conventional time sharing systems.

FACTS COME FAST WITH MICROFILM AND DATA DISPLAY

Fast fact finding is the key to efficient credit control and customer service operations. From the customer's viewpoint, lengthy delay in verification of his good credit standing may be sufficient prod to shop elsewhere. And, when there is an error in his account, he wants it corrected promptly.

The credit grantor wants to ensure that he is not losing money to poor credit risks. This, in addition to a desire to provide the type of fast, accurate service that will keep customers happy and attract new ones.

At Continental Illinois National Bank and Trust Co., Chicago, a smooth blending of microfilm and computer technology in "fact" storage and retrieval systems does an effective job from both the customers' and the bank's points of view.

Credit department personnel have easy access to two major files of complementary information. One file is stored on microfilm and accessed by means of a high speed, automated retrieval system. The other is stored on magnetic discs and accessed by means of data display and entry terminals.

The dual system is used to process and service the accounts of Town & Country credit cardholders. The microfilm part of the system was a belated addition. When Continental entered the credit card business in late 1966, it expected to be handling about one million accounts. The number quickly grew to two million.

Continental is one of 15 member banks in the Midwest Bank Card system which had $240 million in credit card sales in 1967. Town & Country cardholders accounted for about 40 percent of the total. The credit card system involves merchants and cardholders in Southwest Michigan and Indiana as well as Illinois.

The film files are used primarily by the over-limits section of Continental's credit department. As part of the daily processing of transactions, the bank's computer system is programed to print out a list of all accounts that exceed the permissible credit level. For those accounts that exceed the limit for the first time—about 250 a day—cards are punched and interpreted, showing account number, permissible credit level, balance due and the date on which the card was created. Two cards are created for each overlimit account: one card is actually a form on which the overlimits section enters additional information, the other is a preprinted reminder notice sent to the customer.

Reprinted from BUSINESS AUTOMATION, May 1968, Copyright Business Press International, Inc.

A DOCUMENT EXPLOSION

When the cards leave the data processing center, they contain (in punched and written form) only basic data—account number, credit limit, balance due, date and restraint code. This must be supplemented by additional information: identity data (name, address, etc.) from the microfilm files and current account status from the magnetic disc files. Identity data is required to type envelopes in which the preprinted reminder notices are mailed. Account status information is used for follow-up action on the account.

When the system was first set up, identity data was retrieved from printed cards—double tab card size—in filing cabinets. "We had cabinets lined up all around the department. If you put them end-to-end, they probably would have stretched out to a block or two, and they were filled with those cards. When we began getting boxes full of new cards to put in the files, and they had to be stacked on top of those cabinets—well, something had to be done," stated Ed Lenahan, credit manager. "The rest of the system—the data processing aspect of it—worked fine, but the part that we had to deal with simply wasn't adequate for the tremendous volume that began coming in."

The alternatives considered in devising a different system included having the computer print out all pertinent data, but the end result would have been about 30 volumes of paper, each 6-in. thick. At that time, the deaprtment was using microfilm for other applications and considered expansion of that installation. However, manually operated film readers were being used. In order to handle the required look-up volume, a considerable number of readers plus operators and duplicates of film files would have been necessary. There also was a fatigue factor. With manually operated readers, an operator becomes bleary-eyed after using the machine constantly over a two-hour period.

Attention then turned to Eastman Kodak's Miracode, an automated retrieval system that employes index coding on the microfilm. The system reads the codes as the film speeds through the machine and automatically stops the film when the desired index number—keyed in by an operator—passes the reading mechanism. The data adjacent to the code is displayed on the reader screen. The operator does not have to watch the screen nor does she have to manually search through the film.

Data gathered during the pre-installation study provides additional insight into comparative benefits of the alternatives Continental considered. If the computer were used to produce all the data required, approxmiately 45 minutes of costly computer time would be required and the result would be cumbersome paper volumes. One person can perform about 15 look-ups per hour using these volumes. With the manually operated microfilm system, about 30 look-ups per hour are possible; with Miracode, about 100 per hour.

FROM BITS TO IMAGES

Film used in the Miracode system is produced from magnetic tape. Every three months, a computer program is run which calls out required data from the master file of customer accounts (on magnetic tapes). The program also provides for writing on the tape the indexing data which goes onto the film. The tape is sent to MicoPrint Corp., a Chicago service company which uses a Stromberg

Carlson microfilm recorder to transfer the data from tape to film, then loads the film into cartridges.

The look-up operation in the overlimits section begins when a batch of the tab card overlimit notices arrives. The operator selects the cartridge in which the account number is located, inserts it into the Miracode reader and keys six digits of the account number into the adjacent keyboard. The frame of film containing the data she seeks is displayed and she transcribes it to the overlimit notice form. The data includes: name, address, phone number, number of the bank which issued the card, whether or not a credit card application is on file, and number of cards issued to the account (e.g., one for the wife, one for the husband).

Typists use the name and address information to prepare envelopes for mailing the reminder notices. The overlimit notice forms are then sorted according to: amount the account exceeds the limit, presence of absence of a credit application. (Continental's initial issue of cards, like those of nearly all banks embarking on the credit card plan, was based on lists supplied by its customers and 470 participating correspondent banks. Applications were not required.)

The batched cards go to an authorization center where IBM 2260 inquiry-display terminals are used to ascertain account status. Every time a transaction affecting an account is processed by the computer, the status file—on magnetic discs—is updated. The terminal operator keys in the account number and the status file is displayed in front of her within a few seconds. She transcribes the data to the overlimit notice forms, then returns them to the overlimits section. At this point, one of three decisions is made: terminate the account, ask the cardholder if he wants to increase the permissible credit limit, place the card in a "hold" situation pending response of the cardholder to the reminder notice.

"With our fast look-up capability, we can make decisions on 95 percent of those first-time overlimit accounts before they're over by more than $50," stated Dave Damaree, credit supervisor. "The decisions currently follow this pattern: about 80 percent go into 'hold', 10 percent have the credit limit increased, 10 percent are terminated." The percentage in the latter case is likely to go down as the day-to-day operations reduce the number of accounts for which there are no applications.

INSTANT UPDATE

If the credit department decides to alter account status—by increasing credit limit, terminating, or putting a card on a revoke list because it has been lost or stolen—the necessary information is printed on a form used by a display terminal operator. She keys in a security number to obtain access to the disc file, then enters the information from the form. The file is updated immediately.

Display terminals also are used in the credit authorization section which handles inquiries from merchants. There are 10 terminals in this section. Whenever a purchase exceeds the merchant's floor limit—say, $50—the sales clerk phones the authorization section at Continental, gives the credit authorizer the customer's account number and merchant's number. The authorizer keys in this data on the display terminal.

If the transaction is approved, the computer transmits account status information, which is displayed on the authrozer's terminal, and she verbally relays an OK to the merchant.

If a transaction is not approved, i.e., does not fall within pre-set parameters, the system is programed to automatically switch the response to a supervisor's terminal. He picks up his phone, converses with the merchant and possibly the customer, then decides whether to overrule the program. This credit authorization system, MIRA (Merchants Instant Response Authorization), was developed by Continental and is now being marketed to other companies with credit card programs. MIRA's central processor is an IBM System/360 Model 50 computer. The bank has two of these plus a Mod 30 and is currently transferring applications from second generation computers.

Although the Miracode files are used primarily by the overlimits section, they are also referred to occasionally by credit authorizers to verify information. The film file is not updated daily so there are occasions when information on new accounts that are over limit must be obtained from the cardholder services department which issues credit cards.

Microfilm is a staple in the cardholder services department where some 300 customer inquiries are handled each day. Inquiries are batched by cycle numbers; a cycle number represents a group of accounts. Adjusters receive these batches and refer to one or more of the following sources to handle the inquiry: status reports (computer printed), daily transaction journal (microfilm), accounts receivable summation (computer printed), billing journal (computer printed), transaction documents such as checks, statements, sales tickets (microfilm) and a payment list (microfilm). They also have access to a duplicate of the film used in the credit department's Miracode system.

FROM NAME TO NUMBER

Both the credit and cardholder services departments also have an alphabetic list of accounts, on microfilm, for obtaining account numbers when only the name of the cardholder is available.

The daily transaction journals formerly were computer-printed. One of these consists of five-hundred 11 x 15-in. pages. Space saving alone probably would have justified putting these journals on film, but reduced look-up time leading to quicker response to customers' inquiries also was a factor.

Once each day, transaction data is accumulated by the computer and put onto magnetic tape which is sent to MicoPrint for conversion to microfilm. For retrieval of information from this file, the cardholder services department uses a Lodestar reader with Image Control. The latter is a semiautomated retrieval system, less sophisticated than Miracode, which involves a different indexing method.

Computer programs for the daily transaction application are designed so that as the data is being transferred to magnetic tape, every fifth page number is transferred to computer memory. When the transaction list has been posted to magnetic tape, the numbers stored in memory are transferred to the tape and form an index page on the microfilm.

To get at the data on the file, the operator pulls the transaction file (single cartridge) for the appropriate date and inserts it in the viewer. She pushes a button to display the index page and finds which of the "every fifth" numbers the account number she seeks is closest to. After that number is keyed in, the film is searched automatically and stops within four frames of the data she seeks. From that point, scanning is done manually.

About 25 percent of the 300 inquiries processed each day require look-up in the transaction journal. Most of the remaining 75 percent require access to the billing and accounts receivable journals. Programs are now being written to combine these two into one report and produce them on microfilm, via magnetic tape.

Because the billing journals are just as bulky as the paper transaction journals formerly used, "we're starting to film our own from the hard copy," said Robert Podowski, managing supervisor. The bound printout is burst, using a Uarco 1740 burster, then the separate pages are filmed. Instead of a computer picking up every fifth page number, the camera operator writes it down and an index page is prepared manually, then filmed. An Eastman Kodak processing laboratory encodes the film.

"We'll continue to do this until the computer takes over," Podowski stated. "Besides space, there is another factor we have to consider; most of our adjusters are women, and those printed volumes are heavy and difficult to handle."

MICROBILLS

Microfilm is also part of the billing procedure in the Town & Country operations. After sales tickets flow through keypunching for computer input preparation, they are accumulated in the cardholder services section. The tab card size tickets are filed in drawers at random. On the billing date, the tickets are fed into an IBM 083 sorter which puts them in numeric sequence. Then they are fed into a collator, along with computer-printed statements.

A manual inspection ensures that the number of transaction documents collated with each statement is identical with the number printed on the statement. All these documents are filmed, using a Recordak camera, then processed through a Phillipsburg automatic sorting, inserting, envelope-sealing and postage imprinting machine. Sealed envelopes are manually inspected, to make sure the address on the statement card shows through the window envelope, then mailed.

The transaction film becomes part of the audit trial and a source for the adjusters who field customer inquiries. Most are answered within a day-and-a-half of receipt.

There are other ways of handling the various applications at Continental, but the bank believes that it has chosen the most effective from a cost performance viewpoint. The methods and procedures department, which evaluated alternatives and helped establish the systems in use, continually searches for ways of improving and making more effective the means by which the bank moves data.

After working with bulky computer printout and struggling against an increasing volume of work flow, most of those who use the film files agree with Lenahan's comment: "Mircrofilm, as far as I'm concerned, just makes good sense."

Questions:

1. List the good attributes of microfilm storage and retrieval.

2. What objections does the author list to computer produced "hard copy" reports?

III

TECHNOLOGY

SOURCE DATA AUTOMATION

edited by
S. F. DONOVAN

I. INTRODUCTION

During the last 50 years the American economy has become increasingly dependent upon paperwork. The ratio of clerical workers, in the process, has gone from 1 in 40 of the total work force at the beginning of the century to 1 in 6 at the present.

Paperwork processing in this country now costs about $40 billion a year for clerical salaries and for office tools — everything from typists, punchcard operators, and bookkeepers to pencils, paper, typewriters, adding machines, duplicators, and items of electronic hardware. Of this grand total, the annual Federal outlay is nearing $5 billion.

Today about 20 percent of the paperwork in the Federal Government has been automated in one way or another. An account of this would tend to be divided into three parts: (1) automated data processing, (2) automated information storage and retrieval, and (3) source data automation. This article is concerned with the latter, and with the other two only when a controlling interrelation exists.

SHORT HISTORY

Jean Emile Baudot provided the possibility for source data automation when he built a paper-tape punch and reader in the 1870's. About the same time, two other important machines were invented. William Burroughs, a bank clerk, invented the first commercially practical adding machine. Christopher Sholes invented the first commercially practical typewriter. A little later, William Hollerith and Charles Powers, realizing the value of holes as a language carrier, devised punchcards as we know them today.

In those inventions, source data automation machines had their genesis. The adding machine provided the basis for mechanical mathematics; i.e., addition, multiplication (repeat addition), subtraction, and division (repeat subtraction). The typewriter provided the basis for printing. When converted to type segments on tabulators, it provided higher speed printing.

Source data automation has progressed much more slowly than other technological improvements. The reason was probably the reluctance of

---

This is an extract of the General Services Administration Manual FPMR 11-5.

267

executives to accept change. It was difficult to sell the idea that a machine could accurately produce, in 1 day's time, four to five times more work than a clerk could produce manually.

In 1912, John Wahl combined the adding machine with the typewriter to produce the first descriptive accounting machine. This made it possible, for the first time, to type item descriptions and to compute account balances in a single operation, rather than two separate operations.

The first front-carriage-feed accounting machine was marketed in 1928. This machine made it possible to produce, in one writing, multiple forms of differing content. No longer was it necessary to prepare statements, ledgers, and journals in three independent steps. By means of carbon paper, all could be created in one operation. The first accounting machine synchronized with a paper-tape punch was developed in 1935. The first paper-tape typewriter was introduced in the 1940's as an automatic letterwriting machine.

Although punched-card tabulating machines had been available for several decades, it must be noted that more improvements, more new models, and more new applications have been introduced in the last decade than in all preceding years. Thus it was in the early 1950's that "Integrated Data Processing" began to be forcefully and dramatically demonstrated by the equipment industry.

DEFINITIONS OF TERMS

The term "Integrated Data Processing" was first coined to describe systems involving paperwork, mechanized from initiation to completion. Integrated Data Processing was then applied to punched-card systems and, to a certain extent, to computer systems. Finally, it became so closely related to large-scale systems as to take its place with Electronic Data Processing (EDP) and Automatic Data Processing (ADP). In the process the term lost its original meaning of source paperwork handling. The technique, therefore, had to gain its own stature and a more descriptive term. The term chosen was "Source Data Automation" (SDA). Here is the logic of the newer term:

> Source—Where data begins
> Data—Required information
> Automation—In machine language for machine-to-machine processing

Thus the basic principle of capturing information in a usable medium, at the point of origin, for further processing, introduces a number of concepts which require further explanation.

SOURCE

The beginning of a paperwork cycle is the source. This can be anywhere—in different offices, in a different city, across town, or right in the same office. Regardless of the physical location, *the source is always the beginning of the paperwork cycle.*

DATA

Information is always data. It can be on a form. It can be part of a form. It can be on several related or unrelated forms. Data are always recorded on some medium in some manner. The recording may be merely an "X" or a checkmark in a box. It may be handwritten. It may be mechanically transcribed. Data, for source data automation purposes, must have three basic characteristics. First, it must be of a reasonably repetitive nature. Second, it must be machinable. Third, it must exist in sufficient volume to justify the smallest of automated equipments.

THE LANGUAGES OF SOURCE DATA AUTOMATION

Much harm has been done to serious consideration of the technique of source data automation by casual use of the two words "common language." The origin of the phrase is not too hard to pinpoint. Early in the formative period of automation, the only language medium which could be understood by *all* the available machines of that period was the five-channel punched paper tape. While five-channel paper tape is still the only carrier accepted by many final processing machines today, the limitations of this carrier have virtually eliminated it as a true common language.

NATIVE LANGUAGE

Every available automatic machine on today's market operates on a language. It is true the language of one machine may be recognized by the machine of a different manufacturer, but the fact still remains that each machine has its own language built into it by its makers. The languages of machines, therefore, are not common languages but are the native languages of specific machines. In source data automation one should speak of a machine's native language and forget, for the time being at least, the phrase "common language." In illustration of this point, here are some of the basic native languages and carriers of our common systems and machines:

- Communications machines use five-channel punched paper tape.
- Paper tape typewriters use six, seven, and eight-channel paper tape.
- Punched-card systems use a language expressed in round or rectangular holes punched into equal-size cards.
- Scanning machines use special type fonts and magnetic ink impressions.

The requirement for different machines to talk to each other, in some systems, has led to the development of language-converting machines. These will be described in detail later. The only point to be remembered here is that regardless of the native language of any machine, it can be converted into the native language of another machine.

The native language machines in source data automation need the abilities to—

- Create data, including simple calculations when required during the paperwork cycle.
- Accept and record additional data as it occurs in a paperwork system.
- Convert data to another machinable form, if conversion is required in a paperwork system.
- Produce, as byproducts, data for the next step in a paperwork cycle.
- Integrate dissimilar machines into a single coordinated mechanized system.
- Communicate with the more complex machines, such as computers.

COMMON LANGUAGE

The native language impressed on the carries discussed above is a code pattern formed on the carrier by the recording machine. These code patterns, when read by the "mother" machine, result in the creation of an electronic pulse that causes the machine to react in accordance with the instruction indicated by that pulse.

The most common everyday illustration of pulse control is the dial telephone. When a number is dialed, a small contact under the dial makes and breaks a circuit the number of times called for by the dialed number. The circuit make-and-break causes a stepping relay to move to the numeric position of the number. When a person finishes his complete number dialing, the encoded positions of the stepping relays are decoded into a single pulse. This causes the called telephone to be connected with the calling phone and to ring. All source data machines operate on the encoding-decoding principle, and decoded pulses cause—

Reading	Calculating
Writing	Recording
Controlling	Verifying
Communicating	Language Conversion

The electric pulse is identical for a given code pattern of a given carrier, whether transmitted over long distances or short distances—

From Washington, D.C., to San Francisco, Calif., via wire or wireless.
From one machine in a room to another machine in the same room.
From one end of a machine to the other end.

INFORMATION CAPTURE

When Jean Emile Baudot invented the native language and the machine to "automate" sending messages over the telegraph wire, there was only one mode of capturing data, the deliberate creation of the punched paper tape by the manual depression of the keys of a punching device. But, with today's modern equipment, three major modes are available for capturing the selected data in the native language of the machines to be used:

- Deliberate creation.
- Byproduct creation.
- Conversion creation.

The machinery may be capable of performing in more than one mode. For example, a machine which punches a tape as a primary function may also be capable of producing a second byproduct tape in the same or different native language.

Source data automation attempts to obviate person-to-person processing by substituting machine-to-machine processing. Most of the machines involved have been pictured and described in the National Archives and Records Service handbook titled *Source Data Automation Equipment Guide.* (Federal Stock No. 7610–059–2773)

Machine-to-machine processing came of age with the advent of converters. These machines can translate or convert any native language into any other native language. They can, for example, convert the native language of the punched tape typewriter to the native language of the punched card, if such conversion is required for completing the paperwork cycle. Some of the common converters are:

Paper Tape
- Any number of channels of paper tape to any other number of channels of paper tape.
- Any variety of paper tape to any variety of punched card.
- Any variety of paper tape to any variety of magnetic tape.
- Any variety of magnetic tape to any number of channels of paper tape.

Punched Card
- Any variety of punched card to any other variety of punched card.
- Any variety of punched card to any number of channels of paper tape.
- Any variety of punched card to any variety of magnetic tape.

Tag
- Any variety of punched tag to any variety of punched card.
- Any variety of punched tag to any variety of paper tape.

APPLICATION OF SOURCE DATA AUTOMATION

Finding a paperwork function or type of operation in which some Federal agency has not applied the principles of source data automatic would be difficult.

The potential applications are limited principally by the imagination of the person who studies an existing paperwork cycle. Successful applications have been developed in property and supply management, personnel management and statistics, production planning and control, work measurement and reporting, fiscal management and accounting, as well as in the major substantive functions performed in Federal agencies. Over 70 representative applications are contained in the National Archives and Records Service handbook SDA Systems. (Federal Stock No. 7610–985–7272)

Source data automation can bring the advantages of mechanical or electronic operation to all levels of an organization. It can ease the paperwork burden in the small office as well as in the large one involved in voluminous and complicated tasks. It can be developed—

- For any size operation.
- In stages, a step at a time.
- For utilizing dissimilar office machines in "teams."
- As a direct means for communication with the more complex electronic computer.

BENEFITS OF SOURCE DATA AUTOMATION

New achievements are possible for the office with source data automation. It can help integrate communications. To management it provides the ability to systematize operations. It supports forecasting with methodically developed data. Such data are not the result of mere coordination of clerical tasks; it is the result of thorough dovetailing of procedures and functions. This integration often crosses department, agency, or bureau organization lines. It makes the work of all easier, quicker, and more effective.

Tangible benefits include—

Savings—Labor costs, the greatest part of paperwork expense, are reduced.
Accuracy—Errors are decreased or eliminated, as automatic production is more reliable than manual.
Speed—Processing time in the complete paperwork cycle is reduced, as automatic production is faster than manual.
Better Information—More efficient systems are possible since data recorded at birth was used for all processing steps.
Better Decisions—Fast and accurate decisions are based on up-to-date information.

DO'S AND DON'TS OF AUTOMATION

DO—
- Look for repetition, volume, urgency, and error as clues to potential source data automation applications.
- Study the system in depth. Automation requires precision. Machines are less flexible than people. Every detail of the system must be worked out in advance. Machines bind you to the system.
- Study the system from birth (source) of data to its final resting place.

- Consider another approach besides automated equipment.
- Remember that systems improvement is the objective, not necessarily automation.
- Analyze the need for the data being collected. Collect only data which will serve a purpose.
- Remember that each field of data must be completely disciplined from one record to another, from one medium to another.
- Consider necessary controls. A suitable source data automation system must contain: (1) a selected number of controls to assure accuracy of results; (2) a number of checkpoints to which we can return when an error is detected, without having to return all the way to the beginning of the paperwork system.
- Consider standardized coding of information. Codes must be developed for uniform application and each term must be defined to prevent miscoding of information.
- Take advantage of byproduct production of native language media-byproduct to a necessary basic step in the paperwork system.
- Consider training. Either develop in-house, on-the-job programs or arrange to have training conducted by the equipment manufacturers.
- Conduct a trial run to debug your proposal. It is better to discover an error or overlooked item early in the game.
- Make doubly sure that the preparation of input or conversion of already existing data involves—
    Proper recording and validation of raw data.
    Proper coding of data.
    Verification of accuracy of data transcription.
    Periodic machine testing to detect malfunctions.
- Use your *Imagination.*

DON'T—
- Buy equipment first and then attempt to determine what to do with it.
- Try to do the job without putting the facts about the present system and your proposal in writing.
- Try to do the job alone. Instead get the cooperation of the people involved in the operation.
- Over- or undermechanize, or mechanize for the glamour of automation.
- Install an agencywide system overnight. Try a pilot installation first, installing others on a scheduled basis.
- Look at a single step of a paperwork system. Instead study the whole system.
- Try to carry on operations with the present forms. Probably all forms involved in the paperwork cycle will require revision.
- Ignore the problems of converting existing data to the native language you have chosen.
- Blindly prepare the same reports used in the present system.
- Ignore comments and suggestions from the operating personnel.
- Buy a "pig-in-the-poke". Instead get demonstration of the equipment

performing the routine paperwork cycle and all the exceptions to the routine.
- Select a medium for the native language without analysis of the advantages in relation to the specific paperwork system.

Questions:

1. Define "native language", common language.

2. Give an example of the benefits of source data automation.

3. Discuss the origin of the term "source data automation".

4. What major modes are available for capturing data? Which mode best illustrates source data automation?

SCANNING THE WORLD OF OCR

By ALAN DRATTELL

While other EDP developments such as data display and data transmission have captured the spotlight, optical character recognition is continuing to gain wider acceptance among users as a fast, accurate and relatively economical means of providing input from raw source documents.

Although optical scanning—a popular term for OCR—is a relatively new EDP technology in terms of incidence (there are about 400 to 500 machines in use in the U.S. today, not including approximately the same number of MICR units), patents in this field date back to the last century. Most of these were for devices to aid the blind in reading.

OCR units contain certain basic elements such as a paper transport system, a recognition head, memory, code converted and control unit and, in general, optical readers can be defined as machines that can read typed or printed characters directly from documents.

Dr. David H. Shepard, now president of Cognitronics, Inc., which plans to market an OCR numeric recognition system, is credited with inventing the first practical optical reader in 1951. And four years later *Reader's Digest* installed the first machine for commercial use.

About the same time, the First National City Bank in New York City acquired a machine to capture travelers' check numbers. The bank is currently using two Control Data 915 page readers—one for branch file maintenance of savings and demand deposit files, the other to handle a high volume stock transfer operation with input generated from a central typing pool. "By and large we're very happy with optical scanning," reports Charles J. Eder, assistant vice president in the bank's Research Dept. "We realized that it had a great deal of potential in 1955, and even at that time we were happy to accept half a loaf just to get some of the benefits."

OCR's significance as an input medium is continually attested to by its users. For example, Gordon Mills, director of EDP operations for American Airlines, says that there was no other form of source document automation that could solve AA's problem of inputting two million pieces of paper a month.

Optical character recognition equipment can be connected on-line to a computer or be used off-line. In the on-line mode, raw data is machine or hand-printed on source documents of various sizes, including adding machine and cash register tapes. Off-line, the scanner can be connected to a magnetic tape unit, a punched paper tape device or a punched card machine.

Reprinted from BUSINESS AUTOMATION, January 1968, Copyright Business Press International, Inc.

MICR, Magnetic Ink Character Recognition, has for a number of years been used successfully by banks—and without this technique the banking industry may well have faced an insurmountable input problem. However, the application of MICR is essentially limited to one basic use by a single major industry.

POTENT PRODUCTS

There are a number of OCR products on the market, from bar code and mark sense devices to journal tape readers, styled font line and page readers to the more sophisticated multifont and hand-printed character readers.

Although mark sense readers are not really OCR machines since they do not interpret a character into machine language, they have varied uses in business and industry.

Users of OCR machines range from small companies to service bureaus to large concerns and Federal Government agencies.

Food Fair, a supermarket chain of over 200 stores, uses an Optical Scanning Corp. Digitek Model 70 mark sense system to maintain stock levels. Store managers take physical inventory by marking special coded forms which are then optically scanned at a central location, and the data converted to magnetic tape. Computer analysis of the data provides replenishment stock instructions for Food Fair's warehouses and is used as one factor in the chain's profitability calculations.

One small insurance user—Northwestern National Insurance Group in Milwaukee ($100 million in premium writings)—fit the machine to the price it could afford to handle some of its turnaround documentation.

The company needed full alphabetic capability, a machine compatible with its IBM System/360 Mod 40 and one that rented for under $5,000 a month. The installation of a CDC 915 page reader met all three requirements.

At first, company officials were not certain what type of input device would suit their needs. "We thought we should look into an area where our future needs could be met, and we found that OCR was further advanced than we believed," explains Robert F. Whealon, assistant vice president of the insurance firm.

One interesting aspect of Northwestern's move to OCR was its expected and unexpected effect on the keypunch operation. Like other users, the company was apprised by various manufacturers that OCR would help eliminate the keypunching operation. Many opscan manufacturers use this point as a key selling item.

In Northwestern's case, particularly, such producer-generated promotion could have had a deleterious effect since the keypunch group is represented by an office union.

Northwestern management met with union officials and offered to train keypunch personnel as typists—since typed documents remain the prime source of OCR input. Out of 20 girls in the keypunch pool, three expressed interest in the retraining program.

However, as volume increased, Northwestern saw that its keypunch operation involving data capture also increased, maintaining its keypunch operational size.

Users, in general, have found that because of increased volume, staffs remain the same in size or increase despite the use of OCR equipment.

United Air Lines, for example, has increased the number of typists and keypunch operators and is planning additional growth in the next few months.

Input to UAL's OCR machine has expanded rapidly and smaller non-scanning applications volume has also increased. The optical unit presently is used three shifts a day, five days a week, and lower volume tasks in general accounting applications such as work unit measurement and one-time applications such as certain statistical breakdowns can still be handled more economically with the keypunch machines.

Many of these input units, however, have been replaced with typewriter consoles which incorporate standard keypunch keyboards to type source data for United's Electronic Retina Computing Reader, which is manufactured by Recognition Equipment, Inc.

A combination of proofreading and computer editing on a controlling SDS 910 verifies the source data fed into the scanner.

NO CLOUDS IN THE FRIENDLY SKIES

A big plus for UAL is that use of typing equipment has broadened the employment market; the company can now look for typing-level personnel and not just trained keypunches for its typing/keypunch section.

UAL was one of the first companies to install REI's Electronic Retina unit and, in fact, worked directly with the Dallas-based concern in perfecting the machine to fit United's needs.

About seven years ago the airlines formed an industry committee to establish needs and specifications in the recognition hardware area. The data was submitted to about 38 manufacturers; 19 of them replied and there were two, initially, who showed interest. At this point, each airline went on its own.

United's needs included a device that could handle its special 12 lb. carbon-backed paper and that was vacuum-fed so that the carbon-backing would not flake. Changing the industry-wide forms used would have been too costly for the airlines.

The system in use now processes more than one million airline tickets a month plus airbills and refund checks, reading more than four million documents a month.

American Airlines has also discovered the continued need for keypunchers in other areas since the implementation of its REI scanner system for sales and auditing reports, to gather marketing information and to do statistical tasks.

Prior to OCR, American, like most other users, relied on keypunch machines for input. "The method was slow in comparison to the volume of paper," says Mills, "and it often caused mistakes like double entries and missing hunks of information. We were using 36 keypunchers just to process ticket coupons."

One large user—the Social Security Admin.—maintains that its custom-made OCR system, an IBM 1975, will do the work of 120 to 140 keypunch operators, but the agency says that no one will lose his job. The operators will be reassigned to other recordkeeping operations.

The 1975 optical page reader, controlled by an IBM System/360 Model 30, reads the names, social security numbers and quarterly earnings of about half of the 70 million wage-earners in the U.S.

Two vital aspects of OCR equipment are its time- and money-saving capabilities, particularly when compared with the keypunch method of input. At the Social Security Admin. about a quarter million lines of data, contained on a stack of forms four feet high, can be read and recorded on tape in slightly more than eight hours. Manual keying of the same amount of data into punched cards would take a keypunch operator more than 100 days. Robert M. Ball, social security commissioner, estimates an annual savings of more than $750,000.

SAVINGS ADD UP FOR USERS

Other users claim time- and money-saving capabilities too. At United, the Electronic Retina's document carrier is paying for itself about two years earlier than predicted, and the page reader adjunct to the system will pay for itself in about half the time predicted. In all, about $10,000 to $15,000 a week is being saved in input preparation.

For a service bureau operation, such as Chicago Tabulating Service, Inc., OCR enables the company to keep costs down in some areas where keypuncing imposes prohibitive monetary and time factors.

CTS, using an NCR 420-2, scans journal and adding machine tapes submitted by customers who want accounts receivable statements, invoicing reports, sales analysis, profit and loss statements and other accounting documentation. The unit also performs an inventory control application.

The 420-2 is hooked to magnetic tape or disc elements of an IBM 1401 used by the service bureau.

Northwestern National says that even if its machine were to run a minimum of three hours a day, it would justify itself. This is the length of time it takes to get through 2,000 cash tickets.

Says First National City Bank's Eder: "I just can't price opscan and keypunch, except on an item by item basis. For example, in an application like names and addresses, opscan gives us a very high ratio. We probably can do 40 hours of keypunch and verification in one hour with opscan. It varies drastically. Short numeric fields run at a 5 or 10 to 1 hourly ratio. Collectively, we're saving money—but we save money on long numeric listings."

And at Time, Inc., in Chicago, where two Farrington page readers and one Farrington document scanner are being used by the publishing company as basic input on all subscriptions (including new, change of address, payments), OCR is estimated to be 15 percent cheaper than other input sources.

One advantage for American in using OCR has been the resulting evening out of the workload peak. "Surprisingly," says Mills, "we've had no major problems. Our machine arrived during the airline strike in 1966, and although we had planned to implement optical scanning in stages, the sheer volume of our passenger load [American was the only major airline flying during the strike] forced us to plug it in and put it right to work.

"We have found, though, that we have to use different management techniques. For example, we monitor our rejects on magnetic tape and periodically we go over the rejects with the company's technical representative.

Most of our rejects can be traced to the human factor, though, either from our agents in the field or from tickets we get from other airlines."

United had few problems in implementing use of its OCR equipment. The company also has evidence of a fairly low reject rate, and it has not missed a day in its canning operation since the machine was installed three years ago. In the event of enforced downtime, however, results could be catastrophic. United has prepared for such an eventuality by establishing mutual compatibility with Spiegel, Inc.'s REI equipment, located in the mail order firm's Chicago office, several miles from UAL's suburban installation.

THE PIONEERS HAD PROBLEMS

Running for a long period of time—436 hours last October alone—United maintains rigid maintenance schedules. Preventive handling, for example, in October totaled 75 hours; another 44 hours were needed to make repairs.

Reject rate has varied from 0.5 to 0.8 percent, and United personnel have expressed their amazement with the accuracy of the system. The machine has read some documents that it would not ordinarily be expected to scan—such as torn sheets, badly printed items and folded information.

Northwestern's complaint is not with its OCR system, which the company says has given it 99.5 percent character reliability vs. 90 percent punched card verification reliability, but rather one with forms. The quality control of printing on the forms has been a headache for the insurance company.

For some of the pioneer users of optical scanning, however, problems were varied and enormous, despite the fact that today's users for the most part are finding little problem in implementing effective use of these machines.

When the Chicago Board of Education decided to use OCR equipment in 1962, the agency asked opscan manufacturers if they could produce a piece of hardware that could optically read characters recorded on paper from a high speed computer printer, characters recorded on paper from 700 uncontrolled sources on 1,000 typewriters and characters recorded on targets using ordinary pencil.

"We also gave them some idea as to what volumes were," relates Stanley R. Patton, former director of data processing for the Board and currently in a consulting capacity with Benjamin C. Willis Educational Services, Inc. The volumes were "100,000 new student enrollments each year, 2 million student transaction changes each year, 6 million attendance transactions, 5 million lines of supply requisitions, 150,000 subject requests from students and 5 million lines of recorded statistical information.

A $2 MILLION QUESTION MARK

"One manufacturer indicated that if we'd give him $2 million and two years he could make something if we didn't insist that it had to work. One machine would have worked reasonably well if we could have brought all the school secretaries (1,500) under one roof, hired 200 typing supervisors, given them typewriters with one-time carbons and chains to handle the paper, and clean each typewriter every day."

However, REI did come up with its Electronic Retina unit and the Board was off but not winging. "Originally, we trained two programmers to program in octal notation," Patton continues, "designed half a dozen forms that read but not very well, and we begged 50 printing firms to update their processes and prepare forms to our unique specifications—such as bar codes with 0.003 in. tolerance and to maintain this tolerance in a batch of one million printed documents."

The Board had problems the first two years since many of the forms wouldn't read, the programs never worked as they should have, input data was for some time replete with typing errors and preventive maintenance had to be performed four hours out of every eight of operation.

"But today," says Patton, "things are quite different. OCR systems can now read forms prepared by numerous computer printers, read forms prepared by a large number of printers in the industry, have excellent program packages, will read documents prepared out in the field under noncontrolled conditions, will read many different types of fonts, and will read, edit, and format to magnetic tape or disc at a fantastic rate of speed."

Like the Board, many manufacturers who first entered what appeared to be a lucrative market could not cope with the problems they found some like Univac Div. and Radio Corp. of America discontinued marketing in this field, although both admit that they do have new OCR devices in advanced stages of development.

At present, there are 14 manufacturers in the business segment of the field, and a 15th, Scan Data in Norristown, Pa., which is believed to be staffed by ex-Philco-Ford personnel, is expected to have a hardware announcement later this year. In addition, Western Union is working on character readers, but these developments are still in the laboratory stage.

The optical scanning field has provided an opportunity for the small manufacturer to be among the leaders, although Farrington's P. F. McCloskey, vice president, claims that IBM has the largest share of the market. A spokesman for Control Data, however, asserts that his company presently has about two-thirds of the single-font type OCR machine market, as represented by its 915 page reader. CDC is currently developing a multifont machine for probable introduction this spring.

Interestingly, Farrington, a pioneer in the field of optical scanning, turned a profit for the first time last year—$1 million projected for the 1967 calendar period.

The company attributes this profit delay to the long period of time it took people to generally accept OCR, and McCloskey adds that the company did not have the capital to exploit the market.

Recognition Equipment, one of the recognized leaders among OCR manufacturers, has not shown a profit yet; however, the company maintains a positive standing in the eyes of the financial community.

EVEN THE LOSERS MAKE MONEY

Herman L. Philipson Jr., company president, attributes this view to the belief by the financial community that the OCR industry is in its infancy and that this segment of the data processing field will increase more rapidly than the computer industry as a whole in the years ahead. REI has forecast that it will become profitable in its 1969 fiscal reporting period. "We still expect to reach that goal," Philipson says.

Although most manufacturers interviewed by BUSINESS AUTOMATION do not see mergers of small and large producers coming about to a large extent, CDC did enter the field by acquiring Rabinow Electronics. Adds REI's Philipson: "There is not likely to be a fallout among manufacturers in this field since the total demand is greater than the supply."

There has been some question that the cost of OCR is prohibitive and is preventing many users from utilizing this type of equipment. Explains John W. Busby, president of Optical Scanning Corp., "In the original entry market, readers will be cheaper and faster than character reading. There are some times when OCR can be cheaper than keypunching—if the OCR machine is used to at least 50 percent of capacity. Typing always plays a big part. If you don't have to retype, the cost goes down, thus the more steps you eliminate, the better off you are cost-wise.

"If the document needn't be typed at all, the mark readers become even cheaper than OCR. OCR will definitely be the answer to turnaround documents, especially for telephone companies, oil companies, credit card companies, insurance companies and department stores. One way to cut down OCR costs is with specialized forms which eliminate steps, save time and money and enable the user to take advantage of mark coding. Turnaround can be handled either by mark reading or character reading.

"The smaller user will be utilizing mark reading which provides a lower reject rate at less cost. He'll have to give up a little in aesthetics, but he'll gain a great deal in efficiency."

According to Predicasts, Inc., publishers of a $150 report on computer peripheral equipment, "OCR systems costs of between $300,000 and $500,000 have discouraged many applications," and one of scanning's problems, limiting its growth to date, has been the requirement of "highly stylized character fonts and precise document preparation."

ADDING TO THE HARDWARE MUDDLE

However, these drawbacks are being solved by the opscan industry. For example, Optical Scanning this month is introducing a machine that will read hand-printed numeric characters and selected symbols; the OpScan 288 will sell for less than $100,000. CDC's 915 is priced under $92,000.

Other new products are on the horizon including a unit from Farrington to read hand-printed numeric characters. The machine, to be announced shortly, will join hand-printed numeric character recognition systems now marketed by IBM and REI. The latter will install a hand-priting reader module for its Electronic Retina Computing Reader in July. The device reads ordinary hand-printed letters and numbers at speeds up to 1,200 documents per minute.

Philco-Ford has several developments. The company has been testing a hand-print unit that reads alphanumerics at Educational Testing Service in Princeton, N.J., a not-for-profit company that, among other things, administers and scores college board exams. In addition, Philco-Ford will deliver next

December an optical film reader that reads photographic film. The system will be installed at Pacific Telephone & Telegraph Co. in San Francisco, where it will read photographic film of trunk line registers. It is believed to be the first successful marriage of microfilm and optical scanning capabilities.

One major problem the industry must still hurdle, however, is the non-compatibility of its hardware and software. Says REI's Philipson: "I know of no industry where everybody who has entered it has taken such a disparate approach."

The National Bureau of Standards in Washington, D.C. is providing some leadership in developing software standards. And some companies, such as Farrington, IBM and NCR, have developed character sets which have become widely acceptable standards.

Since an optical reader can be said to be only as good as the typewritten material it must scan, a successful offshoot of the OCR industry is the development of input source machines. In this area, Olivetti Underwood Corp., for instance, has several typewriters equipped with standard OCR font. And parameters in these machines are strict since extreme variations can lead to character rejects and increased character substitutions, thus diminishing the value of the optical reader.

Although manufacturers have concentrated in the past largely in the U.S. market, several are making important strides overseas. Farrington, for example, has installed machines in England, Japan, South Africa, France, Scandinavia and Ireland. Several foreign manufacturers are also fairly strong in their markets, and Optical Scanning's Busby says that Japanese companies are working on their own machines. "I believe Hitachi and Nippon Electric are two of the companies."

What's ahead for OCR? Predicasts sees opscan equipment being able to scan over 10,000 pages per hour within the next several years. Major cost reductions will also be achieved. "Although sales of optical character recognition equipment only grew from $500,000 in 1955 to $14.5 million in 1965, the anticipated [figure] for 1975 is $180 million."

THE GLOOM-MONGERS ERR AGAIN

Equipment developments ahead include OCR units that can read handwriting, and adds REI's Philipson: "Some of the biggest opportunities in uses are with computers that don't exist now—for machine translation from one language to another—for information storage and retrieval systems."

That tomorrow promises a brighter world for optical scanning manufacturers and users is apparent. However, the concern for today remains, and undoubtedly opscan has proved that it can help users—big and small—to solve their input problems swiftly and accurately. The variety of machines available offers them a chance to fit the right device to the right application. The only thing that OCR has not successfully achieved, despite its promise, is the replacement of the keypuncher.

It's interesting to note that with the advent of the computer, the gloom-mongers prognosticated the demise of the clerical worker and a dimunition of the general work force. The opposite, of course, has been true. And with optical scanning, business' penchant for paperwork will undoubtedly keep keypunches working with and alongside OCR machines for many years to come.

Questions:

1. Discuss the impact of optical character recognition equipment on United Airlines computer operations.

2. What were some of the problems encountered with the early OCR systems? Are they still problems today?

3. List the major types of optical scanning devices.

PREPARING FOR
DATA COMMUNICATIONS

By GEORGE O'TOOLE

Much of the communications technology used to transfer digital data between computers and remote terminals is not new; it was available in the era of the IBM 701 and the UNIVAC I. But it was the appearance of new developments in computer technology which gave rise to the new field of Data Communications.

THE PROGRAMMER'S WORLD

Consider the world as seen by the computer programmer. It consists of two parts: – the central processing unit (CPU), and everything else. The programmer thinks of the CPU (together with its core storage) as the place in which his program resides. The program operates on data stored in core and is controlled by the registers of the CPU. "Everything else" includes all of the peripheral devices attached to the CPU. The programmer thinks of these as devices through which data are input to the CPU for processing, are stored from time to time (especially large masses of data), and are output as the final results of the processing carried out by his program. He is aware that these peripherals are connected to the CPU by cables and that data are exchanged between peripherals and the CPU by means of electrical impulses, but the physical location of the peripherals is of no particular importance to him: it doesn't affect the way in which he writes his program.

However, the physical fact that electrical impulses are attenuated with distance in cables places a limit on how far a peripheral device may be located from a CPU. In practice this limitation is usually a few hundred feet.

Data, of course, are prepared and collected beyond this limiting radius for peripheral devices. Generally, the users of the results of the data processing function are also located beyond this limit. Traditionally, data have been exchanged between the user and the data processing system by mail, courier, or some equally leisurely medium. This has not usually been unacceptable, since this leisurely time required to transfer the data has been only a small part of the total cycle of accumulating the data for batch processing, the processing itself, and the dissemination of the results.

Reprinted with permission from Computers and Automation (May, 1969) copyright (1969) by and published by Berkeley Enterprises, Inc. 815 Washington Street, Newtonville, Massachusetts, 02160.

REMOTE TERMINALS

Recently, however, this cycle has shrunk. Direct-access storage devices and faster, interruptible CPU's have permitted the development of on-line systems. The remote user frequently wants to take advantage of this capability to process his data immediately. Wherever economy or operational necessity make this attractive, an effort has been made to replace the punch card and the printed listing with the remote terminal.

Suddenly, the programmer's world has acquired a third domain; "everything else" has been subdivided into two groups: peripherals within the radius of cable connection, and devices located beyond this radius, i.e., remote terminals. The physical connection of the remote terminal is not by cable but by some communications medium, usually provided by the common carriers, American Telephone & Telegraph or Western Union. This change requires the introduction of a new device—the communications controller.

The controller is basically a peripheral device which is used to interface the CPU or the remote terminal with the communications medium. Thus, the programmer must use a peripheral device to access another peripheral device, and between these two devices lies the *terra incognita* of Data Communications.

The introduction of Data Communications to an established data processing operation is an essentially revolutionary development: it changes the lives of everyone concerned. It places new demands on the manager, the systems analyst, the programmer, and the computer operator, and presents them with a new set of problems.

AN ADDITIONAL VENDOR

First and foremost among the manager's new problems is his need to deal with an additional vendor, i.e., the common carrier. Presumably, he is already dealing with hardware manufacturers. He may also be contracting with an outside source for some of his software. The introduction of an additional vendor to provide communications presents a number of problems.[1] The first of these is the simple administrative burden which is added to the existing load. The second problem is linguistic—the manager may have mastered the jargon of EDP technology (it may, in fact, be his own jargon) but he is now forced to talk to people who speak a somewhat different dialect. Finally, the new vendor complicates a classical problem. He is, as are the software and hardware contractors, responsible for only a piece of the total system. The manager is responsible, when all the parts are put together, to insure that the totality works. Now, obviously, it is easier to determine that a system is not performing as required, than it is to say why. If things aren't working as they should, there is a natural human tendency to suspect that the trouble lies, not with one's own work, but elsewhere. This puts the manager in the conflicting and unenviable position of being both outraged customer and referee. To face this kind of problem the manager must have unusual personal technical resources, or a very competent staff.

---

[1]These problems are treated at length in, D. C. McNelis, "The Common Carrier as a Second Vendor," *Principles of Data Communications for Professional Programmers and Systems Analysts,* Ernest Heau and Donald McNelis, Computer Methods Corp., 1968, p. 56.

STAFF PROBLEMS

This introduces another thorny problem for the manager. His staff has suddenly become partially incompetent. They are generally ignorant of a new technological area of major importance to the system: Data Communications. There are two possible solutions to this problem: either to hire some more staff with a background in Data Communications or to retrain the present staff. The practical route is a combination of the two, with an emphasis on the latter. Even if it were desirable, it is certainly not feasible to fire all the programmers and systems analysts and replace them with EDP professionals who also have a background in Data Communications. In fact, the supply/demand ratio becomes even worse when the requirement for communications experience is added to the necessary qualification of EDP competence.

The most practical route seems to be to try to recruit one or two individuals with the required Data Communications background, either as in-house employees or as consultants (consultants, of course, represent yet another vendor for the manager to deal with). At the same time, the existing systems and programming personnel should be given intensive training in Data Communications. The objective of this procedure is to provide some people experienced in Data Communications against whose practical background the others can orient their newly acquired theoretical knowledge.

What and how much should be studied by the programming and systems staff? Data Communications is obviously a large subject. The EDP professional cannot expect to become an expert in it overnight or even after some weeks of training. The question reduces to: "Who needs to know what?"

THE MANAGER

First, the manager is faced with acquiring some knowledge. As a minimum he needs a survey course on Data Communications which will orient him to the subject and permit him to converse intelligently on a general level with communications people.

THE SYSTEMS ANALYST

The systems analyst must get somewhat deeper into Data Communications than the data processing manager. He has to be able to talk to communications specialists and representatives of common carriers on a more detailed level. He must also be able to identify his specific communications requirements. He should be able to select from among the variety of communications services available to find the appropriate combination to meet his requirements. He must understand the sometimes complex cost factors associated with these different services. Finally, he must acquire some general understanding of the physical characteristics of remote terminals, the controller devices which interface with the communications medium, and even some features of the central processing unit with which he may not have had reason to become familiar in the past.

THE SYSTEMS PROGRAMMER

The systems programmer has the greatest need for training in Data Communications. Most of what has been said of the systems analyst applies also to the systems programmer and to an even greater degree. He must have a very detailed understanding of the operational characteristics of the remote terminals and controller devices. He must master the art of exchanging data with this new third domain of his universe, peripherals beyond the reach of the old familiar (and simple) cable connection.

He must also adjust himself to a new kind of timing problem. Data are being "pushed" into the system through the communication links and must be processed if they are not to be lost or clog the system. This is different from the conventional system in which data are "pulled" in by the program when it is ready for further processing. This difference means that the systems programmer must pay a new kind of attention to program cycle times and buffer sizes.

The communications medium represents a new source of data error for the systems programmer; these errors must be handled in a new way. When a parity check fails on reading from a local peripheral device, an attempt to repeat the read operation can be made in the hope that the error is transient, before dumping error messages on the operator. In the data communications environment, error correction and recovery procedures must be different. They may include the transmission of a message to the remote terminal to request a retransmission of the lost data. However, if the CPU and the peripheral device are connected by a "store-and-forward" communications link—one or more relay points at which messages are temporarily held until a line becomes available for further transmission—then the erroneous data may have been generated some time ago, the request for retransmission may take a while to get back to the remote terminal, and the retransmission may also suffer similar delays.

All of this means that the program must include the "bookkeeping" necessary to keep track of error conditions over relatively long intervals. This is much more difficult to deal with than the relatively simple problems of data errors in local peripheral devices in which the program can attempt to read the data several times, notify the operator if it is still unsuccessful, and get on with the processing. Here is another dimension of complexity for the systems programmer which is introduced by the advent of Data Communications.

THE COMPUTER OPERATOR

The applications programmer and the computer operator are probably the personnel least affected by the advent of Data Communications. Of course, if the applications programmer has only been exposed to batch processing applications and the new system into which Data Communications is introduced is on-line (as is likely), then he too has a major transition to make. However, this transition is not so much involved in familiarization with Data Communications technology. Instead, it is concerned with the use of direct access storage devices, and programming within the environment of an on-line executive operating system.

The computer operator must adjust to sharing his role with the user; everyone who operates a remote terminal is, in a sense, a computer operator, and, in most cases, an amateur one. The teleprocessing system may include some means for the remote user to talk to the computer operator to ask for assistance. The operator must learn to provide that assistance.

SCHEDULING

If the system includes remote terminals located in time zones different from that in which the CPU is located, problems from schedules of shifts may also be created. If the computer is in Los Angeles and the terminal is in New York, and if someone in New York wants to use the system at 8:00 a.m. Eastern Standard Time, then there must be a computer operator available in Los Angeles at 5:00 a.m. Pacific Standard Time. Some small consolation may be drawn from the fact that it is not a new headache—it is the recurrence of an old one.

Data Communications implies not only new equipment, but also new ideas. The latter are always the more difficult to integrate with an existing system, but the data processing profession is accustomed to making this kind of intellectual leap. The transition from card systems to tape systems, the introduction of higher order languages, direct access storage devices, ... , have all involved mind-stretching to absorb new ideas.

"Well, in our country," said Alice, . . . "you'd generally get to somewhere else—if you ran very fast for as long a time as we've been doing."

"A slow sort of country!" said the Queen. "Now, here, you see, it takes all the running you can do, to keep in the same place. If you want to get somewhere else, you must run at least twice as fast as that."

Data Processing is not a slow sort of country and Data Communications is somewhere else.

Questions:

1. The author points out that management requires some training in the field of data communications. Discuss the adequacy of the level of training the author advocates as a minimum.

2. List the reasons the author feels the introduction of Data Communications is a revolutionary development.

3. What type personnel are affected the most by introducing Data Communications into a system? Why?

THE TECHNOLOGY
OF DISK DATA STORAGE

By ANTHONY D. EPPSTEIN

Modern computers need to access or store large quantities of data in the minimum time possible. This need has led to the design of many types of peripheral equipment able to access information randomly using digital magnetic recording techniques. The most popular type of these devices uses flat, thin, fast rotating disks coated with a very thin layer of magnetic material.

Disk data storage systems range from small capacity, head-per-track units which can hold 10^5 bits of information to very large memories holding more than 10^8 bits. The average access times with present machines range between 7 and 500 milliseconds. Disk systems are 10 to 100 times more reliable than digital magnetic tape systems, largely because in most systems the head floats on a thin air-film and normally does not touch the recording surface.

In this article, the characteristics of currently available disk files are summarized. The major emphasis is placed on aspects of recording rather than mechanical design. This article deals with disk files storing data in binary form only, but another expanding group of disk files should be noted. These files store 20 to 30 seconds of either video signals or analog data which may be replayed for very long periods with no signal deterioration.

MANUFACTURERS OF DISK SYSTEMS

Table I shows that there are, far as can be determined, 18 manufacturers making disk digital recording devices at this time. The list does not include those computer manufacturers which use disk systems made by other companies. Although some companies make more than one type of disk system (e.g. IBM), head-per-track systems are made by the largest number of companies.

Currently, there is much activity in both the U.S. and Europe to design disk files which use interchangeable recording disk packs, and to manufacture the disks themselves. A typical disk drive is shown in figure 1. Up to 5.8 x 10^7 bits of information can be on line on this drive at any one time. Caelus Memories, Inc. and MacPanel Co. also manufacture disk packs for IBM 1311 and 2311 systems.

Reprinted from the September, 1968 issue of DATA PROCESSING MAGAZINE, The Authoritative Publication of Computers and Information Technology.

Table I. Basic Characteristics of Current Disk Systems

MANUFACTURER	SYSTEM TAPE		DISK CHARACTERISTICS		
	HEAD FORMAT	MEDIA	NUMBER	DIAMETER (inches)	RECORDING MEDIA
Applied Magnetics Corp.	Head/Track	Nonexchange	1-4	12	Ni/Co
Burroughs Corp.	Head/Track	Nonexchange	1-4	26	Ni/Co
Data Disc Corp.	Head/Track	Nonexchange	1	12	Ni/Co
Digital Development Corp.	Head/Track	Nonexchange	1-3	12	Ni/Co
Digital Equipment Corp.	Head/Track	Nonexchange	1	10	Ni/Co
Librascope Group, Div. General Precision Corp.	Head/Track	Nonexchange	1-6	10-48	Ni/Co
Magnehead Div. General Instruments Corp.	Head/Track	Nonexchange	1-4	7-13	Ni/Co
Scientific Data Systems	Head/Track	Nonexchange	1-4	—	Ni/Co
Optimized Devices Inc.	Head/Track	Exchange	1	7	Ni/Co
Bryant Computer Products	Moving Arm	Nonexchange	14-16	39	γFe_2O_3
Control Data Corp.	Moving Arm	Nonexchange	36-72	26	γFe_2O_3
Data Products Corp.	Moving Arm	Nonexchange	16-32	31	γFe_2O_3
General Electric	Moving Arm	Nonexchange	16	—	Ni/Co
IBM	Moving Arm	Nonexchange	25	—	γFe_2O_3
Data Disc Corp.	Moving Arm	Exchange	1	12	Ni/Co
Control Data Corp.*	Moving Arm	Exchange	6	14	γFe_2O_3
Friden Corp.	Moving Arm	Exchange	1	12	Ni/Co
IBM*	Moving Arm	Exchange	6-10	14	γFe_2O_3
Memorex Corp.*	Moving Arm	Exchange	6	14	γFe_2O_3
NCR	Moving Arm	Exchange	6	14	Ni/Co
Univac	Fixed Head and Moving Arm	Exchange	1	—	Ni/Co

*Recording media interchangeable between some models in this group of devices.

Table I. Basic Characteristics of Current Disk Systems (Continued)

MANUFACTURER	MAX. MODULE STORAGE CAPACITY (BITS)	HEAD/DISK SPACING x 10⁻⁶ INCH	RECORDING CHARACTERISTICS		
			CODING & PACKING DENSITY (BPI)	TRACKS/RADIAL INCH	DATA TRANSFER RATE (MB/SEC)
Applied Magnetics Corp.	$4.2\text{-}16.8 \times 10^6$	50	1000 PE	30	1.0
Burroughs Corp.	$1.6\text{-}16 \times 10^7$	125	1045 NRZ	33	1.7 to 3.1
Data Disc Corp.	$1.6\text{-}6.4 \times 10^4$	In contact	3333 PE	33	3.0
Digital Development Corp.	$3.8\text{-}10.4 \times 10^6$	100	1000 PE	50	0.2
Digital Equipment Corp.	4.3×10^5	No contact	1100 NRZ	—	—
Librascope Group, Div. General Precision Corp.	$3 \times 10^4\text{-}4.1 \times 10^8$	20	150-1500 NRZ	20 to 50	—
Magnehead Div. General Instruments Corp.	$5.2 \times 10^5\text{-}8.2 \times 10^6$	No contact	600 PE	32 to 40	0.7
Scientific Data Systems	$6\text{-}24 \times 10^6$	—	—	—	1.5
Optimized Devices Inc.	4×10^4	100	200	$\cong 14$	0.1
Bryant Computer Products	$8.5 \times 10^8\text{-}1.2 \times 10^{10}$	No contact	600 PE	64 to 128	—
Control Data Corp.	$1\text{-}12 \times 10^8$	125	850-1075 PE	50	0.84 to 1.07
Data Products Corp.	$2.2 \times 10^8\text{-}3.5 \times 10^9$	200	1000-2000	50	0.7
General Electric	1.4×10^8	No contact	—	—	0.5
IBM	9×10^8	—	1060	100	1.25
Data Disc Corp.	1.3×10^8	In contact	3333 PE	33	1.007
Control Data Corp.*	$2\text{-}5.8 \times 10^7$	125 to 160	1000 NRZ-1000 PE	100	0.7 to 1.25
Friden Corp.	4.9×10^5	In contact	250 NRZ	40	0.08
IBM*	$2\text{-}23 \times 10^7$	125 to 160	1000 NRZ-2000 PE	100	0.7 to 2.5
Memorex Corp.*	5.8×10^7	125 to 160	1000 PE	100	1.25
NCR	3.3×10^7	No contact	—	—	—
Univac	2.6×10^7	—	—	—	—

*Recording media interchangeable between some models in this group of devices.

Figure 1. A Moving Arm Exchangeable Disk Drive

DISK FILE CHARACTERISTICS

The wide range of disk systems available take two basic forms, each with certain performance advantages. There are head-per-track systems, and moving arm systems.

The head-per-track files vary from small capacity systems storing 0.036 x 10^6 bits to large systems with capacities of 4.1 x 10^8 bits. With this type of file, the average access time, apart from a few microseconds for head switching, is set by the rotational speed of the disk. Most systems have only one read or write head per track, but the average access time can be further reduced by using more than one head to scan each track. Head-per-track systems have average access times from 7 milliseconds for small diameter disks up to 35 milliseconds for large 2 to 4 feet diameter disks which rotate at fewer rpm[1]. Data transfer rates are between 200 kb/sec. and 3 mb/sec.

Moving arm disk systems have one or more recording heads mounted at the end of an arm. This arm can sweep the whole area used for recording so that tracks containing information can be assessed in any order desired. Disk systems with moving arms fall into two classes:

1. Those with the recording surfaces an integral part of the machine and which cannot be interchanged without a complete rebuild, and

2. Those which are designed to replace one pack of disks with another when required by the operator. An IBM type 2302 system is the first type, and an IBM 2311 the second type.

Moving arm, noninterchangeable disk systems store between 2×10^8 and 1.25×10^{10} bits,[2] with access times between 100 and 125 milliseconds and transfer rates between 0.5 and 125mb/sec. The increased access times are accounted for partly by the slower rotational speed of the large diameter disks used (about 900-1200 rpm), but in the main the the time needed to unlatch and move the head-carrying arm to the new position.

Moving arm disk systems with interchangeable disks can store between 4×10^6 bits and 2.33×10^8 bits without changing the storage media. The average access times for these systems range between 25 and 500 milliseconds, with transfer rates between 700 kb/sec. and 2.5 mb/sec. This type of system has the very great advantage that an unlimited number of disk packs can be stored off-line.

The type of disk system does not influence the cost per bit of storage. When the total storage capacity of a disk file is plotted against the system cost per bit, for approximately equivalent electronic interfaces, no significant difference between the two types of disk drives emerges. This is shown in figure 2, which reveals a simple power relationship between the cost per bit in cents and the system storage size, given by:

$$\text{Storage Cost/Bit} = \frac{1.08 \times 10^4}{(\text{Total Store Capacity})^{0.68}}$$

That is, with current disk systems the factor which affects the cost per bit is not the system type, but rather the total number of bits of data stored in the system, assuming one storage module in exchangeable media systems.

A plot of the storage capacity versus average access-times for the types of disk systems described above is shown in figure 3.

DISK CONSTRUCTION

The recording medium used with disk files is either a thin nickel-cobalt layer, or a coating containing gamma-ferric oxide similar to that used in magnetic recording tapes. These coatings are normally deposited on a rigid metal substrate.

The substrate material normally used for disks is aluminum 1/8 to 1/4 inch thick. However, Burroughs Corporation use brass as a substrate[3] and Data Products Corporation use a magnesium alloy.[4] Glass has been suggested for substrate use because of the ease of obtaining the required flatness and freedom from surface defects. No disk systems yet announced use glass substrates.

The active surface on metal-plated disks is a thin nickel-cobalt alloy coating. Data Disc drives have the plating 15 micro-inches thick; Digital Equipment Corporation uses a 20-microinch plating coat; and Burroughs a coating less than 30 microinches thick. The Burroughs coating has a coercivity of about 500 oersteds with the remanence approximately 6000 gauss. Data Disc announced that it can coat disks with nickel-cobalt layers 3 to 100 microinches thick with coercivities between 50 to 1000 oersteads as required.

Most metal-plated disks have a thin Rhodium overlay plated over the active layer. This overlay inhibits corrosion of the nickel-cobalt and acts as a wear-resistant surface in an in-contact system. The surface finish of these plated discs is claimed to be less than 0.4 microinch AA.

Ferric-oxide coatings have coercitivite approximately 280 oersteds, remanences of approximately 1900 gauss, and thickness between 100 and 250 microinches. Oxide coated disks have a surface finish better than 3.5 microinches AA.

RECORDING HEAD AND DISK INTERFACE

To reduce wear on the heads and disks to the minimum practicable, the majority of disk systems run with an air film of 50 to 200 microinches between the two. This spacing is self-generated by controlled pressure on a gimbal mounted pad containing the read-write head, such as in the IBM 1311.[5] Figure 4 shows such an air-bearing head which flies at 150 microinches from the recording surface. The mechanism above the head controls the loading, and thus the flying height, pneumatically. Spacing information is summarized in table I.

This spacing between the head and recording surface limits the information packing capability of the coating and should be minimal for a high recording density. The minimum spacing possible is dependent upon the surface roughness of the disc surface. For this reason, as metal-plated surfaces are smoother, the head-to-disk spacings with metal discs are less than for oxide discs by a factor of one or two.

The disk systems manufactured by Data Disc run the heads in contact with the metal-plated disk. This explains the high information packing densities achieved with these systems of 3333 bits per inch, phase encoded.

FACTORS AFFECTING MAXIMUM FILE STORAGE CAPACITY

The major factors affecting the on-line storage capacity of a disk file are:
1. The number of storage surfaces;
2. The surface radial range used and thus, the disk diameter;
3. The radial track density per inch; and
4. The information packing density along a given track.

The number of storage surfaces varies from one in many files up to 144 in Control Data 803 or 808 systems. Disk diameters range from 7 to 48 inches.

The majority of disk files available use 10 to 14 inch diameter disks. However, large diameter disks, 20 to 30 inches in diameter, are used more often in the high capacity disk files than a larger number of small diameter disks, though the IBM 2314 with eighty 14-inch disks goes against this trend. Normally, only the outer annulus of the coated surface is used. This reduces the variation in the head-to-disk linear velocity between the inner and outer diameters.

A change in head-to-disk linear velocity affects the flying height, and thus the replay output from the disk surface. Also, for a constant transfer rate the information packing density will vary with the track diameter used. At high packing densities, this affects the replay signal amplitude, which is another reason for using only the outer part of the disc coated area.

Fixed head-per-track systems write information on between 30 and 50 tracks per inch. Movable arm disk systems achieve a much greater lateral packing density with between 50 and 100 tracks per inch. Head costs affect the radial track density in head-per-track systems. The track density in moving arm systems is controlled by the mechanical tolerances possible with a reasonable track-to-track access time.

With one exception of the Data Disc F series, which writes information at 3333 bpi, all other systems write with a maximum longitudinal packing density between 550 and 1100 bpi. Most systems lie at the top end of this range and use a phase-encoding method of recording.

Therefore, the median information storage density for current disk systems is 10^5 bits/sq. inch for a moving arm system and 5×10^4 bits/sq. inch

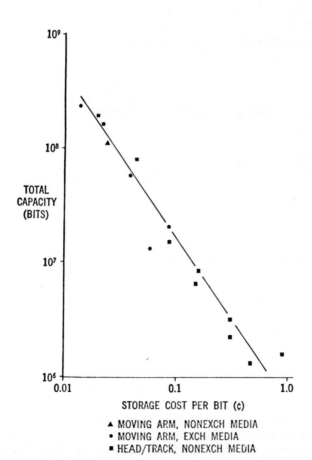

Figure 2. Relationship Between Total Storage Capacity and Cost Per Bit

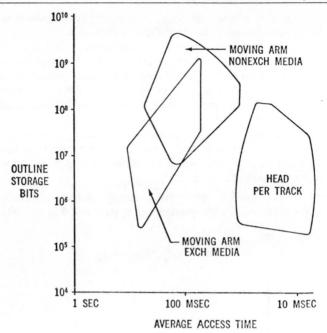

OUTLINE
STORAGE
BITS

Figure 3. Relationship Between Storage Capacity and Average
Access Time by Disk System Type

for a fixed head-per-track system. Present computer digital tape systems achieve
2.9×10^4 bits/sq. inch storage density.

The information summarized in this section is given in greater detail in
table 1.

PARAMETERS AFFECTING SYSTEM RELIABILITY

Whenever disk systems are examined, four parameters necessary for
reliable service must be considered; they are

1. The error rate due to transient and permanent faults,
2. The system life,
3. In exchangeable media systems, the ability to accurately read
information written on another system of the same format, i.e., system
compatibility, and
4. The resistance of disks to contamination which causes errors.

Magnetic tape systems usually achieve an error rate in the region of about
one permanent error in 10^8 to 10^9 bits read. The published error rates for disk
systems are at least 100 to 1000 times better than this. Data Disc states its
systems have less than one transient error in 10^{10} bits, and other manufacturers
claim error rates for their systems better than one error in 10^{11} to 10^{12} bits.

The design life of most disk systems is 10^5 hours. The head and disk lives in Data Disk systems are better than 2400 hours.

The greatest number of disk systems which exchange media use oxide-coated disk packs which are mechanically identical. These systems, such as the IBM 2311, the Control Data 853, or the Memorex 630, achieve high reliability in data interchange. Careful tolerancing of the mounting of the disk pack and the moving arm assembly accomplishes this system compatibility.

The Data Disc M6 and Optimized Devices exchangeable disk systems use a low lateral track density and, in the case of Data Disc, a relatively long track-to-track access time, factors which contribute to reliable data interchange.

A major disadvantage to the use of metal-plated disks is stated to be their inability to withstand abrasion from contaminants or head/disk contact. With two exceptions, all metal-plated disk systems are run in hermetically sealed enclosures. Data Disc states that corrosive atmospheres must be avoided with its disk. In addition, head-per-track systems, which in the main use metal-plated disks, can be so designed that the head never comes in contact with the recording surface. However, the Applied Magnetics MDM-2 system runs with ceramic heads in-contact with the plated disk until the disk is up to speed.

Figure 4. An Out-of-Contact Disk Head Floating on a Self-Generated Air Film

FURTHER DEVELOPMENTS

During the next few years, continued expansion in the use of exchangeable disk memories is probable because of the very great advantage open-ended storage capacity gives. The IBM 2314 system allows 18.6×10^8 bits of storage to be kept on-line, equivalent to previous generation large capacity disk stores, and further increases in the on-line storage capacity of such open-ended stores are likely if multiaccess, real-time computers continue in popularity.

With such exchangeable disk memories, an increased impetus to metal-plated recording media will occur only if reliability, each of manufacture, and freedom from contamination damage is equal to or better than that of oxide-coated disks.

In moving arm systems, an increase of the lateral track density to 150-175 tracks per inch may occur, especially if use of the disk is made in the servo-control circuit.[6,7] Further increases in the longitudinal packing density require improvements to the design of read-write heads,[8] unless a slower rotational speed, smaller head-to-surface spacing, and a corresponding increase in the access time per disk track can be tolerated.

Head-per-track systems may undergo at least a twofold increase in track densities, but a break-through in the cost of head manufacture is needed for the step to be competitive.

Therefore, the area of greatest need in future disk system design is a head/medium system which can take advantage of both the high packing densities possible with metal-plated recording films, and the high head-to-media speeds used in such systems.

REFERENCES

1. Bonn, T. H., "Mass Storage: A Broad Review." *Proc. IEEE, Vol. 54, No. 12, December 1966. 2. Craver, J. S. "A Review of Electromechanical Mass*

    Storage." Datamation, July 1966, pp. 22-28. 3. Jack, R. W., R. G. Groom and R. A. Cleim, "Engineering Description of the Burroughs Disk File."

2. Craver, J. S., "A Review of Electromechanical Mass Storage." *Datamation,* July 1966, pp. 22-28.

3. Jack, R. W., R. G. Groom and R. A. Gleim, "Engineering Description of the Burroughs Disk File." *Proc. FJCC,* 1963, Spartan, Washington, D.C., pp. 341-350.

4. Wieselman, I. L., R. Stuart-Williams and D. K. Sampson, "A Multiple-Access Disk File." *Proc. FJCC* 1963, Spartan, Washington, D.C., pp. 351-364.

5. Carothers, J. D., R. K. Brunner *et al.,* "A New High Density Recording System: The IBM 1311 Disk Storage Drive with Interchangeable Disk Packs." *Proc. FJCC* 1963, Spartan, Washington, D.C., pp. 327-340.

6. Hoagland, A. S., "A High Track-Density Servo-Access System for Magnetic Recording Disk Storage." *IBM Journal,* October 1961, pp. 287-296.

7. Shew, L. F., "Discrete Tracks for Saturation Magnetic Recording." *IEEE Trans. on Electronic Computers,* Vol. EC-12, No. 4, pp. 383-387, August 1963.

8. Louis, H. P., and W. L. Shevel, "Storage Systems—Present Status and Anticipated Development." *IEEE Trans. on Magnetics,* Vol. MAG-1, No. 3, pp. 206-211, September 1965.

Questions:

1. What are the two basic forms of disk systems available?

2. List the advantages of a head per track system. Moving arm system.

3. List the factors which affect the maximum storage capability of a disk system.

4. Discuss the advantages of disk storage systems to tape storage systems.

AUTOMATIC PLOTTING
IN THE THIRD GENERATION

by DALLAS TALLEY

The fine line separating second from third generation computer philosophies may very well have been drawn when the industry at large stopped purring over the internal efficiency of mainframe processing and began a concerted drive to optimize overall systems performance. Improved graphics and graph-plotting devices are part of the forward move into third generation systems. As long as man remains in the decision-making loop—presumably for some time to come—effective display of computed data will be essential. The purpose of this article is to provide an overview of plotting technology, how the various equipment designs were developed, and what the present state of the art offers today's potential users.

THE REASON FOR BEING

One way to assess the importance of automatic plotting is to imagine all of the world's computed data spewing out of electrostatic printers at the rate of 30,000 lines per minute. Multiplexing a number of high speed printers would reduce the output bottleneck. But in what sense would the result be information? Who could digest its meaning? How could it be communicated to others? And outside the immediate confines of the computing room, what effect would this staggering data load have on the larger world of problem solving and decision making?

Plotting one variable against another has always been a quick way of making sense out of a mass of numbers. The message comes with the immediacy of a picture, rather than the serial delay of 1000 words.

Across the wide spectrum of engineering and science to industry and commerce, hand-drawn graphs have been used to depict relationships underlying data long before the advent of electronic data processing. The growth of computer installations merely added to the amount of data which had to be displayed in plotted form.

This growing demand for improved plotting capability was felt most strongly in the engineering/scientific community, which led to the almost simultaneous development, during 1949 and 1950, of three different types of automatic plotting devices.

Of the three types, the most unusual one is no longer manufactured. Designed and built by Telecomputing Corp., it was the first and only pure digital plotter. Its plotting head sensed the lines on the graph paper (30" x 40" bed) and most of its 500 vacuum tubes were used to count the lines in both x and y. Inputs were from parallel keyboard or IBM Summary Punch. Several hundred of these truly fascinating machines were put into service and no doubt some are still plotting today. If ever there is a museum for "computing devices," it should contain one of these "one and only" pure digital plotters.

The forerunners of the present day incremental plotters were originally developed as output devices for digital differential analyzers. This incremental mode fit the punched tape output, which was in the form of a series of incremental changes. These forerunners took two forms: drum and flat bed. The drum machine was pioneered at the Autonetics Division of North American Aviation by a group of engineers who in 1950 left to start California Computer Products. The flat bed equipment was developed by Benson-Lehner Corp. As an output unit for a Madida type of DDA.

The Benson-Lehner Dactylograph was the granddaddy of what is now the "analog controlled digital input plotter." The original units had either a serial keyboard input or input from an oscillograph reading device. Because they used lead screws in the drive system, they were slow but accurate. The Benson-Lehner units that followed, called Electroplotters, were faster and had inputs from card or paper tape units as well as keyboard and graph readers.

About this same time several users of that fine old 30" x 30" Electronics Associates Analog Plotting Board found that the addition of a digital-to-analog converter and some control circuitry gave them digital plotting capability. Electronic Associates, quick to see another market for their boards, started manufacturing input units themselves.

Although a considerable improvement over manual plotting, the early machines were limited. Output speed boundary (for points more than a few inches apart) was 20 points per minute. Maintenance time vs. operating time was 50-50. Input was mostly from manual keyboard, paper tape or punched cards.

IMPROVEMENTS

Over the next several years, plotting equipment designers translated growing user needs into expanded operating capabilities. In addition to conventional curve plotting and data reduction, new applications emerged in map making and cartography, including contour mapping, weather charting, radiation and population density studies, and traffic analysis.

Before the end of 1958, digital drafting also made its debut at Universal Drafting Machine Corp. and Gerber Scientific Instrument Co. By 1959, new plotters were introduced with mag tape input and speeds of 300 points per minute which produced lines, contours, symbols and alphanumeric characters at the rate of three linear inches per second.

Gradually, plotting hardware evolved toward greater flexibility in operation, higher accuracy, improved quality of output and higher operating reliability. Legibility was improved with a greater variety of pens, colors, tonal contrasts, and symbol sets which were not limited to print heads or existing type fonts.

By the turn of the decade, therefore, plotting hardware consisted of three basic equipment designs: analog, digital drafting, and digital incremental. (The old Telecomputing "line counters" were no longer being manufactured.) All three used an electromechanical plot-driving mechanism, actuating either the paper underneath the pen or the pen cursor arm across the paper.

The chief advantage of the digital drafting and digital incremental systems stemmed from their systems design. Both accepted digital data without requiring cumbersome digital-to-analog system interfacing. Basic design simplicity, systems compatibility, and convenient operation particularly marked the digital incremental philosophy. Although limited at first to speeds of three inches per second, digital plotting eliminated the usual problems of dynamic response, drift and gain setting.

Then, in 1960, the first CRT-microfilm system was delivered by Stromberg-Carlson: the SC 4020. The success of this plotting concept led to other units, such as the B-L 120, the DD 80, and the CalComp 835.

ADVANCES & APPLICATIONS

In late 1965, digital drafting became more practical with the incorporation of low-cost, general purpose computers into a plotting system configuration. At little more than $25,000 additional hardware cost, the added flexibility and control of computer logic opened up nearly unlimited applications potential in automatic drafting, tool path drawing, numerical control, circuit card design, engineering schematics, contour map generation, and other fields requiring close graphic tolerances.

In printed circuit production, for example, artwork masters require tolerances up to ±0.001″ so that accumulated errors in the rest of the manufacturing process will not interfere with precise stacking of multi-layer, integrated circuits. Draftsmen cannot meet these tolerances. Computer-controlled drafting systems can. Moreover, the output from a normal eight-hour shift provides the equivalent of the work of 30 draftsmen.

By the end of 1965, automatic plotting may be said to have come of age. An abundance of equipment representing the four basic designs offered exceptional speed and operational flexibility, with accuracies to ±u.001″. New interfacing and software development increased overall systems performance, on-line and off-line.

In addition to improved plotting for conventional requirements in engineering, science, automatic drafting and map making, many new applications began to emerge.

After a slow start, plotters were beginning to demonstrate results in management information systems. Output took the form of readily understood charts, graphs, and other plotted formats. Content included forecast data. cost accounting, investment analysis, economic indicators, and other business statistics of value for management decisions.

Extended-length plotting and butting of frames in electronic (CRT) systems played an important role in flight test analysis, PERT diagramming, and other CPM displays.

High-volume printing via plotter-produced visuals was also becoming more important in the production of stock catalogs, wire lists for fabrication, directory listings, failure report reviews, and statistical abstracts.

BUYING A PLOTTER

Ironically, as plotters have increased in systems compatibility and performance capability, the buying habits and selection criteria of potential users have remained relatively static.

In fact, most plotter hardware still comes as an after-thought, rarely considered in the original systems analysis and frequently purchased without benefit of complete evaluation.

Technologically, an enormous range of plotting wherewithal is represented within the present state of the art. Initial investment can be recouped in many cases within the first year, merely from the savings in reduced man-hours, computer operating time, and other systems overhead now being charged against second-generation plotting procedures.

At the buyers' end of the supply-demand nexus, a wide variety of operating economics are still being overlooked.

The main obstacle to the natural exchange of supply and demand seems to be a lack of awareness on the part of the potential user. This can also be read as the failure of manufacturers to communicate the message of third-generation engineering. In any event, updated guidelines are needed for considering such factors as cost, accuracy, speed, quality of output, software availability, and availability of local maintenance.

Each of the four equipment categories offers a unique mix of cost, applications suitability, and performance advantage. In the past, the mainstay of the plotting industry was the analog plotter. This is changing rapidly, however, due to the improvements ushered in with digital drafting, incremental, and CRT-based systems.

Of the four, digital drafting and CRT-based systems are unquestionably the most sophisticated and most expensive. Fastest are the CRT's, which produce up to two finished 8½" x 11" plotted pages per second. A graph or plot is created at high speed on the face of a cathode ray tube. The image is then photographed by means of a high-speed 35mm or 16mm camera. Standard output media is microfilm, with optional quick-look hard copy produced by ancillary equipment. Plotting is accomplished by incremental or vector and line drawing techniques. Resolution is a function of the cathode ray tube itself. Standard report-size formats are 8" x 8" and 8½" x 11". For larger format sizes, additional processing is required.

Higher cost of the CRT's restricts their applicability and cost justification to a small fraction of the user population. The min-max range for this equipment is from under $50,000 to $300,000. Digital drafting systems run from $90,000 up.

A COMPARISON

By way of comparison with the two more expensive equipment categories, analogs range typically from $30,000 for on-line systems to $50,000 for off-line configurations with mag tape. Digital incremental plotters can be purchased for less than $5,000.

Design differences between analog and digital incremental plotters account for the cost differential, as well as some of the performance advantages inherent in each. Analog systems are generally larger and, in some cases, faster. Analogs also require D-to-A conversion circuitry to provide analog signals which drive the servo motors.

Digital incrementals use a bi-directional stepping motor. Plotting is produced step by step in .01", .005", .002", .0025" and in 0.1mm. and .05mm. increments. Line drawing is not as smooth in appearance as analog or digital drafting output; however, the digital incremental provides better resolution and accuracy than the analog systems.

For purposes of comparison, a typical cost-analysis plotting (revenue vs. shipment was generated on three different categories of equipment. A CRT plotter produced hard-copy output in ½ second. The same plotting requirement took two minutes and 40 seconds on a card-input incremental. Large table analog plotting time was four minutes and 10 seconds. In this example, the CRT speed differential is 320-to-1 compared to the incremental, and 500-to-1 over the analog. In general, any average engineering plot can be produced by CRT plotter in less than a second, or hundreds of times faster than the fastest analog system.

Other salient considerations in equipment evaluation are the format size and printing characteristics suitable to the end use of the plotting output. Will the application require contouring capabilities for geophysical plotting? Close tolerances for automatic mask drafting? Large size formats for aeronautical maps and charts? Smooth, free-line drawing for reproduction lithography? Extended length for CPM reporting? Or some combination of these features for a cost trade-off?

Standard printing in CRT systems is on a roll of microfilm. Optional quick-look hard copy is available in report-size format. Exposed microfilm can also be further processed into transparencies and magnified for direct viewing or photographic reproduction.

Analog plotters and digital drafting equipment offer the largest format sizes, with the additional advantages of smooth line drawing. Standard plotting is one sheet at a time on a flatbed table. For the analogs, general-purpose printing format is 30" x 30". Large table models include 4" x 58" x 60" and other oversizes. Digital drafting formats range from 54" x 72" on up to 60" x 240"'.

RISE OF THE DIGITALS

For many years, analog designs dominated almost 90% of the applications areas due to free-line drawing and large format accommodation. This was especially true in meteorological, geophysical, and other special mapping or contouring applications. The days of this privileged sanctuary, however, are over. CRT's are more suitable for high volume plotting. The digital plotters are less expensive. Digital drafting systems are faster by 50%, and more accurate by an order of magnitude. They also meet size and precise drawing requirements in many areas where analog plotters are inadequate.

At the low-cost end of the price scale, digital incrementals are encroaching on another large segment of traditional analog application areas. Typical plot format sizes are 12" and 30" widths, and up to 120 feet in length. Above 30" in width, pin-registration is the limiting factor.

Line drawing is also less smooth. But due to steadily rising reliability, speed and resolution, the new generation of incremental plotters offers competitive graphic capabilities at unequalled low cost.

In fact, digital incrementals offer several distinctive performance advantages. Printing in the analog systems, for example, is limited to vertical and horizontal axes. Digital incrementals, on the other hand, provide complete annotation and labeling at a wide variety of angles throughout a complete 360°. Software of the new digital incrementals is available for drafting all types and sizes of symbols, providing an unlimited character set which can not be matched by analog systems. Operation is also less complex. For most applications, a single set-up is all that's required.

In 1966, buffered control units were announced by incremental manufacturers. These units combined already available high speed plotting capability (10″ to 20″ per second) with multiple step capabilities to open new avenues of Digital Plotter usage.

Previously digital plotters had faced the inherent design limitations of stepping speed and computer time requirements. The buffered control units incorporate internal programming logic, allowing multiple steps or Delta commands similar to the more expensive digital drafting systems.

Stored program logic of some control units has demonstrated dramatic operational advantages in reducing input instruction, slashing computer mainframe requirements, and multiplexing digital plotters to on-line operation. The new control equipment is compatible with all families of plotters and computers.

Off-line with magnetic tape, one kind of controller (B-L's Delta Control Unit), allows more commands in less write-space with reduced requirements for generating the input tapes. It also reduces the need for "no op" codes and filters.

The Delta Control Unit also made off-line plotting with punched card input practical for the first time. Prior to 1966, each plotting command would have required one complete punched card; i.e., thousands of punched cards to produce a routine graph. With the DCU, 2000 plotting steps can be generated from just one punched card.

The new, stored-logic control subsystems are particularly adaptable for efficient multiplexing via the multi-processing and time-sharing capabilities of third-generation computer systems. A short burst of data from the computer is enough to feed the control memory. Necessary commands for each of the various on-line plotters are then generated until the beginning of the next cycle. If any waiting occurs, it's the plotter waiting for the computer, not the more expensive other way around.

THE FUTURE

Rounding the first quarter of 1967, some exciting new developments in the plotting industry are underway and should be watched with interest by potential users in the immediate future.

Before the end of this year, you can expect to see the introduction of the fifth basic plotting approach, centered around highspeed optical printing without the use of CRT.

Watch for higher speeds and accuracies about to be announced in new incremental and digital drafting systems hardware.

Expanded use of transceivers and other communications equipment will make better use of time-sharing, third-generation computers for remote plotting. Especially for those users who have already paid the basic overhead of time-shared systems—either with in-house computers or as part of a subscriber time-sharing service—remote digital plotting promises unusual report-generating capability for relatively low cost.

In terms of applications development, look for management-information-systems plotting, numerical control and digital drafting to become the center of attention of forthcoming public exhibits, industrial shows and technical conferences.

From the secluded labs of R&D, new printing technologies, lasers, and other advanced research projects may enter the user vocabulary. But, except for the optical plotting systems and interactive light pens, probably no radical new design principles will be implemented in operational hardware before 1970.

As for the four basic design philosophies, you can expect hardware refinements to emanate continually from some 20 manufacturers throughout the nation. This year has already seen announcements of increased speed and resolution in the digital incremental plotting field. Digital drafting systems now include state-of-the-art speed combined with accuracies and resolution previously available only with precise numerical control systems. CRT systems are incorporating integrated circuits and new optical capabilities, thereby providing increased speed, accuracy and reliability.

To support the industry's need for software, plotter manufacturers are developing comprehensive programming packages with subroutines for line drawing, point plotting, contouring, programmed scale setting in linear or logarithmic scales, axes drawing, drafted character generation, and printed annotation.

Automatic plotting has come a long way since its inception in the early '50s, but this is no time to rest on our technological laurels while the gap continues to widen between available potential and implemented reality. Of today's 45,000 computer installations, less than 3000 are equipped for plotting ... the users' need to catch up and absorb a new generation of graphics technology has never been greater.

Questions:

1.   What is the major advantage of a graph over a printed report?

2.   List the major types of plotting devices which have been manufactured.

SOFTWARE: THE ART, THE SCIENCE, THE INDUSTRY

By RUSSELL PAQUETTE

For good or ill, computers manage a great many of your daily affairs. They prepare your bank statements, check your credit rating, determine whether your insurance program is adequate and insure the delivery of your magazines or book club selections. They bill you for purchases and keep track of your smallest payment; they reprimand you for financial delinquency and cajole you into returning a prepunched card in a prestamped and addressed envelope ("Do it now, while you think of it . . .") to order things you may neither need nor want. They even improve your social life by means of hundreds of matching services ("I like the following things—Please check: Legitimate Theater . . . Politics . . . Sex . . . Large Crowds . . . Home Movies . . . Bondage . . . Leather . . . Dominant Women . . .").

On a less personal, but no less important, level, computers are the workhorses of the huge Defense Department complex in Washington; the backbone of American big business; the finest information storage and retrieval instrument ever invented; and the greatest boon to science and education likely to be devised for some time.

Given all this—why, then, are computers widely felt to be cranky, erratic machines, built to harrass, infuriate and intrude on the average citizen? Why do people justly complain when credit payments aren't credited, when bank statements look like double-acrostics and when bills arrive stamped with a threatening "Final Notice" for merchandise never ordered and for which they haven't even received a first notice—which in itself would have been an error? Public opinion believes the machines are faulty; those in the computer business know that poor programming is the real enemy.

Computers are like money—neither good nor evil in themselves. Without proper programming—or software—the machines have no brains, nothing to direct their actions. For, unlike humans, computers are born to do only what they are told—a hard fact many a computer customer is learning to his grief.

There is a misconception common to all un-computer-oriented purchasers that says everything that can be done for the machine has been done for it by the hardware manufacturer; once delivery has been taken; all the buyer has to do is plug it in, learn a few simple operating instructions, and his several-hundred-thousand-dollar investment will roll over and bark. This childlike acceptance of the machine's powers can be traced into the not-so-distant past, when computer sciences were beginning— actually, not

Reprinted with permission from the March, 1968 issue of SDC Magazine, a publication of the System Development Corporation.

much more than twenty years ago—and salesmen were trying to crack a virgin market. Potential buyers were naturally skeptical of anything both untried and expensive, so the computer manufacturers compensated by over-selling the work of their product; the data processing market was too huge—$6 billion in 1966—to stop improving and selling hardware. Customers caught the enthusiasm and clamored for newer, bigger machines, and the manufacturers were delighted to fill that demand.

In the continuing stampede to get even newer computer hardware on the market and delivered, manufacturers are now having difficulty in producing and installing the vital support software without which the machines won't function. It isn't all that rare for a customer to wait six months for delivery of his new computer's compiler or to find that its control programs are not quite ready. Certain sophisticated computer users such as the universities have the skilled personnel to write their own operating programs if necessary, and it is to this kind of independence that certain commentators look. As *Computers and Automation* has pointed out in an article titled "Computers: No Longer a Bargain for Uneducated Users":

"At this point in the development of computers and computer technology, it is most important that manufacturers actively and officially encourage their customers to develop some resident systems skills . . . the user should be encouraged to aim for a level of capability which allows [him] to evaluate the software supplied for [his] machine, and, with only nominal help from the manufacturer, maintain that system and modify any of its features. . ."

Another solution is offered by the rapidly prospering independent software houses springing up to fill the vacuum left by the large manufacturers. Now grossing about $100 million a year, these firms offer programming and consulting services to computer customers, ranging from application programming to sophisticated technical support and total system design.

According to *Time*, "there are now some 2500 of these logic factories, the bulk of them one- to three-man shops. At least two dozen are publicly-owned corporations."

The advantages of the independent software houses are both obvious and enticing. First and most important, they are fully as capable of getting the job done as the large manufacturers, and without the six-month delay customers have come to dread. Almost as important, the independents eliminate the need for large-scale computer buyers to build an in-house programming capability.

In spite of its problems, the software industry is booming. While total business revenues for 1966 came to $1 billion, by 1970 the software market is expected to amount to $7 billion—a sevenfold increase in less than four years. These figures led E. F. Hutton & Company to call software "the fastest growing segment of the computer market . . . it certainly qualifies as one of our fastest growing industries . . ." According to *Time*, more money will be spent on software this year than on the computers themselves. The signs of this phenomenal growth potential dot the business landscape; computer leasing companies, which buy their machines from big companies like IBM and then rent them at substantially reduced rates—at least 10 percent below manufacturers' fees—aim at keeping their wares continuously in action for about ten years, or double the payoff time on which manufacturers base their rents. These comparative small fry, who depend on federal antitrust pressure on the huge IBM complex for survival, are steadily nibbling away at a vast market: last year computer makers installed 13,000 systems worth $5 billion, or twice their 1962 output, and 80 percent of that number are leased. Happily, the smaller companies have even managed to charm the giant under whose shadow they must survive; by purchasing the costly computers, they furnish IBM with the great amounts of hard cash it must have for research and development.

What has come to be known as the software snarl became a real problem with the introduction of the IBM 360 series in April 1964. The 360 and other third-generation computers represent a remarkable advance in hardware design, incorporating microminiaturized solid-logic circuitry into an ever-smaller body, thereby greatly boosting the size of computer memory banks and speed of computation, while simultaneously reducing overall machine bulk. However, there is a price that both manufacturers and buyers have had to pay for these technological marvels—for many of the latest models, the level of sophistication required for their programming is nearly incredible. It is not unusual for programmers to hand-devise 1 million bits of computation for a 360, and, if any *one* is wrong, or if the programmer happens to overlook something, no matter how apparently trifling, the computer that Company X is renting at $160,000 a month will spew out a series of ludicrous errors or simply quit functioning altogether.

Clearly, the gap between hardware technology and software design is becoming critical. The computer industry bulges with horror stories about shiny computers delivered and paid for in anticipation of system programming that never arrived, or arrived faulty, and therefore useless. For example, the city of Los Angeles recently ordered a 360-30 from IBM. After a delay, the machine showed up, minus a workable program. Nine months passed, with the city exacting a $100-a-day penalty from the company. At last count, the tab had climbed to $78,000 in training funds and rental charge concessions.

"IBM is not alone," as Dr. C. Erwin Piper, chairman of the Los Angeles Board of Administrators, told the *Los Angeles Times*. "All companies are having delivery problems. They jumped the gun and sold the hardware before the software was ready. Companies come in here like vultures over a dead bird, cutting each others' throats, saying their equipment wouldn't have been delayed, but then I hear every day that these very same companies also are suffering delays. . . . Part of the problem is traceable to our own personnel. It's difficult to get competent computer programmers, and sometimes you take what you can get."

This shortage of computer programmers, combined with the spiraling cost of support software, closely follows such delivery delays as the industry's biggest headache. For example, a computer costing $60,000 a month will require 20 or 30 programmers to feed it information, write its program and generally keep it in working order. Certain aerospace companies retain 300 programmers for a single computer.

There are about 100,000 men and women currently performing programming tasks for the nation's 37,000 operating digital computers; there is an immediate need for 50,000 more, mostly because buyers are demanding, and the hardware industry producing, computers faster than the specialists can be trained. "If we were to have no advance in hardware for five years," says Walter Bauer, president of Informatics, Inc., ". . . the programs would just be catching up to the capabilities of the machines."

Because of this increasingly serious situation, scores of employment agencies and training schools are filling the classified section of your morning newspaper with ads to entice dishwashers, housewives, high school dropouts and retired policemen into the famously lucrative computer programming field. If you believe the ad copy, anyone can do it—and, up to a point, it's true. Generally speaking, the prime requirements for programming beginners are a logical mind and a liking for time-consuming detail work. The differences between this type of basic programming and the intricacies of system programming, however, are the differences between a toddler and Jesse Owens.

The most immediate need is for application programmers—those people with a minimum of mathematical ability who orient the computer to a specific series of problems. Application programs present the machine with a task—whether of payroll computation for a small trucking firm or the calculation of a satellite's orbit—in a form the machine can understand. They also deal with the myriad instructions stored in the computer's memory that organize and automate its work. To successfully complete his job, the application programmer must be conversant with the particular "language" his computer understands—the code into which all instructions to the machine must be translated.

Such built-in lingual individuality exacerbates the programmer shortage because, when a company buys or leases more recent computer models, the existing application programs must be totally rewritten to conform with the new machines' logic. At best, this type of overhaul is a time-consuming, tedious task requiring a regiment of programmers, and few customers are interested in taking the time or the money required to do the job correctly. For those in a hurry, manufacturers have devised an auxiliary bit of hardware called an emulator. Basically, the emulator imitates the logic of an older computer on a newer one. This, in turn, allows the user to process his data a good deal faster than he could on his original machine, but nowhere near as fast as he might if the new computer were working properly. This trying to have it both ways—a shiny new computer, but a greatly reduced software bill—seems to be a relic of the bad old days, when customers believed their financial investment ceased with the purchase or lease of a piece of hardware.

According to *Fortune,* this is definitely no longer the case, if it ever was. In an article published in March of last year, the magazine pointed out that computer programming, or software, "has emerged as the most expensive, the most problem-plagued component of the . . . electronic data-processing business. Big computer users such as the federal government now spend more on programmers' salaries and on programs than they spend on leasing or buying the computers themselves."

To alleviate the need for new programmers, many companies have started their own schools or are sending trainees to those run by IBM or RCA. Additionally, programming courses are now being offered in approximately 60 universities across the country. But texts date rapidly, and instructors are difficult to keep—a logical consequence of the near-fantastic salaries being offered by private industry to competent programmers. The cut-throat competition for good men has pushed programming among the highest paid professions in the country. People with training–no experience, just training–can start at $7000 a year; that hops to $10,000 after two years, and it's not at all unusual to find a 25-year-old who's been in the business about six years grossing $14,000. Salaries for the top of the profession take off from a base of about $22,000. As James R. Dunlap, president of Digitek Corporation, points out, "The richest man on the earth in the year 2000 will be a programmer."

These sums are well earned. Today's fastest models, which can run off a problem in three seconds that used to take an hour, require an enormous amount of fiddling before they can function. The programmer is faced with control programs–the coordinating mechanism of the computer–of inordinate complexity often containing literally millions of instructions to be stored in the machine's memory on magnetic tapes or disks as part of the total operating system. This closed world of advanced system design accounts for a large part of the computer mystique–the near-occult veneration shown the machines and their programmers by users. For the system analyst, a grasp of the total resources available to the machine and the knowledge of how to employ these resources in the organized, economical solution of a particular set or sets of problems are mandatory. Also, a high percentage of these men have specialized training not only in total system design, but in the various sciences for which the computers will labor.

For a long time, it was impossible even to communicate with computers without the services of one of these high priests; if you didn't know the special language and proper rituals, the mass of metal would simply ignore you. With the development of the higher-order programming languages, such as IBM's FORTRAN and SDC's JOVIAL, however, even a barely competent application programmer can write a satisfactory program without knowing anything about the machine's inner secrets. And finally, with the introduction of English words and phrases into programming languages, which are rapidly becoming more problem- than machine-oriented, users began to dream what had, a scant two or three years ago, been the impossible dream: doing their own programming.

In such languages, each separate symbol generates as many as twenty computer instructions; the compiler accepts each short expression–like "if" or "go"–and transliterates it into the numerical code the machine understands. However, we have not yet reached the every-man-his-own-programmer utopia, and perhaps we never will. Any human language is, by definition, carrier of a heavy load of subjective connotations uncommunicable to any known machine. A completely English programming language would, then, retain only the outward appearance of a living language and would have to rely on a narrowly defined, heavily restricted grammar totally alien to the average person–but quite congenial to a trained programmer.

The single exception to this rule, and possibly still another solution to the software snarl, is time-sharing–simultaneously one of the oldest and most effective means of beating the high cost of machine use. Dating back to the 1950s, when the SAGE (Semi-Automatic Ground Environment) system's programming was designed by SDC to feed the results of multiple radar observations into huge computers converting the data into aircraft displays, time-sharing is becoming the answer to a customer's prayer. High computer prices can be traced directly to the very ease and speed with which the latest machines function; even the most intricate problems use less than 10 percent of the computer's total capacity—so the usual one-user-at-a-time technique must of necessity be expensive. Multiple-access processing, on the other hand, which allows many users to query a central computer almost simultaneously, both keeps the machine in constant use and splits the then-reduced cost among all users.

Whether or not time-sharing is the wave of the future remains to be seen, but big government agencies like the Defense Department and big business alike seem to be getting on the bandwagon now. "General Electric," states the November 1966 *Datamation,* "contends that by 1970, 75 percent of all computers will possess time-sharing capability. Informatics argues that by 1975 nearly all computer usage will be on-line. Western Union estimates that within five years some 60 percent of all computers will be tied into the nation's communication networks. The Bell System predicts that eventually half of the business transmitted over its network will be data. And finally, *Business Week* projects that time-shared services will grow from an estimated volume of $20 million to some $2.5 billion within five years."

According to *Computer Processing Updater Newsletter,* the Los Angeles area alone had, by mid-1967, seventeen active computer time-sharing firms soliciting business; there are nine other Los Angeles firms representing companies with time-sharing capabilities elsewhere in the country, with each of these expected to offer its services to potential buyers in California within the next year. Eight more firms have announced they will probably offer computer time-shared access to schools, laboratories and offices, also within a year. The *Newsletter* points out that: "Only two of the major computer enterprises in Los Angeles stated that they would not in the foreseeable future offer on-line, remote multiple services to customers. Thus the economic war of the century is about to begin among thirty-seven computer firms ... [with] more than $300 million worth of equipment ... already involved."

The case may be overstated, but the fact remains that time-sharing is, at the very least, a potentially revolutionary tool for education, business and government. Obviously, this tool would have remained impossible without the giant strides computer technology took in the 1950s and early 1960s. Within a decade, computing power has increased by a factor of 1000; memory bank size has increased to the point where the large machines can handle several concurrent programs and still furnish astonishingly rapid data access—between 15 and 150 milliseconds. Storage capacities have, since 1958, grown more than a hundredfold, while storage costs per character have fallen by a factor of more than twenty. Also, because many of the larger time-sharing systems contain several processors, and each one of these can be separately programmed, the largest and swiftest computers can cope with up to 1000 users, with the waiting period for an answer stretching to perhaps five seconds.

Speed is not time-sharing's sole recommendation, however. Because such systems offer direct man-machine interaction, programmers are superfluous, except in the building of the original program. There are no cards, tapes or codes; the emphasis is on remote access by many users simultaneously dealing directly with the machine. So, although the computer itself understands only electrical impulses coded in the binary system, the uneducated user can still make himself understood with a minimum of fuss thanks to the invention and perfection of computer languages. These are processed into the operating system to translate the man-machine dialogue.

As time-sharing developed through the early 1960s, software designers quickly found that one of its cardinal uses was in furnishing a multitude of random users access to large data bases. In assessing SDC's Time-Sharing System (TSS), the company's Jules Schwartz and Clark Weissman have written that, in addition to its originally-intended uses, such as natural language processing, group interaction studies, general display programming and the simulation of a mobile military command post, TSS "has proven most popular [in furnishing] on-line access to large data files. Through a general-purpose data management system, a number of users has maintained and queried data bases that range over such diverse applications as personnel files, cancer research statistics and military status information . . . Time-sharing systems are now recognized to be really *resource*-sharing systems, where time, memory programs, data and people are the primary system resources."

Time-sharing represents a reaction against the older method of machine querying called batch processing, through which individual queries were accumulated until there was a sufficient number to warrant the cost of using the machine, at which time each question was fed into the computer, processed and answered. It wasn't at all unusual for users to wait days, or even weeks, for an answer. Significantly, though, batch processing and time-sharing, at first glance almost totally different in approach, seem to be drifting toward reconciliation. As Schwartz and Weissman observe, "There is an increasing tendency for new time-sharing systems to accept off-line inputs and for the major off-line systems to accept some on-line—teleprocessing—activity. Also, most of the major off-line systems have taken on the characteristics of multiprogrammed systems, handling several or more jobs on- and off-line simultaneously. Thus—interestingly—there is a decided possibility that in the next few years there will be some difficulty in differentiating between the two . . ."

Schwartz and Weissman represent one side of the time-sharing question. Although they speak for the majority in the programming world, opinion is far from unanimously favorable to the way things are going. Time-sharing's opponents envision huge, multipurpose computer networks functioning almost as utilities and devoting a disproportionate share of their time to simply maintaining themselves and updating their programs. Under such a monster system, the executive (the computer's control program governing its entire system and ensuring that it functions in sequence) could become so intricate that it might itself appropriate most of the computer's calculating power.

Another adverse factor in time-sharing is the cost of communications between user and machine. According to *Fortune,* "Beyond the range of about ninety miles the [telephone] line charges start to exceed computer charges. Projects to reduce the cost of long-distance computing by means of shared multichannel lines encounter legal complications involving common-carrier regulations. As the Federal Communications Commission has noted, 'Fears are expressed that the cost of communications may prove to be the limiting factor in the future growth of the [computer] industry.' "

And what about the problem of security? The time-shared systems' common memories, possibly filled with confidential data, will have to be safeguarded against unauthorized use. So far the only answer has been the use of codes known only to authorized users—and the incorporation into each system of means to prevent accidental destruction of its data files—but the problem clearly calls for additional research.

As an alternative, or at least supplement, time-sharing opponents point to the relatively recent development of the small, low-cost computer. As SDC Principal Scientist Tom Steel has said, newly developed hardware and breakthroughs in the field of microcircuitry have put the $10,000 to $25,000 computer on a competitive basis with its $5 million and up big brothers, opening a potential market of from 5 to 20 million customers. Steel posits a machine costing about $25,000, available possibly in 1970, which will justify its cost in performing ordinary clerical tasks alone. He estimates that it will do the work of from three to five clerks; more importantly, through recent advances in disk packs and data cells, it will have a storage capacity large enough to contain a program library in many cases competitive with a time-shared, large-scale computer.

Answering the objection that machine efficiency increases with the power of the central processor, Steel also notes that the high telephone communications costs seriously detract from the centralized systems' usefulness. And even where the huge storage capacity of a time-sharing system is required, he says, it will generally be more efficient to establish a data link between the central computer and an on-site (or in-office) machine than to rely on remote processing through communication terminals.

At the moment, proponents of the small computer over time-sharing seem to be reacting in the way time-sharing advocates originally reacted to the once-dominant batch processing method. In computer science, however, there is rarely an either-or, and it is likely that the two approaches will simply attract different aspects of the same market. *Business Week* asserts that the small computer accounts for a $200 million slice of the computer pie, and may very well hit $1 billion by 1970, despite the shying away of the industry giants who dislike one-shot sales at such low prices.

Like any healthy entity, the software industry—or art—is continually changing, growing, acquiring what is useful and discarding the superfluous. Anything with a potential gross of $7 billion by 1970 is bound to be full of conflicting opinions, opposing avenues of research and a good deal of spirited infighting. Batch processing advocates deplore the rapid rise of time-sharing, while time-sharing proponents magnanimously appropriate part of batch processing's methodology; programmers become fewer and make more money with the passing years, but time-sharing and/or the minicomputer, with their easy-to-operate mechanisms, may solve that problem in the comparatively near future. Despite the notorious troubles manufacturers are fighting in delivering hardware complete with all necessary operating programs, business has never been better—and the difficulties harassing the computer giants have allowed the beginning of still another branch of an already booming industry, the independent software house.

Only when software is viewed within the context of all its paradoxes and hugger-mugger, its continuous twenty-year effort to simultaneously keep up with its orders and ahead of the times, does its actual strength become obvious. In a scant two decades it has advanced from nothing to one of the most important facets of civilization; and, through the momentum it has built up during that time, it can be expected to keep climbing indefinitely. As SDC's president, Wesley Melahn, has said,

"The future of information technology and its contribution to our way of life will be limited only by our imagination."

Questions:

1.　What is software? Hardware?

2.　Compare the development of hardware to that of software.

3.　What is an applications programmer? How might higher level languages such as FORTRAN affect his job?

4.　List the attributes of time-sharing, both favorable and unfavorable.

THE FIRST TIME-SHARING
GENERATION IS HERE

By JEFFREY N. BAIRSTOW

The computer can help to create effective engineering. And do it at fraction-of-a-second speeds. But the designer who has a problem to feed into the digital computer may be forced to wait hours, days or even weeks for his results—unless he has access to one of the few time-sharing systems now in operation.

Time-sharing offers him faster use of the machine than he can hope to obtain by waiting his turn at a busy batch-processing computer. Some engineers believe that time-sharing computers are the wave of the future. Utilized to the fullest, they argue, such systems can make the computer the instant calculating servant not only of the engineer but also of the businessman, the storekeeper and even the householder.

Why does it take so long to use the average computer today? First, the designer must give his problem and data to a programmer, who after lengthy and frequent consultation with the engineer, produces a computer program. The program is coded—that is to say, put into a language the computer can understand, and the coded program is punched onto cards or paper tape. It then goes to the computer, where it is stacked in a pile to await its turn at the machine. A few hours later, perhaps, it is fed into the computer, which puts out its replies in seconds. If the replies are satisfactory, back they go to the engineer. But if not, the program has bugs—faults that the computer will not correct, since it can only follow instructions. The programmer will need to debug his program, a procedure that may require several computer runs with consequent delay. Finally the harried designer gets his results. Total time in this case: three days to three weeks perhaps. The designer's reaction? "Maybe a slide-rule would have been faster."

The alternative? The engineer has a teletype console in his office with an ordinary telephone line to a time-shared computer service center. He dials the computer, he writes his programs himself in a language that closely resembles ordinary math, he instantly debugs his own programs, often helped by the computer itself, and he gets his results back instantly (Fig. 1). Total time to write, debug and run his program? Probably much less than 30 minutes, even for an inexperienced user. When the program has been debugged it can be stored on the time-sharing system for use at a later date. The user only has to request the program from his personal file.

What is time-sharing? There are many definitions. A general one might be that time-sharing is the use of a device, such as a central processor, for two or more purposes during the same overall time interval by interspersing

Reprinted with permission from the April 25, 1968 issue of ELECTRONIC DESIGN.

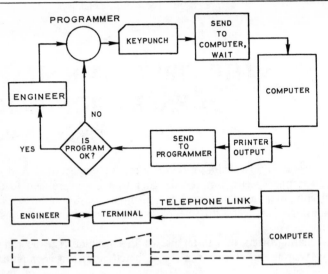

1. **The engineer is separated from the computer** when he uses a conventional batch-processing system (a), but the time-sharing system (b) gives him direct access.

component actions in time. This definition covers the use just described—the interactive conversational use of a computer. It also covers the use of a computer for monitoring and controlling several functions, as in a nuclear reactor. Such a system, where computation is controlled by events outside the system, is called a real-time system. Yet another time-sharing system is the single-purpose system, as used in reservation systems—for example, the Sabre system used by American Airlines for passenger reservations.

The system that the design engineer is most likely to use is the conversational, interactive variety. It will allow him to write his own programs, to store his own files and generally to use the main computer as through it were his and his alone. So we'll concentrate on this particular type of time-sharing system.

A time-sharing system is actually a time-and-space-sharing system. It enables several users to share space in the computer's memory and to share the computation time available (Fig. 2). In a simple system the user programs are kept in an auxiliary memory and moved in and out of the central core memory (swapped) as needed. The computer uses a special program, the executive program, to do the swapping and all the other housekeeping operations needed in a time-sharing system.

Thus in Fig. 2 assume that program A is already in the core memory and being executed. While this is going on, programs B and C are being loaded into the core. At the end of A's time slice, program A is stopped and program B is started. In the meantime the executive wants to bring in program D, so it has to get rid of A; thus it begins to send A back to the auxiliary memory. B's time slice finishes, and C begins to execute. The executive doesn't have room yet for D, so it sends B back to the auxiliary memory also and begins to swap D into the core. C's time slice ends, D begins to compute, and now

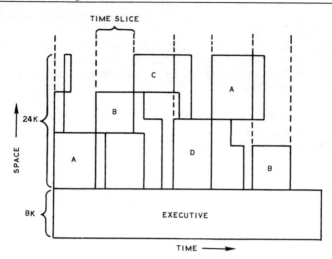

2. **Time-sharing** implies that both time and space are shared. To share space, users must be swapped into and out of memory so that their programs may run.

the executive realizes that A must be brought in again. So C is swapped out, A is swapped in, and the cycle run through once more. Note that A is not necessarily in the same position as previously (dynamic relocation). This is a simplified operation of a time-sharing system, but it does contain the elements of time and space sharing essential to any time-sharing system.

THE TYPICAL TIME-SHARING SYSTEM

The time-sharing computer uses the same basic equipment as the batch-processing computer. But not all batch-processing machines are suitable for time-sharing. This may be either because the software is not available or because the computer does not possess the extra hardware needed for time-sharing.

In addition to extra hardware within the computer itself, two items peculiar to interactive, on-line time-sharing are needed: These are the terminals, one for each user, and the communication control to handle the input and output to and from the computer and the terminals.

Before examining the needs of a typical system, consider the four basic problems in time-sharing that are not encountered in a batch-processing system. They are:

■ Many users will need to use the time and space resources of the central processor at the same time.

■ The system and all the user programs must be protected from each other and from deliberate or inadvertent attempts to invade the privacy of the system.

■ Reliability becomes of major importance when possibly 50 users could be on line together. Fifty irate users can be expected to produce almost as many simultaneous phone calls to the computer center when a total hardware or software failure occurs.

■ Because the user is isolated from the computer, he is not inclined to be tolerant if the response time of the system is too long, or the computer's replies are too long or too short, or if the assistance available from the computer center is inadequate.

All these problems will be met and solved by an efficient time-sharing system. Let's look at the basic hardware needs.

A typical system is like that in Fig. 3.

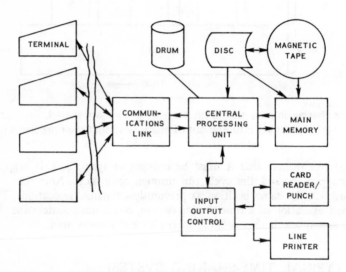

3. A typical conversational time-sharing system will need special communications equipment and more storage than the normal batch-processing computer.

It could be a normal computer system, in that it has a central processing unit (CPU), a main memory, disc drum and tape files, and input-output equipment. Remote terminals and the communications link are additional equipment.

The remote terminals will most likely be electric typewriters or teletype machines that can input information directly from the keyboard or output information by using the printing part of the typewriter.

The communications link acts like a telephone exchange in routing incoming calls to the computer and outgoing information to the correct terminal. In a batch-processing computer, the computer does one job at a time and the input is a stack of punched cards. In a time-sharing computer the communications device takes the place of that input and directs all the jobs into the computer, which then assembles its own stack or queue of jobs.

To keep the whole thing running smoothly, the computer needs a special scheduler. It is the function of the scheduler to assemble the various jobs and give them a priority, dependent on their urgency. To see what the scheduler does and how it does it, let's take a sample journey through the system.

A TIME-SHARING TRIP

Imagine that you are at a teletype console and wish to use the computer. You dial the computer by using the telephone mounted on the teletype. This call goes through the normal exchange network and establishes contact with the communications link.

Assume that the machine is not being used by anyone. The scheduler examines the queues of jobs and finds nothing to do on them. The system is in an idle state. Now let us assume that your call is received. When the call is received by the communication equipment, an interrupt signal is generated. This causes the scheduler to stop examining the queues; instead an interrupt processing routine is run. This routine marks in a table (kept in the core memory) that a call has been received on a particular telephone line. Control is then returned to the scheduler, which continues to examine the queues.

The scheduler recognizes that a telephone call has been made and calls upon a routine to handle your call. This routine sets up a program for you, generally called the main executive program. The executive program is placed on one of the queues and marked as a running program.

Control then returns to the scheduler, which continues to process the queues.

When the scheduler examines the queue that contains the executive program, it calls upon a disc-swapping routine to put the program in the main memory, so that it can be run. If the program (the executive in this case) is not in the main memory, the swapper finds somewhere to put it and reads it in off the swapping drum. If not, the scheduler takes a program out of the core and puts it on the drum, in order to have room to bring in the executive program.

Now the executive sends out a message to the user to log in. Since it usually takes some time for the user to press the teletype keys, the program is placed on a queue to await the input. A program is on the teletype queue for one of two reasons: either it was asking for characters from the teletype and there were none, or it was sending out to a teletype but the buffer could not hold any more characters for that teletype.

You'll then see a message appear on your teletype, "Please identify yourself." At this time you type in your proper account number, password, etc. Each time you type a key on the teletype, an interrupt is generated in the computer. The character is stored in the proper buffer, and whatever was going on before the interrupt occurred is continued. In this case, with only one user on, the scheduler would see only the entry on the queue that cannot be run because the program is waiting for teletype input.

Then a user finally types a break character, such as a carriage return. When the interrupt routine processes the carriage return, it marks the program on the queues as being an "activatable" one—that is, one ready to be run. Control goes back to the scheduler after the interrupt has been processed. When the scheduler finds an activatable program, it calls upon the swapping routine again to get the program into the core. In this particular case the program would already be in the core. Control is transferred to the program. The program then re-executes the character-request instruction, and the character is given to the program.

The program continues to ask for characters until either the time limitation that the monitor imposes upon the program is exceeded—that is, the program computes longer than is allowed in one quantum—or the program asks for something that can't be done, such as asking for another character when the input is finished.

Therefore every time the program asks for something that cannot be done, or it exceeds its time allotment, the program is packed up and put back on the queues, to be run again when it is activatable. If it has exceeded its time slice, it is activatable and will be run again as soon as the scheduler sees it on a queue. If there are five programs that all need several slices of computer time—called by programmers "compute bound" programs—the scheduler will run them in sequence and return them to the end of the queue. Only one program is ever running at any time in the machine. All the other programs are put away on queues, and all the information necessary to restart them from the point at which they were stopped is kept in tables.

The only things that can mark programs activatable are interrupt routines—that is, if a program asks for a character input and is waiting for teletype input, the interrupt routine, when it sees the carriage return, will mark the program activatable. The only exception to this case is when a program exceeds its time limitation, in which case the program is marked as activatable but it goes to the end of the last queue until nothing else is available to run.

So far as memory allocation by the swapping routine is concerned, if a program has been running and is dismissed and the room that it took in the main memory is needed to run the next program, it will be written on the swapping drum and the new program will be read into the space that was occupied by the old program. When the first program is ready to be run again, the swapper will be required to find room for it, and possibly write out another program to find room to read the old program back in.

To perform all the operations just described, the hardware must have several features peculiar to a time-sharing system.

TIME-SHARING NEEDS SPECIAL HARDWARE

The central processing unit (CPU) must have interrupt hardware that will stop the execution of a program without losing any information. When the CPU is interrupted, the values must be stored, or 'trapped,' so the program can be resumed again. This can be done by software, but this method is usually slow.

To generate timing interrupts, a real-time clock can be used. This clock is also used for accounting purposes—that is to say, for charging each user for the service he has received.

The requirement for user programs to be swapped in and out of the main memory often means that the actual position of a program in the core memory may not be the same each time it enters the main memory. Although the executive program will recognize this, the user will not. Thus the computer must generate revised addresses each time a program is swapped into the core. This dynamic memory relocation is most efficiently handled by hardware.

Combined with the relocation register is another register for memory protection. This memory protection register is used to make sure that a program will not address an area of memory not assigned to it.

The storage requirements in a time-sharing system normally mean more storage than in an average, single-user computer. If there are 50 users, then up to 50 times more storage may be needed. However, to put all these users in the main memory would be prohibitively expensive. To deal with this problem, a hierarchy of storage is used, with a ferrite core main memory, a disc or drum, and a back-up store that uses magnetic tapes. Thus when a user has written a successful program he wishes to keep, it may be stored on the disc or on magnetic tape.

A time-sharing computer must be able to service all the communication lines that connect the users to the computer. This may be done in two ways: either by using a multiplexer or by using a separate communications computer. A multiplexer will operate asynchronously with the central processor. When a character is received, the CPU is interrupted and it services the channel that produced the interrupt. Thus a fraction of CPU time is required to service the input-output channels.

When a separate computer is used, as on the early Dartmouth College GE 235 system, this processor services the individual terminals. It collects characters until an entire line is assembled. At that point the CPU is interrupted, and the entire message is sent to the main memory or onto a disc. Often this communication computer itself has time available for various functions, such as editing and interpretation of commands.

The terminal links the user to a time-sharing system. It may be a teletype, a typewriter, a CRT display with an input keyboard or a special-purpose terminal. The most common terminals are the teletype—an example of which is the Teletype Corp.'s Model 33—and the typewriter—such as the IBM 2741 Communications Terminal.

Keyboard devices suffer from these disadvantages:

■ They are slow. An output speed of 10 characters per second is too slow for the output of large quantities of text or tables.

■ They are noisy. The presently available keyboard devices are motor-driven and electro-mechanically operated. A considerable amount of noise and heat are generated.

■ They are inflexible. The input and output to a typewriter is serial, which makes it poorly suited for certain operations—for example, text editing and graphical output.

A CRT console overcomes many of the disadvantages of a keyboard console. It is quiet, and its display rate is high. The principal disadvantages are the high cost and special communication facilities needed to handle the high transfer rates. Additional circuitry may be needed to relieve the CPU of the time-consuming task of refreshing the CRT image.

To understand how these requirements may be met, we'll look at three current systems, all realistic time-sharing systems.

THE MEN FROM MAYNARD

The Digital Equipment Corp. of Maynard, Mass., was probably the first manufacturer to offer a working time-sharing system with conversational facilities on the PDP-6. The PDP-6 was developed in 1963, and the first user in a time-sharing environment was the Brookhaven National Laboratory on Long Island, N. Y.

An important concept was the use of 16 general-purpose registers, an idea now used by the current IBM 360 line of computers. These registers are available as accumulators, index registers and normal memory locations. Small loops of repeated instructions can be executed very rapidly from these registers.

The PDP-10, developed in 1966, is a later version of the PDP-6. It has the 16 general-purpose registers and a very large instruction repertoire of 365 basic instructions. The time-sharing version PDP-10/50 (Fig. 4a) also includes a Burroughs disc file. The time-sharing system configuration has a memory protection and relocation option that allows the executive routine to assign part of the main memory to a user, prevents the user from having access to other areas and also provides for the automatic relocation of memory addresses.

For memory protection, all user programs are divided into 1024-word blocks. The executive routine stores the number of blocks, minus one, in a memory protection register. When the user program demands access to the memory, the first eight bits of the unrelocated address are compared with the contents of the protection register. If the address exceeds the allowed value, memory reference is inhibited and an interrupt occurs. Each user is kept in a continuous block (Fig. 4b) and moved so as to keep as much core as possible empty for new user programs. The movement or relocation of programs is done by an eight-bit relocation register, which is loaded by the executive routine. The relocation increment is added to the address to obtain the actual memory address.

The PDP-10/50 time-sharing system includes a monitor to handle the swapping of programs into and out of the core and the disc files. The monitor has two portions: the scheduling algorithm and the swapping algorithm. The scheduling algorithm takes the user programs and places them in various queues according to the status of the job. Thus a job may be in one of three run queues (depending on how long the job has run previously), an input-output "wait" queue, an input-output "satisfied" queue and various queues associated with the interpretation of commands. The scheduler can examine the queues, after an interrupt to determine the next job to be run.

The earlier PDP-6 suffered from noise and intermittent contacts, but these appear to have been ironed out on the PDP-10. The only commercial time-sharing user of a PDP-6, the Applied Logic Corp., has taken delivery of a PDP-10 that it hopes will be on-line early this year. However, Applied Logic has written its own software, primarily to provide suitable accounting routines and to modify the command structure.

The Digital Equipment Corp. has had success with its PDP-6 in a research environment, where requirements are not as severe as in a commercial setup. Its extended instruction set makes it useful for real-time, on-line research operations.

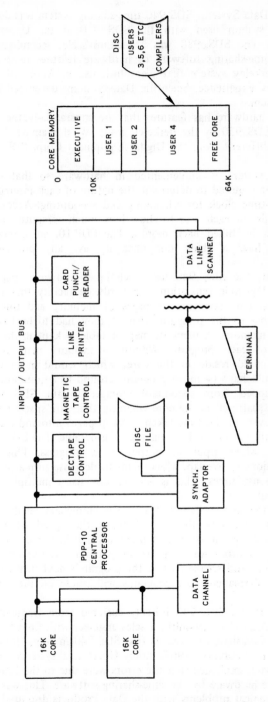

4. **A large instruction repertoire and 16 general-purpose registers made the PDP-6 a suitable machine for time-sharing. The later PDP-10 (a) uses the same features and also has a simple memory allocation scheme (b).**

AID FROM THE UNIVERSITY

The Scientific Data Systems SDS 940 time-sharing system was developed from the Berkeley system used with the SDS 930 at the University of California, Berkeley. The SDS 930 was a medium-scale, second-generation computer without time-sharing software or hardware features necessary for time-sharing. The Berkeley system first went into use in April, 1965. As a result of the Berkeley experience, Scientific Data Systems developed the SDS 940 time-sharing system.

The SDS 940 hardware has features that are substantially the same as those added to the SDS 930 by the Berkeley group. We'll examine those that make the SDS 940 different from the Digital Equipment Corp. PDP-10 (Fig. 5a).

The interrupt system is implemented in hardware so that software techniques will not be required to determine the nature of each interrupt. The SDS 940 uses a real-time clock for scheduling and accounting. Accounting is the keeping of records for each user to show how much computer time each has used, so he can be billed each month. The PDP-10, an asynchronous machine, does not have a clock nor does it have any provisions for accounting.

More important, the SDS 940 uses techniques known as paging and dynamic relocation. Dynamic relocation is a hardware facility that relocates programs within scattered fragments or pages of memory and thus makes more memory available to the programs than if they had to be fitted in a contiguous block of memory. A memory map or table is kept in the core to show the location of each program. Without a memory map, only one program at a time could reside in the core, which would mean that the operating system would have to move programs around to accommodate new programs being swapped from secondary storage. In the SDS 940 the 2000-word pages are scattered in the core wherever there are spaces (Fig. 5b).

With a paging system, the time taken to swap pages into and out of the secondary storage, either drum or disc, may be considerable. The SDS 940 can execute instructions while input or output is in progress. This enables swap-compute operations to overlap, which helps to decrease turn-around time and to improve response times. This is achieved by using multiple memory paths to each core unit.

A feature available in the SDS 940 is an 8-million-character drum store. The drum has a transfer rate that is 10 times the speed of the disc. Consequently it is used for the storage of programs that have reached a delay point, such as an input-output wait. At the delay point the user's program is dumped onto the drum and recalled when the program's next turn for use of the machine occurs. Permanent user programs will reside on the disc until needed.

The hardware of the SDS 940 initially suffered from frequent parity errors, according to Alan Hammersmith, a sales engineer with Comshare, Inc., of Ann Arbor, Mich. Comshare received its first SDS 940 in July, 1966, and it became operational in February, 1967. Louis Guertin, a systems' specialist formerly with Comshare, explained that the errors were due to the heavy duty cycles imposed on the hardware by the time-sharing software. This was further accentuated by mechanical problems with the Data Products disc used for file

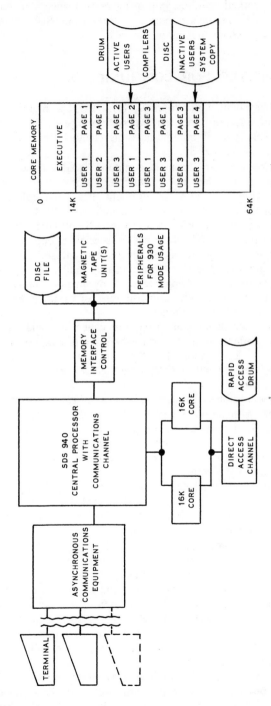

5. **The SDS 940 uses both a drum and a disc** (a). The drum holds user programs that are still active (b) but are waiting for some action such as input. The disc stores inactive user programs and system programs.

storage, Guertin said. Both Hammersmith and Guertin agree that Scientific Data Systems has worked hard on improving performance. An indication of success is evident in Comshare's purchase of three more SDS 940's last year and its intention to purchase four more this year.

USING A COMPUTER FOR COMMUNICATIONS

The GE 420 system, a development from the Dartmouth College GE 265 system, is quite different from the two systems already described. Instead of using a multiplex type of communications channel, the GE 420 uses a separate computer, the Datanet 30.

Communication between the main computer, a GE 415, the Datanet 30 and the disc unit is handled by a switching unit called a programmed peripheral switch (Fig. 6). This arrangement has been called the delta configuration as opposed to the straight line, data channel, CPU, disc feature of the Digital Equipment Corp. PDP-10 and the SDS-940 (Fig. 7).

For time-sharing, the GE 415 has a special direct-access hardware package that permits memory protection, includes an interval timer (similar to a real-time-clock) and gives the GE 415 a non-stop mode. The non-stop mode prevents the processor from stopping except by manual intervention. This could be done by the use of an illegal instruction, for example. Extra channels allow the addition of further peripherals.

Memory protection uses a pair of registers called base and limit registers. These registers are loaded by the executive before a program is run. The base register establishes a lower limit for the program and the limit register provides an address beyond which the program cannot go without creating an interrupt.

As with other machines, the GE 415 has a hardware floating point unit to enable it to deal with numbers having differing decimal point positions. A frequent comment from both GE and non-GE users is that this unit is the fastest floating point unit yet available on a time-sharing system. Although few 420's are yet in the field, early experience seems to indicate that the GE 420 hardware will be very reliable.

To shorten the over-all response time to users, the GE 420 uses a simple multiprogramming system for the GE 415 CPU (Fig. 6b). This allows simultaneous computation and input/output. One user will be in operation while another user is either being swapped into or out of core.

To determine the programs to be run, the GE 415 executive has five queues, each with a different priority level. These queues are for edits, old program fetches, initial runs, continued runs and large program runs. Each job is given a three-second time slice and, at the end of that time slice, the job is returned to the end of its queue. If, as is more likely, an interrupt occurs before the time slice is completed, the job will be returned to the appropriate queue as determined by the interrupt. Jobs requiring input/output will be swapped onto the disc and I/O handled by the Datanet 30. Thus I/O can proceed in parallel with computation.

Like SDS, General Electric has had considerable assistance from their early users in the development of time-sharing software. Presently offered on the GE 420 are BASIC and a version of FORTRAN IV. BASIC is a

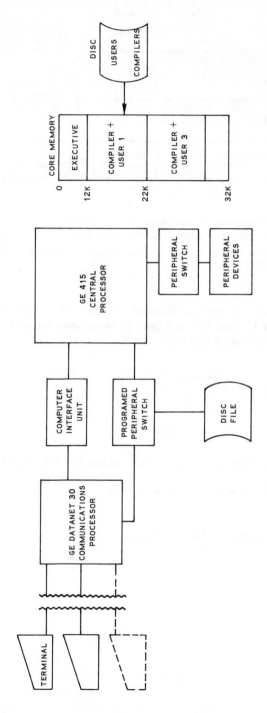

6. **A communications computer is the link** between the central processor and the users of the GE 420 system (a). Only two users are ever in the core, one active and the other one being swapped into or out to the disc (b).

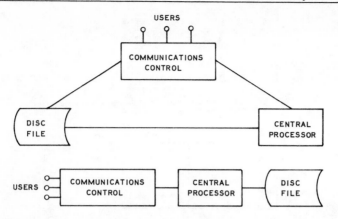

7. **The delta configuration** (a) allows either the communications computer or the central processor to have access to the disc file. In the straight-line configuration (b) access to the disc file must always go through the central processor, thus using CPU time.

conversational language developed at Dartmouth College. The original BASIC has been extended by GE and GE 265 users so that it now can handle larger files and has some direct access capability.

Questions:

1. Discuss and define the term time-sharing.

2. Discuss the four basic problems that are encountered in a time-shared system.

3. List the special hardware and software required to operate in a time-shared mode.

4. Write a short analogy to describe time-sharing.

OPTIMIZING PERFORMANCE IN A MULTI-PROGRAMMING SYSTEM

by PHILLIP C. HOWARD

Since the first computer system was installed, users have searched for ways to squeeze out maximum throughput from their systems. Measurements of one sort or another have influenced programming techniques, systems design, hardware selection, and configuration requirements, usually for the purpose of realizing some improved performance level. Until recently, performance measurement has been fairly simple and straightforward: run a program, time it, calculate the I/O to compute ratio and the degree of overlap, and make a decision on whether the time could be decreased appreciably by making a change. There were few outside influences to consider; a job that ran in 20 minutes one day would run in 20 minutes the next day on the same system.

The advent of multiprogramming and multi-processing has required some changes in the approach to performance measurement, however. The emphasis has shifted away from the optimization of individual programs to the optimization of total system throughput. It is no longer quite so important how an individual program performs, if that program shares the resources of a system with one or more other programs. In such an environment, the goal is to utilize all system resources as close to their full capacity as possible.

Fig. 1 shows this goal in terms of resource utilization in a multi-programming system as opposed to the use of resources in a uni-programming system operating on a hypothetical scientific calculation. In uni-programming systems, the speed of an individual program is always limited by one of the system resources. A program may be processor bound or peripheral bound but, in any case, the entire system runs at the rate of the limiting resource. The remainder of the system components will be idle to varying degrees. For example, if a processor-bound scientific calculation, using two tape drives, is run on a system with 16 tape drives, then 14 drives will be idle for the duration of the run. This run may be followed by a sort which uses all 16 tapes but very little of the processor, and the processor will then be mostly idle for the duration of the sort. The total throughput of a uni-programming system is simply the sum of the individual run times plus set-up time. It is apparent that if each run uses only a part of the total system resources, then over the course of a day the total utilization of each resource will be considerably less than its capacity.

The basic objective of multiprogramming is to overlap programs of various types so as to maximize the use of all resources, all the time, and thereby increase the total throughput of the system. However, the mix of work in a multiprogramming environment does not automatically insure that resources will be uniformly and heavily loaded. In fact, the very nature of an installation's over-all workload may result in a prevailing system bottleneck that limits system performance to something less than full capacity. The objective of performance measurement is to identify such bottlenecks and take the necessary steps to remove them, thus buying an additional amount of computing power at little or no expense. In this context, performance measurement takes on a completely new meaning. The problem of measuring, and ultimately optimizing, over-all system performance is far more complex in a system that shares its resources among several programs than the equivalent procedure in a uni-programming system.

The key resources that contribute to the performance of a system have not changed. However, the manner in which these resources are used is subject to a somewhat different set of ground rules.

Memory utilization: The objective of every system designer and programmer in the past has been to use the maximum amount of memory available to combine runs, reduce I/O activity, and in general to speed up the individual program. Should this same general rule be followed in a multiprogramming system, it is obvious that the level of multiprogramming, or multiprogramming depth, would be extremely low. In fact, without some rules

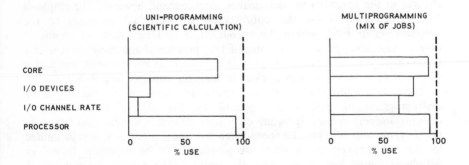

Fig. 1 Comparative use of resources: uni-programming versus multiprogramming.

to control the use of memory the system may be forced into a uni-programming mode, thus negating any possible performance gain.

Processor utilization: The optimization of processor usage has always been, and remains, a basic objective with respect to optimum system performance. However, in a multiprogramming system we are more interested in the efficient utilization of the processor in servicing all user programs in execution rather than its efficiency with respect to any single program.

Channel loading: Channel capacity is the major factor in the selection of peripheral devices and in the establishment of I/O buffering and blocking strategies. For a single program, it is not difficult to determine which device is the limiting factor and to optimize the program around the file or files that are most critical. The same general rule, of course, holds true for a single program in a multiprogramming system. However, from an over-all system viewpoint, channel loading is a function of *all* programs in execution plus any operating system functions that require input/output. Care must be taken to avoid saturation of one particular channel which in turn becomes a performance limiter for the entire system.

Resource allocation: In a uni-programming environment the objective of most programmers is to make maximum use of all system resources in order to minimize run time. In a multi-programming system these rules may no longer apply. For example, while a tape sort will undoubtedly be faster if it is allowed 12 tape handlers rather than six, it may very well be that two six-tape sorts could be completed in parallel faster than the same sorts run serially, each with 12 handlers.

Only a limited amount of each system resource exists. In order to optimize system performance a balance must be reached between the demands of individual programs and the total available resources. In other words, there is a need to protect the system against a user who requires all of a particular resource, thus locking out other programs and causing the system to run at something less than its full performance capability.

There are many other elements which influence the performance of a multiprogramming system, but in general the objective is always to maximize the use of system resources in terms of both speed and space.

It is not particularly difficult to measure, on a rather gross basis, how a system performs over a certain period of time. On the GE-600 series, for example, the operating system (GECOS) produces job accounting information for each job that enters the system. By processing this data "after the fact," it is possible to reconstruct the multiprogramming mix, processor and channel loading, memory utilization, and peripheral usage. While this information is valuable as a general measure of system performance, it does not help significantly to answer the question of *why* the system operated as it did. The fact that such information does exist within the operating system is, however, extremely important in the development of other measurement techniques.

A considerable amount of work has been done on the GE-600 series in the development of monitoring techniques. To date most of these techniques have been software oriented, although one approach has included some special hardware additions to the processor. In all cases the fundamental purpose of the monitor is to "freeze" the state of the system momentarily and "snapshot" core-resident data that describes the current state of the system. By taking these snapshots at some fixed rate of speed, we obtain a continuous record of the system's actual performance, analogous in many respects to a motion picture. This record permits the user to reconstruct the details of the system's operation after the fact and to analyze resource utilization as a function of the events, both internal and external, which took place. The objective, naturally, is to locate the causes for poor system performance and to correct them.

Several considerations are essential in the design and implementation of such a monitor:

1. The system must have an accurate internal clock which allows events and resource loading to be pin-pointed accurately in time, and permits an accurate accounting of resource usage.

2. The monitor should impose as little additional load on the system as

possible. In fact, the closer it is to being "invisible" the better, since any significant load will distort the operation of the system and destroy the value of the data as a reflection of real-life system operation.

3. The operating system must maintain, in core, certain basic statistics and data which constantly reflect the true system state. This is basically an operating system design problem, and if the original design did not include such capabilities it is not likely that these functions can be appended.

4. An appropriate frequency for the data sampling function must be selected. This period must be small enough so that all major system events can be observed, but not so small that the monitoring function becomes a burden on the system, nor that the volume of output overwhelms the analyst.

5. The monitor function itself should be simple to use. That is, it should not be a major operational problem to enable and disable the monitor while the system operates normally. Just as it is important that the internal operation of the system not be distorted, it is also important that the external operation not be distorted, particularly if such a tool is to be used in a production environment.

6. Finally, the display of the results, whether in the form of printed reports, plots, or some other media, must be easy to read and interpret. In fact, the value of the data from any monitoring technique is in direct correlation to its simplicity and clarity. Considerable attention should be paid to the data reduction programs, to minimize the human analysis.

A software monitor, known as the system resource monitor, has been used extensively at General Electric for performance measurement and evaluation of the GE-600 series, and in customer installations for configuration, workload, and operations analysis. Fig. 2 shows the operation of the system resource monitor under the operating system, GECOS.

The only basic changes to GECOS involve the operator control module and the dispatcher, which performs the program selection function. The basic timing mechanism is in the dispatcher. Since the time quantum allowed for each program is 15 milliseconds, the program selection process takes place at least that often. As a part of this routine, the time since the last "snapshot" is calculated and compared against the desired frequency (delta-t) which is set by the operator. If the time elapsed is equal to or greater than this value, the monitor program is enabled; otherwise, the normal program selection process continues. The monitor program moves certain tables and status information from GECOS core to a holding buffer, issues a tape write command, and returns control to the dispatcher, which continues in the normal program selection process.

The delta-t interval of the monitor can range from about 50 milliseconds up. Experience has shown, however, that an interval of about four seconds is quite satisfactory for all but the most detailed software analysis. At this rate, the additional processor load is less than four-tenths of one percent and nearly all events of any significance can be observed.

The data that is collected by the system resource monitor at each delta-t interval can be categorized as follows:

Time of day: The basic timer in the GE-600 series is accurate to 1/64 millisecond and a software time of day clock is accurate within a few milliseconds. Time of day establishes the precise time of each snapshot.

Programs in execution: All user programs in execution are identified as well as active GECOS functions.

Job queue contents: GECOS automatically schedules user jobs and maintains a queue of jobs on the systems storage device (normally a drum). The contents of this queue are reported to provide information on queue empty conditions as well as the allocation requirements of waiting jobs.

Processor utilization: GECOS accounts for all processor time charged to user jobs, operating system functions, and idle time. This data allows the user to isolate periods when processor utilization was below the expected level and

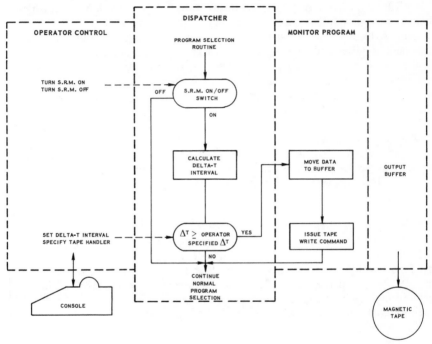

Fig. 2 System resource monitor operation.

to determine where processor time was being charged during a particular period.

Core utilization: Data on core assignments for both user and GECOS programs permits the reconstruction of a complete, time-oriented memory map. This allows the user to identify bottlenecks caused by lack of core or, alternatively, to isolate periods when core was not fully used, possibly indicating a bottleneck elsewhere in the system.

Peripheral assignments: Peripheral allocation is reported in order to identify which units were allocated to which programs, or were available for allocation. With knowledge of the job queue contents, it is a simple matter to determine whether the lack of a particular peripheral resource prevented new programs from entering the system.

Channel loading: Specific accounting of channel use time permits the user to observe channel loading as a function of the workload and to identify possible channel bottlenecks that limit system performance.

The system resource monitor analysis program produces six basic reports from the data collected. For example, one of these shows processor usage and channel loading for the major system peripherals in histogram form, as a percent of the delta-t interval. Other reports include a distribution of processor utilization among user programs and GECOS functions, a memory map, a resource allocation report, and a report of jobs in queue. All reports are keyed to time of day for cross-referencing.

APPLICATION OF RESULTS

The data collected by monitoring a system's operation is worthless unless some new intelligence can be applied to the operation and use of the system. A feedback loop must be set up whereby changes are instituted that test new premises and, hopefully, lead to an improved performance level. As stated earlier, the ultimate goal is to keep all system resources busy and avoid conditions wherein one particular resource is the limiting factor in the system and all others remain at least partly idle. Naturally, performance is always limited by some system resource but to the extent any such limitation leaves other resources working far below their capability, the capacity of the system as a whole is being wasted.

The types of changes that have come about as a result of the monitor techniques described for the GE-600 series fall into four categories:
1. Operating system, software, and user program design;
2. Hardware configuration;
3. Job scheduling and operational procedures;
4. Peripheral selection and file placement.

The first is of primary importance to the manufacturer in the design of software. It is difficult to predict in the design phase how events, occurring randomly within the system, will interact, and what the possible consequences to total system performance will be. By observing these interactions through monitoring techniques, a number of changes have been tested and incorporated into GECOS and other software to substantially improve performance.

The last three areas mentioned above apply primarily to the user environment. Monitoring techniques are extremely helpful in identifying mismatches between a user's workload and a particular configuration, which result in a performance bottleneck. Such bottlenecks, however, may also be caused by poor job scheduling or operational practices. New guidelines or rules for peripheral selection, file placement, and programming techniques may, also be indicated.

As more experience is gained with these measurement tools, some degree of self-optimization will undoubtedly become a part of operating systems. In general, the great complexity of large-scale, third-generation computers demands a sophisticated self-measuring and optimization procedure. Until such time as this becomes a reality, performance measurement is essential to insure that system performance is optimized to the greatest extent possible.

Questions:

1. In this article the statement is made that "a job that ran in 20 minutes one day would run in 20 minutes the next day on the same (uni-programming)

system." Discuss why this is not necessarily true utilizing a multi-programming system.

2. What are some of the major considerations in the design and implementation of a system monitor? Discuss each.

3. The system resource monitor operating under GECOS collects a variety of data. Explain how this information can be used to improve the performance of the computer system?

AN INTRODUCTION TO ANALOG/HYBRID COMPUTATIONS AND ITS APPLICATIONS

By R. VICHNEVETSKY and J. P. LANDAUER*

Analog computation has been present on the scientific and engineering scene since the time of Lord Kelvin's ball-and-disk integrator, or, perhaps, more accurately, since the invention of the slide rule four hundred years ago. Mechanical analog computers, known as differential analyzers, were widely used at the time of the second World War, and the electronic analog computer was developed after that war.

It has often been said that the appearance of electronic computers on the scene of scientific and engineering research has completely revolutionized the way in which mathematics is used as a tool by scientists and engineers. In the course of this revolution, the two different types of computers, analog and digital, have dichotomized users into two partly dissociated groups each praising the virtues of the type of computer with which they were most familiar. More recently, a *de facto* proof that both types had good and valid reasons to exist, and be used, was made when some engineers found out that the best way to solve certain types of problems requiring computers was to use the two simultaneously in the form which has been since named the hybrid computer. *A posteriori* justification of the superiority of hybrid computers in many different types of scientific and engineering applications will be found in a survey of the hybrid computers used since that time, i.e., since the late 1950's. But to organize the scene, it is appropriate to review the history of their development.

The first hybrid systems, such as the installations at Space Technology Laboratories[1] and Convair Astronautics in 1958, were composed of existing analog-digital computers interconnected by a slow speed data conversion system. About 1960, it was realized that the digital computer could also serve an important function in automating the setup and operation of the analog computer, and the HYCOL system, at the General Electric Missile and Space Vehicle Department,[2] had a linkage which permitted the digital computer to set pots, read components, control analog modes, etc.

At the same time, advances were being made in analog hardware to permit much higher computing speeds and, therefore, much shorter run times. This high-speed capability permitted the use of new iterative techniques which expanded the scope of application of the analog computer, however, a significant expansion of the control and logical capability of the analog computer was required to implement these iterative methods. This need was met in about 1962 by the introduction of high-speed electronic switching and

---

*The authors are affiliated with Electronic Associates, Inc.

Reprinted from *Modern Data Magazine,* February, 1968 issue.

An Introduction to Computer Systems

patchable logic elements, and these features are now available in nearly all modern analog computers.

Modern hybrid computing systems consist of an analog computer, a digital computer, and a linkage system which performs the double role of transferring data and general control signals between these two machines.

THE BASICS OF
ANALOG COMPUTATION

To appreciate the advantages which hybrid computation offers, it is necessary to understand the basic functions of the two major sections of the hybrid system, namely, the analog computer and the digital computer. All applications are essentially a combination of these basic functions.

The major purpose of the analog computer is to provide high-speed solution of ordinary differential equations; since the dynamics of many physical systems are defined by sets of differential equations, this function is essential. In addition to this basic mathematical function, the modern analog computer can simulate any type of discontinuity and logical function which may be present in the physical system or the set of equations representing that system.

The electronic analog computer operates by generating and measuring voltages and currents which represent physical or mathematical variables in the problems being solved. Each variable in the problem appears continuously as a separate voltage or current waveform at the output of a particular element within the computer. All variables are generated simultaneously, and, therefore, the analog computer is inherently a parallel machine.

In brief, an analog computer exists for, and is capable of, solving ordinary differential equations, with an accuracy and speed determined by the electrical properties and tolerances of its circuits.

In engineering, the analog computer can be an effective tool in either of two categories. In the first of these, the inductive process of model building, an analytical relation between variables is hypothesized to describe the physical system of interest. Forcing functions identical to those in the physical system then can be applied to the hypothetical model so that a comparison of the response of the model with that of the actual physical system will indicate changes that should be made in the model to fit it to the system better and thus establish the validity of the model. Because of the ease with which parameter variations and model changes can be accomplished, the analog computer is useful in conducting many "trial and error" experiments on the model to obtain the best fit to the physical system.

In the second category, the deductive process of systems analysis, it is necessary to have a mathematical statement available which describes the physical system to be studied. These mathematical statements (equations) are often supplemented by graphical information as well as logic statements, and definite ranges for the parameter values are assigned for the study. Experiments are then performed, varying the inputs and the parameters describing the system, to obtain, finally, an optimum response for the system, or to develop a better understanding of the intrinsic nature of the system by studying input/output relations. Here, again, because of its speed, flexibility, and similarity to the physical system, the analog computer is an effective engineering tool.

CONCEPT OF THE ANALOG COMPUTER

An analog computer is a collection of operational devices which are capable of performing basic mathematical operations. By interconnecting components which can integrate, add, generate functions, multiply by a constant, and multiply variables, we can analyze dynamic systems which are described by ordinary differential equations. Analog computers range from small desk-top computers (20 to 80 amplifiers and a related number of multipliers, attenuators, and function generators) to medium-scale computers (150 to 200 amplifiers) and large-scale systems with capabilities of the maximum values of the variables which will occur in the problem, guided by the experience of the engineer and coupled with information obtained from the analysis of simplified forms of the equations describing the physical system. However, errors in estimating maximum values are not serious since, once the problem is put on the computer, these errors are quickly indicated by overloads of computing elements, and then one can rescale as necessary. In addition to not exceeding the voltage limitation of the computing elements, proper scaling also requires that the voltages be greater than some minimum voltage level at some time during a problem.

The problem is then run on the computer using not the original variables (e.g.,x), but the scaled variables (e.g., $10x$, $100 \sin x$, $10^{-3} e^{-kx}$, etc.). A detailed treatise on scaling is not appropriate here, but it can be seen to be a significant part of the programmer's task.

Whether or not time scaling is required in a problem is determined by several factors:

- Limitation of dynamic response of computing elements;
- Limitation of dynamic response of recording elements;
- Length of time required for problem solution.

Time scaling can be reduced to a straight-forward procedure which will not affect the voltage scale factors previously established for the dependent variables of the problem.

To increase or decrease the time required for a phenomenon to occur, it is necessary simply to increase or decrease the rate at which the phenomenon takes place. Since the inputs to all integrators are rates, to increase or decrease the rate of problem solution on the computer we have only to increase or decrease the gain of the integrators.

CONTROL AND READOUT

Analog computers have three basic operating modes plus two auxiliary modes. The operating modes are:

Operate – The computer computes the dynamic solution to the given problem;
Hold – Solution time is frozen and variables are held at the last computed values;

Reset – all computer variables are reset to predetermined initial conditions.

The auxiliary modes are:

Potentiometer Set – potentiometers may be adjusted to their assigned numerical values;

Static Check – a set of prescribed initial values is applied to the integrators, against which all derivatives of the problem can be measured to verify agreement with problem equations.

On the computer, mode control is accomplished by means of switching associated with the integrators. In a typical intregator network, relays are used to produce the RESET (initial condition) and OPERATE modes. The relays for all integrators are thrown simultaneously and controlled by master "Operate" and "Initial Condition" switches located on the control panel of the computer. The HOLD mode is implemented by opening all of the "Operate" switches (inputs to the integrators) during a problem run, thus freezing the variables and their derivatives at a particular instant in the problem solution. When the computer is again returned to the OPERATE mode, it will have, in effect, a new set of initial conditions, i.e., the conditions existing when the computer was placed in the HOLD mode.

There are several methods available for displaying the results obtained in a computer solution. A Digital Voltmeter-Printer combination allows monitoring and subsequent printout of all voltages in a problem at a particular instant. Readout accuracy is available to 0.01%. In addition to the digital voltmeter readout, a continuous record can be made of problem variables as functions of time, using multi-channel strip chart recorders, two-axis (X-Y) recorders, or CRT displays for high-speed solutions.

SIMULATION

The primary use of analog computers and their hybrid progeny is to simulate the behavior of physical systems. Through simulation techniques, one is saved the cost of building a system and changing the components for a parameter study. Simulation on the computer enables one to study a system, with all of its variations, without physically building it.

Computer simulation in the hybrid world is the modeling of complex physical systems—represented by sets of differential equations, algebraic equations, and logic equations—in order to study their dynamic behavior; the objectives of simulation may be experimental design, prediction and control, design evaluation, verification, and optimization.

Applications for hybrid computer simulation are generally complex problems. Data processing system simulations are more effectively done by digital computer. The simulation of circuits and devices is usually more appropriate to the analog computer. It is in simulation of total systems, that bring together a combination of components, some suited for digital and some for analog simulation, that the modern hybrid computers are required. Hybrid computation offers the most economical and efficient means for solving a broad spectrum of problems which arise in many fields of science and engineering: some classes of applications are shown in Table 1. The major applications in

TABLE I

CLASSES OF HYBRID COMPUTER APPLICATIONS

Field of Application	Type of Problem
Aerospace	1. Aerospace Vehicle Mission Simulations 2. V/STOL Vehicle Stimulations 3. Aircraft Adaptive Control 4. Control System Studies 5. Boundary Value Problems 6. Nose Cone Ablation 7. Launch Window Studies 8. Terrain Avoidance Simulation
Chemical	1. Chemical Reactor Simulations 2. Heat Exchanger Simulations 3. Distillation Columns 4. Kinetics Curve Fitting 5. Process Optimizations 6. Plant Optimization 7. Process Control Simulation
Bio-Medical	1. EKG and EEG Data Analysis 2. Physiological Simulation
Communication	1. Wave Propagation 2. Ionospheric Ray Tracing 3. Antenna Pattern Calculations 4. Radio Signal Data Processing 5. Learning and Recognition Studies
Others	1. Submarine Simulations 2. Nuclear Reactor Simulations 3. Gas Pipeline Analysis

aerospace have been for vehicle simulations, to train pilots, design and evaluate automatic control systems, determine fuel requirements for optimal space missions, etc. In the chemical field, the major applications involve various types of simulation and optimization problems for chemical reactors, heat exchanges, etc. In the biomedical field, the most significant applications have been for analysis and identification of signals derived from sensors attached to humans and animals[3,4]; as well as significant contributions in the mathematical modelling of organs and body functions.

The applications for hybrid computation in the communications field have been rather specialized, as can be seen in the list in Table 1. Some of these have been research studies such as the ionospheric ray tracing which involved the solution of the equations of the path of a radio wave under the influence of a changing refractive index. In this problem, the analog computer solved all of the equations defining the ray path and the digital computer provided the complex function generation to represent the ionosphere. The overall economic savings in solving this problem on the hybrid computer was approximately 600/1 over an all-digital solution. The learning and recognition studies used the hybrid computer to analyze the spectrum of a voice signal and develop functions which would permit recognition of arbitrary words within a given vocabulary.

THE HYBRID COMPUTER

Hybrid computation has developed in the short period of about ten years from an experimental technique for the solution of a particular type of problem to a broadly-accepted computing discipline with applications in diverse fields. In over 100 hybrid computing laboratories which have been established since 1958, hybrid computation has proved to be superior to either pure analog or digital methods in problems which range from the solution of six-degree of freedom aerospace vehicle simulations to analysis of electrocardiographic data.

A hybrid computer consists of the interconnection into a single computing system of one or more analog computers, and one small-to-medium-scale, general-purpose digital computer. The interconnection equipment consists of:

★ Multi-channel analog-to-digital conversion equipment:
★ Multi-channel digital-to-analog conversion equipment:
★ Logic linkage affording the bilateral transfer of logic information;
★ Monitoring and control system linkage, permitting the analog and digital computers to be controlled by signals originating from either machine.

The combination of computers to form a hybrid system opens the door to new capabilities which were lacking in either the analog or the digital.
● The capability to solve partial differential equations at high speed by methods requiring the storage and playback of functions in the digital, and continuous integration in the analog.

● The capability to solve dynamic optimization problems requiring the iterative solution of state and adjoint differential equations, and the storage of intermediate iteration results.

- The capability to store, in the digital computer, numerical data to be used by the analog computer, either in a data processing function, or in the solution of modelling, data fitting, or parameter identification problems.

- The capability to solve problems requiring high accuracy, combined with high-frequency-response subsystems, the two of which are usually disjoint in actual problems.

- The capability to pre-program sequences of solutions to be obtained at high speed by the analog computer, and recorded or operated upon by the digital.

- The capability to program the analog computer, set up the attenuators, and perform the checking operations automatically from the digital.

THE DIGITAL COMPUTER SUBSYSTEM

The five basic categories of application for the digital computer in a hybrid laboratory are:

1. Off-line digital processing;
2. Analog programming aid;
3. Analog computer setup and checkout;
4. Automatic operation of the analog computer;
5. Closed-loop hybrid computation.

The non-hybrid uses of the digital computer include assemblies and compilations of the stored program portion of hybrid problems, checkout of the digital portion independent of the analog computer and linkage system, and pure digital computation. In many cases, the digital computation will be performed to obtain dynamic check solutions for the analog program.

The digital computer can serve a variety of purposes in aiding the analog programmer in the preparation of a problem.[5] These include calculation of pot settings and static check values, preparation of pot and amplifier assignment sheets, etc.

Analog computer setup and checkout includes use of the digital computer to set the attenuators and execute the static check in the analog computer. This results in a significant reduction in the time required to begin obtaining useful results from an analog program. Another unique facility provided by the digital computer to aid setup and checkout as well as operation is mnemonic addressing of analog variables and constants without referring to the particular amplifier or attenuator.

Automatic operation of the analog computer is applied in several ways. The stored program capability of the digital computer permits the implementation of techniques for comparing the results from the simulation of a hypothetical system to data from the physical system which is stored in the digital memory and modifying parameters of the simulated system to obtain a better fit. Also, sophisticated optimization algorithms can be implemented conveniently by the digital computer. The digital computer can also be used effectively to automate closed-loop iteration of hybrid problems, provide automatic control of displays, etc.

HYBRID COMPUTATION

Closed-loop hybrid computation represents the major class of application in which hybrid systems are employed. Closed-loop hybrid computation implies continuous data transfer between the analog and digital domains. Typical functions which the digital computer performs in closed-loop hybrid computation are listed as follows:

> Numerical solution of differential equations
> Arbitrary function generation
> Function storage and playback
> Transport delay simulation
> Digital control computer simulation
> Complex algebraic computations.

The use of the digital computer for the numerical solution of differential equations arises whenever the accuracy of the analog computer is not sufficient to represent the physical system adequately or when the size of the problem exceeds the capacity of the analog computer. The major application for this function of the digital computer is in the simulation of aerospace vehicles. In this case, the trajectory equations, which must be solved at a high accuracy, are simulated on the digital computer while the attitude equations, requiring less accuracy, but much higher speeds, are solved on the analog computer.[6,7] It is fortunate that the trajectory equations have much lower frequency components so that the resulting hybrid simulation can be run faster than real time. Whenever the solution of the differential equations must be divided between the analog and digital computers, it is generally possible to keep the high-frequency computations on the analog computer so that the hybrid solution is much more efficient than pure digital computation.

The generation of arbitrary functions represents one of the major uses of the digital computer in hybrid systems.[6,8] Although units for the generation of functions of one argument are available with nearly all analog computers, the setup time for a large number of functions is often prohibitive. For functions of two or more arguments, there is no adequate means provided in analog hardware. Using the digital computer, setup simply involves loading the data tables into memory from some medium such as paper tape or cards.

Analog function storage and playback, using the digital memory, permits the implementation of sequential computing techniques which result in the compatibility of new classes of problems. The major application for this function is in the serial solution of partial differential equations.[9,10] Function storage and playback involves sampling, converting, and storing the results of an analog run while, simultaneously, the stored results of a previous run are played back to produce a continuous input function to the analog computation.

Transport delay simulation is very restricted by pure analog techniques, while it is a simple extension of the function storage and playback function in the hybrid system. The hybrid technique offers the possibility of any number of channels of delay, with fixed or variable periods.[11]

The ability to simulate digital control computers has become increasingly important as larger numbers of digital computers are used for aerospace vehicle guidance and process control. These simulations permit complete design of the control program and its evaluation in control of the system.

For some mathematical models, the right hand sides of the differential equations are so complex that they cannot be solved within the available analog hardware. In this case, the digital computer is used to compute the complex non-linear algebraic expressions while the analog computer integrates the computed rates. In general, the higher frequency loops are established with analog components while the digital computations are used in the lower frequency loops. A special case of this function, which is related to the generation of arbitrary functions, is the use of the digital computer to calculate coordinate transformations. Although the digital computer is slower than analog resolvers, it offers the advantage that there is essentially no limit to the number of transformations, and a significant saving of analog hardware is obtained.

HYBRID COMPUTER APPLICATIONS

On a world-wide basis, there are today more than 2,000 analog and analog/hybrid laboratories in operation. A good proportion are large-scale simulation laboratories, and a recent survey indicated that of these, more than half are hybrid laboratories, or are in the process of hybridizing their existing analog equipment. A measure of the dimension of the use of hybrid computers is obtained by reviewing the spectrum of their current applications.

The first large-scale electronic analog computers were developed for the needs of the aircraft industry. This industry, and its adjunct, the space industry, still represent the largest users of hybrid computers today. However, hybrid computation has spread out to other segments of users, and in proportion, non-aerospace industrial and university users of analog and hybrid computers are much more important today than they were even five years ago.

Analog and hybrid computers provide an excellent man-machine interface, and this important fact may have a great bearing upon the future role of hybrid computers in the computing industry.

This article has described the basics of analog computation and the structure of the hybrid computer, with only superficial reference to the application in which they are used.

REFERENCES

1. Truitt, T. D., "Hybrid Computation — What is It? — Who Needs It?" AFIPS Conference Proceedings, *Vol. 25, pp 249-269, 1964.*
2. Paskman, M., Heid, J., *"Combined Analog-Digital Computer System,"* Proceedings of the Combined Analog-Digital Computer Systems Symposium, 1960.
3. "Hybrid Computer Analysis of Electrocardiographic Data." EAI Application Reference Library No. 4.41h.
4. Cameron, W. D., "Determination of Probability Distribution Using Hybrid Computer Techniques," International Symposium on Analogue and Digital Techniques Applied to Aeronautics, Liege, Belgium, September 1963.
5. Ocker, W., Teger, S., "HYTRAN — A Software System to Aid the Analog Programmer," *Proc. FJCC*, pp 291-298, 1964.
6. "Hybrid Simulation of a Temperature Rate Flight Control System for Re-Entry Vehicles," EAI Applications Reference Library No. 3.413h.

7. Wilson, A., "Use of Combined Analog-Digital System for Re-Entry Vehicle Flight Simulation," *Proc. EJCC,* Vol. 20, pp 105-113, December 1961.
8. Chapelle, W. E., "Hybrid Techniques for Analog Function Generation," *Proc. SJCC,* pp 213-227, 1963.
9. Carlson, A., "Hybrid Simulation of a Control System for a Tubular Chemical Reactor," EAI Education and Training Memo No. 65-2.
10. Shapiro, S., Lapidus, L., "A Combined Analog-Digital Computer for Simulation of Chemical Processes." Proceedings of the Combined Analog-Digest Computer Systems Symposium, 1960.
11. "The Simulation of Transport Delay with the HYDAC Computing System," EAI Applications Reference Library No. 1.3.7h.

Questions:

1.   Discuss the advantages of simulating the behavior of physical systems by analog computers versus digital computers.

2.   List several uses of a digital computer which aide the analog programmer in the preparation of a problem.

3.   Trace the development of present day hybrid systems from those in use in the late 1950's.

4.   In hybrid computation, when would the digital portion be used for the numerical solution of differential equations.

5.   List some probable application areas where hybrid computers would be useful.

HIGH SPEED LOGIC AND MEMORY - PAST, PRESENT, AND FUTURE

by ARTHUR W. LO

INTRODUCTION

By 1950 the logic and memory functions required in data processing were successfully implemented by vacuum-tube technology to demonstrate the feasibility of electronic computers. In the decade of 1950-1960 a large variety of solid-state switching and storage elements and associated circuit schemes were proposed, and pursued to various extent through the research, development and production phases. The present decade, 1960-1970, has witnessed the consolidation of hardware technology to semiconductor logic circuits and magnetic random-access memories to achieve cost and performance advantages in practical systems. The overwhelming success of the semiconductors and the magnetics appears to deter the development of other technologies. Whether or not this trend will continue in the next decade, 1970-1980, depends on the magnitude of the demand and the advancement of science and technology.

This article provides a brief account of what was promised, what we have, and what is being promised in high-speed logic and memory hardware. It aims to show the reasoning behind the past promises, why we have what we have, and what is reasonable to expect for the near future. A chronological sketch of the major developments in hardware technologies for high-speed logic and memory is shown in Tables I and II to aid the discussion.

No hardware technology can be successful unless it lends itself to the fulfillment of certain universal device and circuit requirements pertinent to digital operation. The "function-composition" nature of digital information processing systems makes possible the synthesis of complex system functions from primitive operations. The physical realization of such systems relies on the interconnection of a larger number of elementary circuits to form complex electronic networks. The requirement of extensive and flexible *interconnection* dictates the fundamental properties of the elementary circuits. In order that arbitrary combinational and sequential logic functions may be implemented with least constraint, it is essential that the elementary circuits (the logic gates which performs the primitive logic functions) can be "freely" interconnected with one another without obstructing their basic operations. The interconnected gates must respond to one another according to the design and with little delay. These basic requirements demand that the elementary logic circuits must have the following characteristics:

Reprinted with permission from AFIPS Conference Proceedings (Fall, 1968), a publication of the Thompson Book Company.

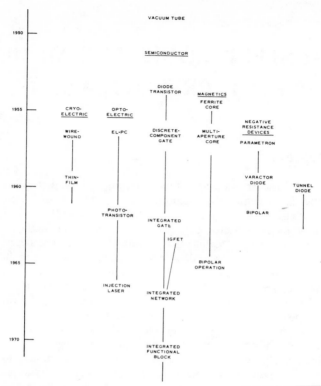

TABLE I—Chronology of high-speed logic development

(a) Signal Quantization. The provision of signal quantization ensures that the output signal of the elementary circuit is more true to the specified "0" or "1" representation than the input signal, so that there is no signal deterioration in a logic network of any size.

(b) Directivity and Isolation. The provision of directivity and isolation of signal flow ensures clear designation of "cause and effect" to prevent spurious interactions between connected circuits.

(c) Fast Switching. The minimization of the switching delay time between switching circuits ensures the operation speed of the digital system.

Most of these desired characteristics of the elementary circuit are provided by the *switching element(s)* employed in the circuit. The quantization requirement demands switching elements having a sharp and uniform switching threshold, as well as an operating region of high gain. These properties ensure reliable switching of the element by small input voltage and current excursions, under the realistic constraints of noise, component tolerance, and fan-in and fan-out loading. The requirement of directivity and isolation of signal flow calls for switching elements of unilateral isolation property or the use of unidirectional coupling elements. The switching delay time of a digital circuit is essentially determined by the time required to charge or discharge reactances in

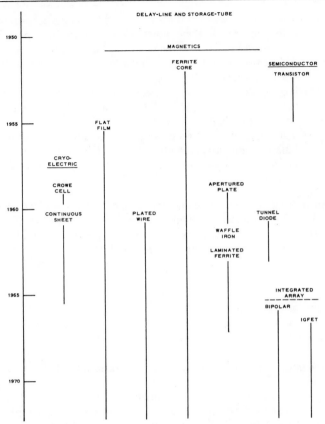

TABLE II—Chronology of high-speed memory development

the circuit to produce the specified signal voltage or current excursion. Reduction of component size and high density circuit construction are essential to reduce the intrinsic and parasitic reactances associated with the devices and their interconnections. In summary, the physical implementation of high-speed logic demands high-grain, highly nonlinear unilateral switching elements which can be readily fabricated to very small size and high uniformity, and interconnected to one another in high density.

In the case of memory, very-high-speed, small-capacity information storage is usually intimately connected to the logic circuits, and the same hardware technology serves for both logic and memory. For memories of storage capacity of thousands of bits to millions of bits, some efficient, random-access address-selection arrangement is indispensable. Such memory is usually arranged in the form of an array, or planes of array, of storage elements with provision of selective addressing. The major considerations for high-speed, medium and large capacity memories are as follows:

(a) The storage elements must provide discrete, static or dynamic remanent states to retain the stored information, with little or no standby power.

(b) The storage elements should provide simple means of selective addressing, and they must be immune to repeated disturbs (produced by digit-drive, partial word-drive, and spurious coupling). A foremost requirement is that the storage cell has a sharp, stable and uniform switching threshold.

(c) High-speed operation requires that the storage elements can be made to minimal physical size (and with high uniformity) and "wired" into high density arrays.

(d) The large number of storage elements needed in each memory unit puts the emphasis on high-yield mass fabrication techniques for the production of storage elements and memory arrays at reasonable cost.

This outline of the fundamental device and circuit requirements for high-speed logic and memory implementation provides the basis of a systematic appraisal of the merits and limitations (leading to the success and failure) of the various hardware technologies, present, past and future.

High-speed logic

What was promised?

The large variety of promised hardware approaches for the implementation of high-speed logic are summarized under the following categories.

Semiconductor diode, transistor and integrated circuits

From the earliest stage of development, the semiconductor transistors and diodes, with their obvious advantages in size and power consumption, offered good promise of their replacement of the vacuum-tubes in logic circuits. The advancement of semiconductor technology soon revealed the significant advantages in reliability and life, switching speed, and manufacturing cost of the semiconductor devices, several orders of magnitude over what could be achieved with vacuum-tubes. A unique property of the semiconductor junction devices is that the pn junction voltage-current characteristic provides a switching threshold which is not only very sharp but also "naturally" uniform in the sense that the threshold value is insensitive to the physical dimensions and the fabrication processes of the device. Thus diodes and transistors can be readily fabricated to extremely small size (where dimensional variance is unavoidably large) and in large quantity, while having uniform switching thresholds. The sharp and uniform threshold permits reliable switching by voltage excursion of less than a volt. The minimal device capacitance (from the small physical size) and the high transconductance of the device provide fast switching. Early promise of logic subsystems composed of thousands of transistor logic gates with logic delay of a fraction of a microsecond and cost below $1.00 per gate were readily surpassed in the late 1950's. The phenomenal success of planar silicon transistor technology, consisting of the processing steps of epitaxial growth, oxide passivation, photolithographically controlled selective impurity-diffusion and metal-deposition, made practical the batch-fabrication of large number of components (diodes, transistors and resistors) of extremely small size and great uniformity at low cost. The same technology readily makes the interconnections between components to form logic gates, and the interconnections between gates to form logic networks, all at the surface of a silicon chip. Following the undisputed demonstration of the producibility of integrated-circuits and their advantage over discrete-element assembly, came speculations of larger- and-larger scales of integration, all the way to "computer on a chip," as well as delay-time "limited only by the speed of light" and cost of "practically nothing."

In the decade 1950-1960, when the need of practical high-speed logic hardware was urgent and much of the potentials of transistor logic circuits were not fully appreciated or realized, a large number of solid-state devices and circuits were seriously considered for logic implementation. The major developments and expectations of these approaches are outlined in the following sections:

Cryotron logic circuits

The early wire-wound cryotron offered an electronic analog of the electromechanical relay, with the potential advantages of higher speed, longer life and lower power consumption, despite the obvious cryogenic requirement. The advent of thin-film cryotron structure prompted great expectation of batch-fabrication of large and complex logic networks by the simple process of vacuum-deposition of homogeneous materials. An inherent drawback of cryotron logic circuit is the low operation speed dictated by the large L/R time constant (even after the introduction of super-conductive ground-plane which drastically reduced the circuit inductance). Efforts to improve operation speed by size miniaturization and the use of higher-resistance metal-alloy encountered difficulties in the uniformity of the switching threshold, which is directly related to line-width and critically dependent on temperature (thus ohmic heating in switching), as well as material and fabrication imperfections. The success of cryo-electric logic system hinges on the ability to batch-fabricate large, complex logic networks economically, but the present status of cryogenic science and technology has not warranted such undertaking. The promise of entire logic and memory system batch-fabricated at low cost by the cryo-electric technology is not likely to be fulfilled in the near future.

Opto-electric logic circuits

The early EL-PC pair, employing polycrystalline electro-luminescent phosphor and cadium-sulfide photoconducting material, promised low-cost production of logic circuits by the "printing-press" process. However, the cost of assembling, interconnecting, and protective packaging of these circuits for sizable logic systems was not low, and the operation speed was intolerable. More recent opto-electric logic, using semiconductor light-emitting injector-laser and light-sensitive photo-diode (or transistor) still could not achieve operation speed comparable to transistors. The major difficulty is that, for any realistic network interconnection, only a small fraction of the emitted light from a driving element can be effectively coupled to the active region of a receiving element to realize the high gain required to achieve effective quantization and fast switching. There has been few promises of practical opto-electric logic except for special purpose applications.

Magnetic logic circuits

Square-loop magnetics provide static storage and stable switching-threshold, but they are handicapped by the lack of gain and unilateral property. The development of "all-magnetic" logic was more a challenge than a practical solution. The use of sequenced clock-pulse energization and multi-aperture cores has produced logic circuits operating at low speed and high power level. The more recently developed "bipolar" operation overcame much of the earlier drawbacks, but the cost and performance advantages of the magnetic circuit were, by then, lagging far behind transistor circuits. The promises of magnetic logic were limited to its high reliability against noise, its immunity to radiation damage and its apparently unlimited life.

Parametric phase-lock oscillator logic circuits

The phase-script, carrier-powered, logic circuits (beginning with the Parametron) promised immunity to noise (but not spurious interaction between circuits) and the potential of extremely high frequency operation (using varactor diode and microwave structure). The majority-logic operation, however, demands uniform oscillation amplitude and coupling attenuators, as well as precision phase-control of the transmission of signal and carrier power at microwave frequency. The practical aspects of interconnecting complex microwave structures make the implementation difficult and costly even for small logic systems.

Tunnel-diode logic circuit

The two-terminal, negative-resistance, semiconductor device (with its majority-carrier conduction mechanism) attracted early attention on account of its subnanosecond switching time. The problem of uniformity of switching thresholds among units (their peak-current being directly proportional to the tiny junction area) resulted in low gain, and consequently longer switching time than promised. The balanced-pair circuit (requiring only matched-pair instead of uniformity of all units) overcame some of the operation difficulties, but the need of sequenced clock-pulse supply and precision coupling attenuators makes the realizable operation speed no better than modern transistor logic circuits. The voltage-limiting property of the high-speed device might still be useful if it could be conveniently integrated to the more useful conventional semiconductor elements.

What we have

Presently the field of high-speed logic is monopolized by the seminconductor integrated-circuit technology. Technical developments are concentrated on smaller component-size and higher component density. A typical transistor at present may have emitter strip-width of 0.1 mil and base width of 0.4 . Such a transistor can be switched reliably in one nanosecond by a voltage excursion of less than one volt. The basic logic gages, composed of transistors, diodes and low-precision resistors have logic delay time of 2-20 ns and power consumption of 10-15 mW. (The integrated-circuit technology has all but obsoleted the TRL and DCTL gates, in favor of the DTL and the TTL gates for cost-oriented applications, and the ECL gates for speed-oriented applications.) The present scale of integration is 10 to 50 interconnected gates on a chip (corresponding to density of $10^4 - 10^5$ components per square inch), for the cost of about 25 cents per gate.

The Insulated-gate Field-effect Transistor has been successfuly developed to rival the bipolar transistor as practical basic switching element. In comparison with the bipolar transistor, the IGFET is handicapped by the lack of a "naturally" uniform switching threshold and its low trans-conductance at lower operating voltage. Thus the basic IGFET inverter requires a larger voltage-excursion and a larger "load" resistance for reliable switching, and consequently has a longer switching delay time (ten times that of the bipolar transistor inverter). The shortcomings of the basic IGFET circuit are partially overcome by the pulse-mode circuit (at the expense of sequenced-pulse power-supply) and the complementary-symmetry circuit (at the expense of more complex device fabrication). The IGFET circuits are not likely to match the performance of the bipolar-transistor circuits for general-purpose, high-speed logic, without some significant advancement in IGFET technology. The inherent advantage of the IGFET is its simpler device structure which lends itself to higher degree of miniaturization and higher fabrication yield (than the bipolar transistor), thus more suitable for practical large-scale integration.

The limiting factor of larger-and-larger scale of integration on a chip is essentially determined by the yield of the completed network. Presently there are two distinct approaches to large-scale integration. The fixed-pattern wiring (metalization) approach requires all the components covered by the interconnection pattern to be free of defects. Integrated logic networks of 10 - 30 bipolar transistor gates and over 100 IGFET gates have been produced in this manner. Larger integration by this approach suffers severe yield shrinkage. The discretionary-wiring approach allows reasonable imperfections among the fabricated components to make larger integration feasible, only at the expense of tedious testing at the component level, considerable data processing to formulate interconnection patterns, and the cost of preparing individual metalization masks. At the present time the fixed-pattern technique is used for the majority of integrated-circuit production, and the discretionary-wiring technique is used for some products.

What is being promised

The present trend of *logic* hardware is larger- and-larger scale of integration on a chip, since the interconnection between chips is largely responsible for the degradation of speed, reliability and cost of present logic systems. This fact prompts the promise that by early 1970's we will have 1,000 - 10,000 interconnected gates on a chip, with component density of $10^5 - 10^6$ components per square inch and switching delay time of 2 - 5 ns, at the cost of 5 cents per gate. With this many interconnected gates a single chip would constitute the entire electronic network of a complete logic subsystem, thus greatly reducing the number of terminal leads to the chip. The manufacturing of "functional-units" of such complexity can be achieved only by automation to handle the tasks of logical design, device and circuit layout, and diffusion (and metalization) mask design, as well as automatic fabrication and testing. The fulfillment of such promise is largely governed by the law of demand and supply. The functional-units which have large-volume demand will be developed and produced, and the others will be neglected. The progress in this direction will depend heavily on the standardization of computer structure and the consolidation of computer types. Never before is there such urgent need for interaction between software and hardware planning. "What to make" and "How to test them, when made" deserves as much attention as the technology of producing the hardware.

It is of interest to note that the sobering experience of past developments and a better understanding of the basic requirements of digital circuits have refrained speculations of revolutionary logic-implementation in recent years. Nevertheless, there are expectations that new and significant progress will be made *if* and *when* certain difficulties associated with a number of hardware technologies are overcome or bypassed. Germanium transistor operating at low temperature can provide very high speed logic if the fabrication techniques of germanium can reach the same level of silicon technology. The feasibility of all-optic logic for extremely high speed operation depends on the development of practical means of efficient light-coupling between laser-like elements. Large-scale cryoelectric logic and memory systems (at extremely low fabrication cost) could become practical through the discovery of superconductor material of higher normal resistance and higher operating temperature (say, liquid nitrogen temperature). Practical use of two-terminal, bulk-effect semiconductor devices for high-speed logic awaits the development of uncomplicated means of providing directivity and isolation. All-magnetic logic based on flux steering of magnetic domains within homogeneous material (thus eliminating signal-path interconnections) could be feasible with the development of practical means of providing flux quantization and signal directivity.

High-speed memory

What was promised

A major consideration in the development of high-speed, large-capacity memory systems is the cost of producing and assembling the large quantities of storage cells. The magnetics has been, and still is, the dominating memory technology.

Ferrite core-memory

The ferrite core memory technology has the distinction of having promised little (in storage capacity, cycle time and system cost), and delivered much. By 1955 the main memories of all major computers were being implemented with this technology. The ferrite core, with its inherent static-storage property (without standby-power) and material stability (polycrystalline ceramic material), easily obsoleted the electroacoustic delay-lines and the storage tubes. The switching threshold of the magnetic core is directly related to its physical dimensions and material imperfections, which are difficult to control in the high-temperature, high-pressure processing of the polycrystalline material. The cores, therefore, are tested individually to meet the actual operating conditions (including the large number of disturbs) before wired into the array. This enforced device uniformity, and the tremendous demand of random-access memory of adequate speed and capacity to match the existing logic circuitry, resulted in the production of million-bit memory with read-write cycle time around 5 us by 1960. The cost of the core-memory systems was found to depend more and more on the driving and sensing circuitry, which followed closely the advancement of the semiconductor technology. Three types of memory organizations, 3D, 2D and the middleground 2½D, were adopted to fit the compromise between storage capacity, cycle time, and system cost for any particular, random-access memory application. The feasibility of multi-aperture core for reliable nondestructive read-out, and two-core-per-bit partial-switching operation for higher speed were also demonstrated, but not widely adopted on account of the added complexity and cost. The promised batch-fabricated ferrite memory, such as apertured-plate, laminated ferrite and waffle-iron, did not achieve the expected cost advantage, mainly because of yield and the burden (of switching excess magnetic material) imposed on the drive-and sense-circuitry.

Magnetic thin-film memory

The anisotropic magnetic thin-film shows the promise of exceedingly fast coherent-rotation switching, convenient orthogonal drive operation, and planar structure for easy batch-fabrication. The development of practical flat-film memory, however, has been slower than expected. The open-flux path structure imposes a compromise between dot size and film thickness, and the output signal voltage, thus prohibiting very high density array structure. The desired uniformity of switching and disturb thresholds are difficult to achieve with present material and batch fabrication techniques. The more recently developed cylindrical-film (plated-wire) memory elements provide a closed flux-path in the easy axis (thus permitting the use of small-radius wire and thicker film) to overcome some of the difficulties (particularly disturb sensitivity) of the planar thin-film. The promise for these thin-film memories is that, once the material and fabrication problems are solved, improvement of memory storage capacity, cycle time, and system cost by one order of magnitude over the core memory should be readily achievable. A comfortable thought is that there is no lack of large demand for multi-million-bit, sub-microsecond memory at present and in the foreseeable future, provided the price is not outrageous.

Cryoelectric persistent current memory

The development of cryoelectric memory, (from cryotron-cell, to Crowe cell, to continuous-sheet and cavity-sensing) promised very-large capacity random-access memory operating at modest speed. The task of producing high-uniform, high-density array with good yield remains a challenge to our material and fabrication technology.

What we have

Core memories of 3D or 2½D organization, with capacity of multi-million-bits and cycle-time of 1 - 2 us, dominate the field of internal main memory in the present generation of computers. Some flat-film and cylindrical-film memories of 10^6 bit and 0.5 us cycle-time have been installed in working systems. Memory systems cost is difficult to assess, but it appears to be in the range of 1 - 5¢ per bit. In the area of high-speed, small-capacity random-access memory, the magnetic thin-film technology (both flat-film and cylindrical film) has produced memories of 5 x 10^4 bits with access-time (for read or write) of 100 - 200 ns.

Semiconductor, integrated-circuit technology is making an inroad to the field of very high-speed memory. Development efforts on the fabrication of large arrays of semiconductor memory cells and interconnections has shown that IGFET memory of 10^4 bits with access-time of 100 ns, and bipolar-transistor memory of 10^3 bits with access-time less than 50 ns are technically feasible.

What is being promised

The normal progress of core-memory technology will see some further reduction of cost so that it will be economically feasible to have tens of million bits of random-access storage (with cycle-time around 1us) in the present generation of computers. There is strong expectation that the evolution of thin-film technology (flat-film and plated-wire) will finally reach the goal of low-cost batch-fabrication, thus providing memories of 10^6 − 10^7 bits capacity, 200 - 500 ns cycle-time, at the cost of a fraction of a cent per bit. Integrated IGFET memory is expected to dominate the area of small-capacity storage (less than 10^6 bits) with access time of 100 - 200 ns, at the cost of 1¢ per bit. The semiconductor technology also shows good promise for merging the logic and the memory functions to make medium-capacity associative-memory economically feasible and to allow much more sophisticated computer organizations.

Much attention is currently focused on the development of block-oriented random-access memories. One prospect is the magnetosonic delay-line memory which employs magnetic storage and block-access by semiconductor electronics (to cause the propagation of a sonic wave in the selected line). Nondestructive read-out is derived on the digit lines in sequence by the propagation sonic wave, and write-in is carried out by the coincidence of digit currents and the propagating wave. Another prospect is the opto-electric read-only memory, where the stored information on high resolution photographic plate is block-selected by optical means, employing light-beam deflection or an array of light-emitting elements. The optical readout (of all the bits in the block in parallel) is converted to electric signal by an array of photosensitive elements. Holographic techniques are proposed for the implementation of the high-density photographic processing. The practicality of these block-oriented systems are too early to be realistically appraised.

CONCLUDING REMARKS

The present hardware technologies for high-speed logic and memory have reached a high level of proficiency, making the central processing unit far ahead in cost and performance in computer systems. Evolutionary progress of these technologies, particularly in batch-fabrication techniques, will provide more logic and memory at less cost, but only slight improvement in operation speed.

There is, however, no sign of any revolutionary hardware implementation of high-speed logic and memory in the near future.

Questions:

1. Trace the development of logic circuitry.

2. What is the present tend of logic hardware?

3. List the different types of memory technology currently in use.

4. Discuss the advantages and disadvantages of magnetic type memories.

FOURTH-GENERATION HARDWARE

BY G.M. and L.D. AMDAHL

It has been recently discovered that a third generation of computer technology has been entered. With the clarity of this observation we need no longer obliquely ask what the trend is in computer hardware or software, but we can ask directly and forcefully, "What will the next generation bring?" Accepting the notion that there will be a fourth generation of computers (by the principle of binary powers, eight years after the third) the following observations and extrapolations are put forward.

The third generation of computer technology can be characterized as one of unification. An attempt has been made to unify in once computer structure the effective capability to perform commercial, scientific and real-time tasks. Time-sharing is being elaborately analyzed, with conversational mode systems in early use. Monolithic integrated circuits are coming into widespread computer use, but with their greatest potential yet to be realized.

To achieve software interchangeability, the concept of upward compatibility, giving rise to families of computers differing only in speed and price. Manufacturers such as IBM found that this could be accomplished only by drastic means—design of a totally new line of computers having basic differences from predecessor equipment. The transition to the third generation has therefore been arduous, with techniques such as microprogramming and emulation being employed and with complete new software being required.

FOURTH-GENERATION HARDWARE: BATCH FABRICATION

Computer hardware of the fourth generation is anticipated to be most strongly characterized by batch fabrication. In areas of logic circuits and high-speed memory, complex arrays of switching circuits on single silicon chips will be batch fabricated. This is referred to as large scale integration, or more simply, LSI. It should be noted that batch fabrication does not necessarily mean the concurrent fabrication of identical items; rather, it means the concurrent fabrication of many different items passed through identical process steps. This permits economically produced silicon chips to logically differ. While large parallel computers (such as the proposed Illiac IV) could have many identical chips, small computers would be denied this luxury. Therefore the economic

---

365

production of many different kinds of chips would benefit the manufacturer of the small computer.

Integrated circuits offer benefits of batch fabrication both in the area of logic circuits and memory. The benefits of LSI for logic circuits will be reduced cost, greater density and greater speed. The limitations of LSI in this use arise in interconnections, heat dissipation and chip complexity. To use LSI, a problem of the first magnitude will have to be solved: the compete automation of chip design. This problem is vastly complicated if yield must be enhanced by adjustment of the interconnection pattern of cellular circuits as a function of test results.

LSI memories can be very high speed and can permit multiple-access use. Because select and sense circuits are fabricated by the same process steps as those used for memory cells, high performance memories are expected to be relatively inexpensive. An economic property of considerable advantage for small memories is the relatively linear cost per bit as a function of size exhibited by LSI memories. But these speed and cost advantages will not apply to large LSI memories. Another factor to be considered by systems designers is the volatile nature of the LSI storage cell, permitting loss of information stored when power is removed.

Other batch fabrication techniques for memories will undoubtedly emerge in each of the areas of wired ferrite arrays, woven plated wire arrays and thin films. Any of these will be suitable for large quantities of lower-speed random-access memories and would not have the volatile characteristics of the LSI memory.

Mass storage still appears to be dependent on electromechanical devices for lowers cost implementation. To a large extent this is due to the fact that batch fabrication is always easier to achieve when detailed structure is unnecessary, and the fabrication of the surface of a disc or drum is indeed batch fabrication of an enormous number of storage cells. However, the feverish activity in the development of static (nonrotating) mass storage will surely result in its use in fourth-generation equipment, particularly for systems requiring rapid information retrieval.

ARCHITECTURE: AN ATTEMPT TO BALANCE

The economic consequences of batch fabrication are expected to have the greatest effect on fourth-generation architecture. Even in the third generation, processor costs are relatively low compared to other system cost factors such as I/O channels, peripherals, marketing and software. In the fourth generation this imbalance will tend to increase, with the system architect offsetting it by greater instruction capability, more processing overlap and parallelism, and additional hardware features for multiprogramming and multiprocessing.

The use of the high-speed LSI memory will tend to impose an additional level in the memory hierarchy. This will emphasize the need for semi-automatic control of memory, perhaps along the lines of paging techniques. We would expect that considerable emphasis will have been applied to this area due to difficulties incurred in third generation systems. The problem here is to make the memory appear to be a very large and homogenous virtual memory (techniques which permit viewing main memory as unrestricted by actual main memory limitations), yet without imposing virtual response and virtual solution times.

Basically the computer can only deal with information residing in real memory. It must in some manner be provided with instructions which, during its operation, can cause it to control the transmission of information between hierarchy levels with as much preplanned structure as is possible. In circumstances where preplanning is inadequate, multiprogramming must be able to fill the voids.

Failure to provide any preplanning would raise the level of multiprogramming, requiring memory capacity that would be considered excessive even in the era of batch fabrication. The solution time for individual large problems may become excessively long in a multiprogrammed environment, making the system unsuitable for this purpose. Algorithmic control, suited to access characteristics of data sets, will undoubtedly become important. The nature of the control would be governed by programmer specification or by recognition of historical referencing properties as determined by the hardware.

Another area of architecture is the employment of microprogramming to an extent that compiler languages might be optimized. In a companion article, Ascher Opler predicts a fuller utilization of this technique in the fourth generation and the emergence of *firmware* specialists.

The question of equipment dependability will come under careful scrutiny in the fourth generation despite the fact that LSI will offer high reliability. The reason for this scrutiny will be the customer's concern for nearly absolute computer up-time in time-sharing environments. While in the past he was willing to accept turnaround delays due to the computer being down, he will not accept inoperative on-line terminals. Partial redundancy, multiple processors and in-line diagnostics should result from this emphasis. With LSI, redundancy can more economically be achieved than with discrete components.

SOFTWARE: MORE FREEDOM

The role of software has been changing from generation to generation. From an initial start of freeing man from dealing directly with the computer by the provision of input-output utility programs, the role has progressed from having to deal in absolute terms by means of symbolic program assembly, from having to deal in basic terms by means of macro assembly and compilation, and finally from having to deal with space-time boundaries by means of data-management programs and virtual memory. One of the current activities is aimed at freeing man from space and time separation from the computer by time-sharing.

One can speculate as to those freedoms which will be sought for the next generation. A number of likely candidates come to mind, many of which have been started and have varying degrees of progress. Some fairly basic ones are (1) freedom from redundant effort by means of common libraries of programs and data sets in the information utility, (2) freedom from limited forms of man-machine communication by means of better techniques for the identification, extraction and display of meaningful information, (3) freedom from necessity to recognize the particular machine type being used by software standardization, and (4) freedom from painful recovery on machine malfunction by automatic detection and by maintenance of user transaction journals.

It is interesting to note that these freedoms contribute to a layer of basic concepts. These concepts relate the more abstract notions of computing to the detailed dynamic activity of the hardware computer. As more freedoms are added which release the user from primitive representation of his problem, he is further insulated from the hardware. This intervening software structure will develop into a capability for self-generation of programs for specific computational actions. Such programs will enjoy an existence so brief that they deserve a unique name, for which *bubbleware* is advanced.

One can deduce that significant overhead will be added in the execution of hardware functions as the user gains freedom in detailed program declaration. Despite this, the hope for fuller realization of human creativity will give continued impetus for this trend to greater abstraction.

BEYOND THE FOURTH

It may be appropriate to speculate beyond the fourth generation, but it appears that the logical conclusion to be drawn is that the ultimate goal must be freedom from having to deal with the computer at all. When this level of development has been reached, creative intellect will have burst its final shackles, free to wing to new Olympian heights.

Questions:

1. What are some of the characteristics of third generation hardware?

2. What is LSI? What will be the impact of LSI on the fourth generation of computers?

3. List other characteristics of fourth generation computers the author expects we will see.

FOURTH-GENERATION SOFTWARE

BY ASCHER OPLER

On the assumption that the next generation of information processing systems should try to correct the shortcomings of its predecessors, let's preface our sneak preview of the fourth generation with a quick review of the major general failures of third-generation software.

Third generation dissatisfaction centers on the disappointing price/performance ratio of the hardware/software combination (from now on we'd better say "software/ hardware"!) and conversion difficulties. The disappointing performance is generally attributed to software.

At one time we used hardware price/performance ratio as a useful measure. When software became an indispensible part of hardware, we measured only the performance of the combination. Since the separate pricing of sofware is upon us (e.g., Sigma 7 COBOL), it is likely that we'll soon be measuring software price/performance ratio. With this in mind, we can look at the price/performance ratio of the third-generation combination and observe that the *hardware* ratio is excellent but the combined ratio is generally disappointing.

The conversion picture is generally bleak. Those who used FORTRAN and COBOL heavily with second-generation equipment and those who can emulate their second-generation computer on their third come off well compared to those who didn't use the two languages or who can't emulate.

PROJECTED FOURTH-GENERATION COMPUTERS

This article is based on one man's guess about the next generation. The guess is that fourth-generation hardware will use large-scale integration (LSI) logic specialized by microprogramming. Integrated logic chips will be needed to obtain the required fast circuitry and the microprogrammed specialization will be needed to obtain the required software and user interfaces.

The elements of one of these computers might have these characteristics:

circuitry (LSI)	5 nanoseconds
micromemory access	10 nanoseconds (read time)
main memory access	400 nanoseconds

In the most radical departure from present architecture, the computer would have *no order set* and *no data structure*. The computer would be specialized for the various roles it is to play by *replaceable microprograms*.

Reprinted with permission from DATAMATION ®, (January), published and copyrighted (1967) by F. D. Thompson Publications, Inc., 35 Mason St., Greenwich, Conn. 06830.

Third-generation microprogrammed computers are delivered with a pre-designed, pre-installed microprogram of the read-only type. and in most members of the product line, the option of an additional read-only memory carrying a *second* microprogram set is available. This second set serves to provide full or partial compatibility with the order set of an older computer.

In fourth-generation computers, *many* microprograms will be available from the manufacturer. Software and user specialists will also prepare and use their own. This should throw the whole field wide open.

To better understand the nature of microprogramming a no-order-set/no-data-structure computer, I believe it worthwhile to introduce a new word into our vocabulary: *firmware*. I use this term to designate microprograms resident in the computer's control memory, which specializes the logical design for a special purpose, e.g., the emulation of another computer. I project a tremendous expansion of firmware—obviously at the expense of hardware but also at the expense of software.

Microprogramming has, of course, been known since the early days of computing. The principle is simple—build a small micro-processor and drive it with a stored microprogram.

Take floating-point addition as an example. In the first generation, it was performed with a normally-programmed subroutine. In the second generation, it was implemented in circuitry. In third-generation microprogrammed computers, the floating-point addition is performed using a microprogram stored in read-only memory.

One major factor making this possible is the ratio between main memory access time and circuitry speed. With integrated circuits (IC) and now LSI, times have *plunged* to 1-5 nanoseconds while the access time of main memory has *slowly* declined. This allows 30 to 70 micro-steps to be performed by circuitry between each main memory fetch or store. These 30 to 70 steps permit the implementation of third-generation order sets.

The memories are called read-only memories but, of course, the contents had to be written once in order to "load" the memory. Today this is done as part of the computer fabrication process. For the fourth generation, extension to slow-write fast-read (SW/FR) memory is anticipated.

The interface between "normal" programs and microprograms comes via the operation code. In effect, when each instruction is decoded, the operation code calls upon a specific microprogrammed "routine" stored in the micro-memory.

To visualize the preparation of firmware, consider a special keypunch not available to software and user programmers. This punches 67-column cards (4 x 8 inches) with triangular holes (try that on you keypunch and card reader!). A special card reader loads decks of these 67-colmn cards into the fourth-generation SW/FR memory. This card reader probably will be locked so that only firmware specialists have access to it (we hope)!

WHAT FIRMWARE CAN DO NOW

Even in the third generation, firmware is expanding the capabilities of hardware and software. Its effect on reducing the cost of hardware is central to third-generation economics. Unprecedented production rates with reduced requirements for system checkout and delivery are due to both integrated circuitry and to microprogramming.

Specialized versions of standard product line computers have been prepared primarily by altering the microprogram in the read-only memory. The most spectacular success has been achieved with all-hardware compatibility via a special microprogram. The success of the IBM System/360 Model 30 in running IBM 1401 programs attests to this fact.

Emulation, a combination of sofware and hardware, operates by using two different microprogrammed features. Basically, an emulator is an interpretive simulator made much more efficient by using a microprogram to perform the basic interpreting loop—fetch an instruction, decode the address, access the contents of the address and perform the indicated operation. In addition, the op-codes that are most time- (or space-) consuming to simulate are directly executed by microprogramming those orders into the micromemory. Emulation is, of course, required when the micromemory is too small to contain the entire order set of the second-generation computer.

An interesting example of the power of extending existing capability by microprogramming is the evaluate (EVAL) instruction added to the IBM System/360 Model 50 delivered to Allen-Babcock Computing Ind. This command is reported to evaluate a PL/I expression in standard form directly in hardware. Other added facilities include *floating decimal* instructions.

FIRMWARE IN THE FOURTH GENERATION

Assuming the availability and accessibility of adequate SW/FR memories in the next generation, the entire *hardware/software* interface problems disappear only to be replaced by the more complex *hardware/firmware/software* interfaces. First, there is the hierarchy of components and corresponding responsibility.

Component	Responsibility	Organization
1. Circuitry	Hardware Designer	Manufacturer
2. Micromemory	Firmware Specialist	Manufacturer*
3. Control Programs	Software Specialist	Manufacturer*
4. Processors, Utilities, etc.	Software Specialist	Manufacturer*
5. Application programs	Application Specialist	User

*and/or software (firmware) producing organizations.

Secondly, firmware will assume a dominant role in structuring the computer. Manufacturers could (potentially) supply firmware decks allowing their fourth-generation computer to execute the order set of most popular third-generation computers—their own and competitors'. There could be a standard fourth-generation industry-wide order set and data structure.

But an even more significant impact would be felt by software. There is a general consensus that present software is too large. too complex and too slow. It is in the tradeoffs between software and firmware that most price/ performance improvement should be obtained.

Third-generation computers require control programs to resolve and handle interrupts, to control multiprogramming and input/output dispatching, and to provide useful services such as resource allocation and protection, etc. The demands placed on control programs by the hardware and by the user have forced the current programs to swell to enormous size with concomitant reduction in performance.

For fourth-generation computers, the answer will lie in using firmware for major portions of the control program functions and in using special features built into the firmware to facilitate other control program functions.

For instance, one problem that contemporary software must solve is to provide flexibility so that any particular installed configuration can be used with "general purpose" control programs. Even though "system generation" is used to specialize a generalized control program for a given configuration, the resultant code often contains lengthy subroutines to handle such functions as resolving device error signals, providing special user error recovery or interrupting the processing routine. The point is this—to provide modularity and flexibility, manufacturers are currently forced to delegate obvious hardware functions to software since this is the only means by which the user of the computer can specialize it for his use.

In fourth-generation equipment using SW/FR micromemory, microprograms can be prepared by the firmware specialist—manufacturer, programming company or the user—to carry out the specific interrupt and input/output control function specified by the user. This alone will go far to simplify control programs.

Further simplification can be obtained by making the data structure and order set work for, not against, the implementors of control programs. The basic implementation involves techniques of queue management, control block handling, table reference, internal sorting, pointer handling, etc.

Since microprogramming permits extensive data structuring for control program implementors, it will permit the addition of instructions to enqueue, dequeue control blocks build search and sort tables of specified structure, etc. These new commands should prove a boon to expediting the running of supervisory programs.

Time-sharing and multiprogramming both require very fast switching among programs. Many fourth-generation computer programs (processors and utility programs) will be written in the form of re-entrant code. The new hardware must be able to preserve the status of each user's computation and, when re-entrant code is used, to preserve blocks containing variables and other parameters. Currently much of this preserve/restore function is performed by software. Delegating this function to firmware should reduce the milliseconds performance time to microseconds.

COMPILERS AND FIRMWARE

Last year, a paper by Melbourne and Pugmire[1] described the design of a small computer for *directly executing* FORTRAN *statements.* The machine,

---

[1]Melboune, A.J. and Pugmire, J.M.: "A Small Computer for the Direct Processing of Fortran Statements" The Computer Journal, Vol., 8, pp. 24-28 (1965).

which was simulated but not built, was "controlled by a microprogram held in a fixed store." Marketing men can determine the reception of a FORTRAN-only computer—but it is certainly one reasonable approach for the fourth generation. With SW/FR firmware, the FORTRAN microprogram can be read into micromemory—instead of the order set of a computer.

Short of a computer which executes programming language directly, firmware can add many features to fourth-generation computers to facilitate compilation and execution. Special instructions corresponding to the POP (programmed operators) of Digitek compilers can be microprogrammed to facilitate compilation. Facilities like the "hardware algorithms"[2] of System/360 Model 91 can operate on object code to permute computational order and even eliminate redundancies. Direct execution of statements in Polish string notation—a technique first used in the KDF9 and B5000—can add to the power of new computers which handle programming languages with unprecedented speed and economy.

It is quite likely that the bulk of programs run on fourth-generation computers will be written using standard programming languages. These may be run in some multiprogrammed (or time-shared) manner with other programs on a large computer run as a "powerhouse utility" serving many users—or on smaller "private" computers dedicated to a single application use (e.g., message switching) or the needs of a single isolated user (e.g., small engineering laboratory). The latter may very well prefer to use the FORTRAN—only (PL/I only?) computer while the user of the dedicated equipment may find it to his advantage to start from scratch and write the central portion of his program in firmware using normal core (or thin film) storage only for bulk tables and transient storage.

Depending on the ease of preparing, debugging and loading firmware, the whole application area might be radically altered. But it will probably be worthwhile to prepare firmware only for real-time, dedicated applications where every microsecond (nanosecond?) counts!

At the present time, there is a limited supply of microprogrammers and a *relatively* small demand for such services. The only firmware under preparation is in the shops of manufacturers and is performed under careful supervision of hardware designers. Preparing microprograms is considerably different from writing programs. It requires a more detailed knowledge of the function of circuits and registers.

Automatic preparation of microprograms starting with some "higher" level language—like FLOATING ADD A,B—has not been achieved. However, as firmware becomes more important, increased effort to facilitate its preparation will certainly be made. Indeed, if some of the many roles that firmware is to play in the fourth generation are to be realized, a new generation of specialists must be trained and effective tools provided for their use.

---

[2]Chen, T.C., "The Overlap Design of System/360 Model 92 CPU" AFIPS Proceedings, Vol. 26, Part II, pp. 73-80, (1964).

PERSPECTIVE

The following chart shows the relative effort (compared to the manpower involved in the production of the hardware of a computer) expended by manufacturers for different computer generations.

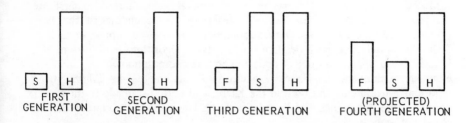

With increased demand for low-cost, high-performance total systems, the emphasis continually shifts to means of buttressing hardware to make it easier and more efficient to use. The third generation has seen the peak of the effort in software. No doubt the fourth generation will require equivalent effort—but placing much of what was software into the firmware area should go far to prevent some of our current difficulties.

———————

Questions:

1. What is firmware?

2. How will the disappointing cost/performance ratio of the third generation of computer systems be alleviated by the fourth generation? Give some examples.

HARDWARE DESIGN REFLECTING SOFTWARE REQUIREMENTS

By SAUL ROSEN

WHAT WAS PROMISED

All of the features that have been designed into digital computers may be considered to be, at least to some extent, reflections of software needs.

Starting with some of the earliest machines, the EDSAC[1] provided for address modification on input to make it convenient to use relocatable subroutines. The 4-address code of the EDVAC[2] was designed to make it possible to do minimum access time coding. The Datatron[3] provided off-line tape search, the RCA Bizmac[4] and the Univac File Computer provided special hardware-programmed tape sorting machines. Floating point hardware[5] was introduced on many computers to eliminate the need for software scaling systems and for interpretive floating point systems.

New computing systems, and whole new generations of computers have been introduced at an astonishing rate.[6] Even the small computers of a new generation are powerful machines, comparing favorably with some of the very large machines of earlier generations.

The component design engineers have made great advances over the years in the development of high speed memories, and in the development of circuit components that are cheap and fast and small. There seems to be an order of magnitude improvement in these areas every few years, and the concept of large scale integration[7] promises additional advances on the same scale.

It is the job of the hardware system designers and the software system programmers to translate these advances in components into improvements in system effectiveness.

Perhaps the most important part of the job of computer system design is to determine which functions are best handled by hardware, and which should be provided by software. All of the traditional engineering considerations come into play here. One must consider the added cost of additional hardware measured against possible gains in operating efficiency. One must consider the availability of manpower with the appropriate skills for design and for implementation. One must also consider intangible factors such as the inherent advantages of simplicity and the hidden costs of complexity.

Reprinted with permission from AFIPS Conference Proceedings (Fall, 1968), a publication of the Thompson Book Company.

From the point of view of the computer user it makes no difference which features are incorporated into the hardware and which are programmed in software.

It is the combined hardware-software system, the "extended machine"* that the user must rely on to provide the power and flexibility and convenience that have been promised with each new generation of computing equipment. Multiprogramming and interactive systems, problem-oriented languages, on-line debugging, automatic storage and retrieval of information—these and many other developments of modern computer technology promise the user convenience in problem statement, in program preparation, and debugging. They promise to make it possible to obtain timely, useful, meaningful results without the waste of personnel time and equipment time that has been so characteristic of computer problem solving.

So far at least the promises have not been kept. Most problems that are solved on the new generation of computers are solved very much in the same way as they were solved on earlier computers. Most debugging is off-line. Programmers, even in so-called higher level languages still wait through hours and days of turn-around time for their octal and hexadecimal dumps. The hardware machine has changed and developed and improved at a great rate, but the capabilities of the extended machine have grown disappointingly slowly.

WHAT WE HAVE

It would take a large volume devoted to the subject of computer organization to discuss all of the hardware features of existing computing systems that reflect software needs. There have been many hardware developments that have contributed to the development and the performance of multiprogramming and multiprocessor operating systems and compiling and translating systems. A few of these are discussed in this section.

MICROPROGRAMMING

The word microporgramming has been used in a number of different though related ways from the earliest days of computer design.[8]

In the most usual current usage of the word a computer is said to be microprogrammed if it interprets the user or programmer instructions (add, multiply, branch, etc.) as calls on routines (the microprogram routines) stored in a microprogram memory. These routines are themselves sequences of the more elementary operations that are built into the machine hardware. For reasons of speed and economy in the technology now available, the microprogram memory is usually a read-only storage device.[9]

For this reason, the microprogram routines are usually designed and written by hardware engineers rather than by software programmers.

There are microprogrammed computers in which the microprograms are stored in fast read-write storage which is logically or even physically the same as the ordinary program and data storage of the computer. The elementary operations of the computer thus become available to the problem programmers. This kind of system may in a sense permit each programmer to design his own instruction code. If that were true on a sufficienty basic level, it would be very difficult to supply software in the same sense as it is now supplied. Typically, in such systems, only software programmers (i.e., systems programmers) are permitted to design instructions.

Microprogramming in a read-only memory is a relatively simple, easy to understand technique whereby it is possible to "build-in" quite complex operations.

It makes it clearer perhaps than it was before that much of the sequencing that is done by hardware is the same kind of thing that is done in programming.

With the popularization of microprogramming it is easier to talk about performing some traditional software functions in the hardware, i.e., in programs on the elementary operation level rather than on the instruction level.

Such programs could be done in the hardware without the formalism of microprogram control. We shall use the term hardware programming to indicate programming built into hardware, either through a microprogramming system or by other hardware sequencing methods.

EMULATION AND SIMULATION

One of the most successful applications of the recent microprogramming technology is in the simulation of computers on computers.

The microprogram control and the set of microprogram routines are in effect a simulation program that simulates the programmer's instruction set on a computer whose instruction set is the set of elementary operations. It may be equally possible to simulate computers with other programmer instruction sets in terms of the same set of elementary operations. This, slightly oversimplified perhaps, is the idea of hardware assisted simulation that is now usually called emulation.[10]

Simulation of one computer on another had been done for many years using the programmer instructions. The resulting systems were inevitably so slow as to be almost useless for general computation, and were limited in use to special applications such as checkout, etc. The speed that makes emulation practical for much wider areas of application can only be achieved by operating at the hardware level.

INTERRUPT SYSTEMS

One of the critical areas in most operating systems is the handling of interrupts, especially routine input-output interrupts. The time it takes to recognize an interrupt, handle the functions required by the interrupt, initiate new operations where needed, and finally return to the interrupted program, is usually one of the most important performance parameters of the system. If a great many instructions must be executed in response to each interrupt, an otherwise fast computer may become intolerably slow.

This is an area of programming in which the programmer deals directly with the idiosyncracies of the computer hardware. It is, almost by definition, an area that cannot be handled by software alone. Much of the programming here is best done at the elementary operation level. There are many hardware features of many computing systems that have been designed in response to the need for efficient handling of interrupts. Some of these perform the following functions.

1. Identify the device that interrupted, either by transferring control to a location that is specific to that device or class of devices, or by storing a device identification code in a special register or storage location.

2. Provide special locations into which information about the state of the device is automatically recorded.

3. Provide for automatic storage of the most important registers that will then be automatically restored when the interrupted program is resumed.

4. Switch automatically into a special supervisory mode. In some systems the special mode has its own instruction control register and its own special registers for temporary storage and for control functions.

Also important in this area are hardware devices that cut down on the number of interrupts that have to be handled by the central computer. An example is the so-called multiplexer channel that automatically transfers streams of information between core memory and a large number of slow devices, interrupting the central computer only at the beginning and end of each stream.

DYNAMIC STORAGE ALLOCATION

There have been a number of interesting and useful hardware developments to assist in the allocation and addressing of storage. In the Burroughs 5000-6000-7000[11] series an array (or a subprogram) may be addressed as if it is present in main memory even though it may actually be in peripheral storage. Addressing is indirect, by way of a descriptor. A "presence" bit in the descriptor causes an interrupt if the addressed array (or subprogram) is not in core storage. The supervisor may then fetch it from peripheral storage and place it, without change, in any area of core memory that is large enough to hold it. The origin of the assigned storage area is placed in the descriptor, and all subsequent references to any elements are interpreted as relative to this origin. The descriptor also contains the length of the array and the hardware automatically checks for and interrupts on any reference beyond the limits of the array.

Another, perhaps more influential design was the Atlas one-level storage system.[12] In that system core storage is organized into 512-word pages, and programs are organized into 512-word blocks. A block in peripheral storage may be loaded into any page in core storage. The block number is placed in a page address register. The page address registers form an associative memory that is searched by hardware. A program address that consists of a block number and a displacement within the block is automatically translated into a hardware address that is a page number and the same displacement within the page. A reference to an address in a block that is not physically present in memory causes an interrupt to the supervisor which will fetch the block from peripheral storage and place it in any available page and place its block number in the page address register for that page.

A three level addressing scheme[13] was introduced on the General Electric 645[14] and on the IBM 360 model 67.[15] There a program address is interpreted as a segment number, a page number, and a displacement. An active segment has a page table which correlates physical page numbers with logical block numbers. A segment table gives the location of the beginning of the page table for each segment. A program address is converted into a hardware address by an automatic two level table look-up. In both the IBM and GE systems a small associative memory stores a few of the most recent translations, and the address translation is very much speeded up if the segment-page combination has been used recently enough so that its translation is still available in the associative memory.

The GE645 and IBM 360/67 address translation system, and other hardware address mapping schemes that were introduced since the Atlas development were designed as hardware aids to time-sharing systems. Computer manufacturers, and many users tend to refer to any computer that has any kind of hardware address translation as a time-sharing computer.

It takes much more than adding an automatic scheme for address translation to an existing general-purpose computer design to produce an effective time-sharing system.

SUPERVISORY FUNCTIONS

In most systems supervisory functions are initiated in response to interrupts, but they are too varied and complex to be considered as part of the interrupt system.

With the recent and continuing developments in integrated circuits and large scale integration it is becoming both technically and economically feasible to handle supervisory functions by hardware rather than software programming.

In the input-output area such functions may include the maintenance of input-output queues, the handling of priorities and issuance of input-output commands, the response to error conditions and other special conditions.

In the job management area they include once again the management of priority queues. They also include the handling of address translation tables in systems that provide automatic translation, and more generally the management of a multi-level hierarchical storage system.

There are dangers and pitfalls in attempts to handle these functions in the hardware. Programs on the microprogram level may become excessively long. They may be difficult or even impossible to debug. Hardware programmers are not necessarily better than software programmers. They make errors that must be corrected. Their first versions of programs are often incomplete and inefficient and must be replaced by later better versions. Hardware programming for really complicated tasks will only be feasible when it is relatively easy to make changes to the programs.

This is still a research area. It seems reasonably certain that some of the functions mentioned above will be handled by hardware programming. Eventually they all may be handled that way.

COMPILATION

Compilation of programs written in Fortran, Algol, Cobol and other higher level languages is another critical area in the performance of software systems. It is an area in which hardware programming can and in some cases already does handle at least part of the job.

With the microprogramming systems that now exist it is reasonable to handle all of the process that is usually called lexical analysis on the microprogramming level. Microprograms can also be used in the construction and manipulation of tables, and to provide arithmetic capabilities not otherwise provided in the hardware. Much of this has already been done in the Allen-Babcock PL-1 System by adding microprograms to those already present in the IBM 360/50.

As in the case of supervisory systems, here too by making use of the integrated circuit and LS1 technologies it may become economically feasible to do the whole compiling process by hardware rather than by software programming. This too is a research area, and so far none of the proposed designs for building higher-level language capabilities into hardware seem both practical and attractive.[16]

The Burroughs 5500-6500-7500 computers represent a very interesting approach in this area. The machines, especially the later ones, contain very elaborate hardware programs to help in the processing and running of Algol programs. One might say that the block structure of Algol is built into the hardware, along with the automatic interpretation of Polish strings and the automatic handling of push-down lists or stacks. The logic of the 6500-7500 computers is described in some detail in.[17]

WHAT WE NEED

The most important need is for a design philosophy that aims at the design of total information processing systems, and that will eliminate the mostly artificial deistinction between hardware systems and software systems. We need a continuing development of the trend toward combined hardware-software programming discussed in part 2. Practically no one would deny that these are desirable goals, and it would serve little purpose to elaborate on them here. The remainder of this section will therefore discuss a few more specific and perhaps less obvious needs.

PERIPHERAL STORAGE

Writers in the computer field have overemphasized the importance of central processor speeds and capabilities in discussing the performance of computing systems. This is understandable, since there have been such dramatic advances in speed and compactness of circuits and central memories.

The advances in peripheral storage have been fewer and less spectacular. Software programs, along with almost all other information-processing programs, can profit far more from hardware advances in the area of periperal storage, than from improvements in central computer logic and speed.

At a SHARE meeting in 1966, representatives of IBM presented figures concerning the performance of an initial version of the OS 360, the operating system for the 360 computer. For the areas covered in that presentation, the operating system ran almost as fast with the slow model 40 central processor as it did with the very much faster model 65. Both used the same disc storage system, and it was the very frequent reference to disc storage, not the speed of internal processing, that was the limiting factor in the performance of the system.

I have been told that the design philosophy of OS 360 that permits frequent reference to system routines resident in peripheral storage, was influenced by a hardware development program that was to provide very much faster-access peripheral storage for system residence than is provided in current disc or drum storage systems.

A peripheral storage system large enough, cheap enough, and fast enough to permit its use as a rapid access device for system residence would be the most important contribution that hardware designers could make to software systems.

Peripheral core storage devices such as IBM's LCS and Control Data's ECS are too expensive. The cost per bit of bulk core is roughly 100 times the cost per bit of large disc storage (2¢ – 4¢ per bits vs. .002¢ –.004¢ per bit). The random access time differs by a factor of about 10000. The most obvious design point between these two would aim at a device with random access 100 times as fast as disc at about 10 times the cost per bit—i.e., access time less than 1 millisecond at a cost of .02¢ to .04¢ per bit.

Software systems deal with file management, with the cataloging, the storage and the retrieval of information. Catalogues and glossaries must be kept in peripheral storage. If the files are at all extensive, the catalogues must be several levels deep. One glossary leads to another which in turn leads to another, all requiring additional accesses to peripheral storage. The faster access peripheral storage mentioned above would be of great help, but even there, and more so in connection with disc and drum systems, hardware that provides for automatic search, for branching from one catalogue to another, for parallel readout from a number of index tracks—these would all provide major assistance to a large segment of software programming.

TIME SHARING

In recent years there has been a great deal of interest in, and a great deal of effort expended on the design and implementation of large interactive time-sharing systems. The results achieved in 1968 are very disappointing when compared with the promises of 1965.

Hardware performance is only one aspect of time-sharing system performance. Improvements in computer hardware alone will have little effect without corresponding developments in areas of software and communications. However, new computer hardware developments are essential before the promise of interactive time-sharing systems can be realized.

There are many general hardware design improvements that are relevant to time-sharing systems. These include improvements in peripheral storage, faster channels with greater bandwidth, and hardware programming of many operating system functions.

Specific to the time-sharing field there is a need for the development of adequate consoles, especially graphical input-output consoles. There are conflicting requirements for low cost and for many built-in features that minimize the load on the central computer. An adequate graphical console may require built-in hardware equivalent to that required in a fairly sophisticated computer.

This is an area in which analogue as well as digital techniques may be important. It is an area in which the new component technologies may make significant contributions.

ANALYSIS AND DEBUGGING

Software systems, especially on large computers are systems of great complexity. Hardware design can and should contribute to the analysis, to the debugging and to the documentation of such systems.

In order to improve the performance of a software system, we need to be able to evaluate its performance. In the case of a number of computing systems, separate and very complicated hardware was built to gather information needed in such analyses. The problem is to get the necessary information without loading the system and thereby distorting the information gathered. This can be very difficult to do in software alone. Hardware aids built-in to the initial design may represent a trivial cost compared to the cost of external monitoring equipment that may otherwise be needed.

There has been far too little concern on the part of the hardware system designers with the problems of debugging complex programs. Hardware aids to program debugging would be among the most important hardware aids to software production. On-line debugging is essential. It should be possible to monitor the performance of software on a cathode ray tube console, without interfering with the performance of the software. It should be possible to examine areas of peripheral storage as well as areas of core storage.

One of the most interesting features of the recently announced IBM 360 model 85 is the microfiche reader built into the system console. This reader will permit reference to the software documentation and at the same time permit reference to the state of various hardware registers.

We should perhaps aim for a software system design and implementation technique that will make it unnecessary to have a microfiche reader at the console for debugging and maintenance, but in systems where documentation has to be voluminous, a simple hardware retrieval system can be of great value.

COMPATIBILITY AND STANDARDS

Advances in the area of standardization and compatibility in computer hardware can be of importance to software developments in a great many ways. There is always a danger that standardization will inhibit progress, but at some point in time this danger must be faced. Over the years the computer industry has become accustomed to change at a frenetic pace, and such change is often but not always accompanied by progress.

The time may be near, or already at hand when there should be standardization of computer instructions, of input-output interfaces, of character sets. Duplication and multiplication of identical and nearly identical programming efforts is typical of the computer field today. It is hard to overestimate the saving in manpower and computer power if such duplication could be eliminated. Standardization of computer hardware would be the major step in the elimination of such duplication. We might even then find that there exists a surplus and not a shortage of system programmers.

REFERENCES

1 M V WILKES D J WHEELER S GILL
   The preparation of programs for an electronic digital computer
   Addison-Wesley 1951 1957
2. Functional description of the EDVAC
   University of Penna Moore School of EE Research Division Report 50-9
   under contract W—36—03400RD—7593 with the Ordnance Dept Dept of the
   Army Nov 1 1949
3 J C ALRICH
   Engineering description of the electro data digital computer
   IRE Trans on electronic computers EC—4 March 1955 p 1—10
4 W K HALSTEAD et al
   Purpose and application of the RCA BIZMAC system
   Proc of the WJCC Feb 1956 p 119—124
5 S G CAMPBELL
   Floating-point operation
   In W Buchholz Editor Planning a computer system McGraw-Hill 1962
6 S ROSEN
   Electronic Computers—a historical survey
   Document CSDTR 25 Computer Sciences Dept Purdue University July 1968
7 D F FARINA
   Large-scale integration: A status report
   Datamation 14 Feb 1968 p 22—29
8 M V WILKES J B STRINGER
   *Microprogramming and the design of the control circuits in an electronic
   digital computer*
   Proc Cambridge Philosophical Society 49 Part 2 April 1949 p 230—238
9 S G TUCKER
   Microprogram control for system/360
   IBM Systems Journal 64 1967 p 222—241
10 J GREEN
   Microprogramming, emulators and programming languages
   Comm ACM 9 March 1966 p 230—232
11 R S BARTON
   A new approach to the functional design of a digital computer
   Proc of the WJCC 1961 p 393—396
12 T KILBURN et al
   One-level storage system
   IRE Trans on Electronic Computers EC—11 April 1962 p 223—235
13 J B DENNIS
   Segmentation and the design of multiprogrammed computer systems
   Journal of the ACM 12 Oct 1965 p 580—602 Reprinted in S Rosen Editor
   Programming systems and languages McGraw-Hill 1967
14 R C DALEY J B DENNIS
   Virtual memory, process, and sharing in MULTICS
   Comm of the ACM 11 May 1968 p 306—312
15 B W ARDEN B A GALLER T C O'BRIEN F H WESTERVELT
   Program and addressing structure in a time-sharing environment
   Journal of the ACM 13 January 1966 p 1—16

16　T R BASHKOW A SASSON A KRONFELD
System design of a FORTRAN machine
IEEE Trans on Electronic Computers EC—16 Aug 1967 p 485—499
17　A A HAUCK B A DENT
Burrough's B6500/B7500 stack mechanism
Proc of the SJCC AFIPS Vol 32 1968 p 245—251

Questions:

1.　Compare emulation and simulation.

2.　List several hardware features which have been designed to aid the handling of interrupts.

3.　Define microprogramming.

BIBLIOGRAPHY

Arnold, Robert R. and Hill, Harold C. and Nichols, Aylmer V. *Introduction to Data Processing.* John Wiley & Sons, Inc. 1966, 328 pp.

Awad, E. *Business Data Processing.* Prentice Hall. 1965, 310 pp.

Bernstein, Jeremy. *The Analytical Engine.* Random House, 1963. 113 pp.

Brown, Harry L. *EDP for Auditors.* John Wiley & Sons. 1968. 195 pp.

Buckingham, Walter. *Automation: Its Impact of Business and People.* The New American Library. 1961. 176 pp.

Canning, Richard G. *The Management of Data Processing.* John Wiley & Sons. 1967.

Chapin, Ned. *An Introduction to Automatic Computers.* 2nd ed. D. Van Nostrand Company. 1963. 503 pp.

Churchman, C. *Introduction to Operations Research.* John Wiley & Sons. 1967.

Davies, D. W. *Digital Techniques.* Chemical Publishing. 1967. 158 pp.

Davis, Gordon B. *An Introduction to Electronic Computers.* McGraw-Hill. 1965.

Dearden, John, and Warren McFarlan. *Management Information Systems.* Richard D. Irwin, Inc. 1966. 427 pp.

Desmonde, William H. *Computers and Their Uses.* Prentice-Hall. 1964. 296 pp.

Desmonde, William H. *Real Time Data Processing Systems: Introductory Concepts.* Prentice-Hall. 1964. 186 pp.

Favret, Andrew G. *Introduction to Digital Computer Applications.* Reinhold Publishing Corp. 1965. 246 pp.

Greenberger, Martin, editor. *Computers and the World of the Future.* MIT Press. 1962. 340 pp.

Greenfield, Maynard S., et al. *Designing Systems for Data Processing.* Automation Institute Publishers Co., Inc. 1965. 358 pp.

Gregory, Robert H. and Van Horn, Richard L. *Automatic Data Processing Systems.* 2nd ed. Wadsworth Publishing Co. 1963. 816 pp.

Joslin, Edward O., *Computer Selection.* Addison-Wesley Publishing Company, Inc., 1968

Ledley, Robert S. *Programming and Utilizing Digital Computers.* McGraw-Hill. 1962.

Martin, E. Wainwright, Jr. *Electronic Data Processing: An Introduction.* Revised edition. Richard D. Irwin, Inc. 1965. 423 pp.

Sammet, Jean E. *PROGRAMMING LANGUAGES: History and Fundamentals,* Prentice-Hall, Inc., 1969.

Sherman, Harvey. *It all Depends.* University of Alabama Press. 1966. 218 pp.
Simon, Herbert A. *The Shape of Automation.* Harper & Row, Inc. 1965. 111 pp.
Sipple, Charles J. *Computer Dictionary and Handbook.* Howard W. Sams. 1966.
Smith, Paul T. *How to Live with Your Computer.* American Management
    Association. 1965. 207 pp.
Van Ness, Robert G. *Principles of Punched Card Data Processing.* The Business
    Press. 1964. 288 pp.
Van Ness, Robert G. *Principles of Data Processing with Computers.* The Business
    Press. 1966. 375 pp.
Weiner, M. G. *War Gaming Methodology.* Rand Corp. 1959.
Wiener, Norbert. *Cybernetics or Control and Communication in the Animal and
    the Machine.* 2nd ed. MIT Press. 1961.
Wofsey, Marvin M. *Management of Automatic Data Processing.* Thompson Book
    Co. 1968. 213 pp.

AUTHORS REPRESENTED

Willis W. Alexander, President, American Bankers Association.
Bernard A. Galler, President, Association for Computing Machinery.
Ralph E. Kent, President, American Institute of Certified Public Accountants.
Issac L. Auerbach, President, Auerbach Corp.
C. Mathews Dick, Jr., President, Business Equipment Manufacturers Association.
Dick Brandon, President, Brandon Applied Systems, Inc.
J. Daniel Couger, Assistant Dean, School of Business, University of Colorado.
Dr. Harvey S. Gellman, President, DCF Systems, Ltd.
J. A. Campise, General Consultant.
Dr. Marvin M. Wofsey, Professor, The George Washington University.
S. F. Keating, President, Honeywell, Inc.
S. D. Baxter, Chief, Computation Centre, National Research Council of Canada
Norman F. Kallaus, Chairman, Dept. of Office Management and Business Education, The University of Iowa.
Thomas J. Watson, Chairman of the Board, IBM Corporation.
R. Stanley Laing, President, The National Cash Register Company.
Robert E. McDonald, President, UNIVAC.
Frank W. Field, Assistant Vice-President, Business Information Systems, BELL CANADA.
Neal J. Dean, Vice President, Booz, Allen, & Hamilton, Inc.
Roger W. Bolz, Consultant.
Ira S. Gottfried, Executive Vice-President Norris and Gottfried, Inc.
Dr. Frank Greenwood, Director of Computer Services, Wright State University.
Herbert A. Simon, Carnegie-Mellon University
Gilbert Burck, Editor, Fortune Magazine.
Alan Drattel, Managing Editor, Business Automation.
Jean E. Sammet, Federal Systems Division, IBM.
Roy M. Salzman, Management Sciences Division, Arthur D. Little, Inc.
Richard H. Hill, Informatics, Inc.
Brooke W. Boering, Systems Analyst and Senior Programmer, Talman Savings and Loan Assn.
R. L. Patrick, Computer Specialist.
I. Prakash, Editor, DP Focus.
U. Prakash, Editor, DP Focus.
Steven B. Lipner, The Massachussetts Institute of Technology.
R. E. Montijo, Jr., Manager of Special Programs, EDP Division, RCA.
Robert M. Smith, Editor, Management Services.
Erwin M. Danziger, Director of Administrative Data Processing, University of North Carolina.

W. Sandy Hobgood, University of North Carolina.

Richard Lanham, Editorial Staff, SDC Magazine.

John P. Malloy, President and Board Chairman, Modern Machine Works, Inc.

John B. Tingleff, Second Vice-President, Continental Illinois National Bank and Trust Co.

William E. Jenkins, Division Vice-President, Eastern Airlines.

W. E. Miller, Manager, Metal Industry Systems Engineering, General Electric Co.

Albert L. Zobrist, University of Wisconsin.

Richard I. Miller, Senior Consultant, Harbridge House, Inc.

Gerald J. Smolen, Manager, Transportation and Communications Systems, ARIES Corp.

George O'Toole, Pace Computing.

Anthony D. Eppstein, Research Engineer, Memorex Corporation.

Dallas Talley, Marketing Director, Systems Engineering Laboratories.

Russell Paquette, Editorial Staff, SDC Magazine.

Jeffrey N. Bairstow, Editor, Computer Decisions.

Phillip C. Howard, Manager of Systems Planning, General Electric Co.

R. Vichnevetsky, Electronic Associates, Inc.

J. P. Landauer, Electronic Associates, Inc.

G. M. Amdahl, IBM Fellow.

L. D. Amdahl, President, COMPATA, Inc.

Ascher Opler, deceased.

Saul Rosen, Purdue University.

INDEX